ROADSIDE GEOLOGY
of TENNESSEE

MARCY B. DAVIS

2019
Mountain Press Publishing Company
Missoula, Montana

Maps constructed by Chelsea Feeney (www.cmcfeeney.com) using
GIS data from the US Geological Survey, National Park Service,
and the GIS Clearinghouse for Tennessee.

Roadside Geology is a registered trademark
of Mountain Press Publishing Company

Library of Congress Cataloging-in-Publication Data

Names: Davis, Marcy B., author.
Title: Roadside geology of Tennessee / Marcy B. Davis.
Description: Missoula, Montana : Mountain Press Publishing Company, [2019] |
  Series: Roadside geology | Includes bibliographical references and index.
Identifiers: LCCN 2018058320 | ISBN 9780878426911 (pbk. : alk. paper)
Subjects: LCSH: Geology—Tennessee—Guidebooks. | Tennessee—Guidebooks.
Classification: LCC QE165 .D38 2019 | DDC 557.68—dc23
LC record available at https://lccn.loc.gov/2018058320

PRINTED IN THE UNITED STATES

P.O. Box 2399 · Missoula, MT 59806 · 406-728-1900
800-234-5308 · info@mtnpress.com
www.mountain-press.com

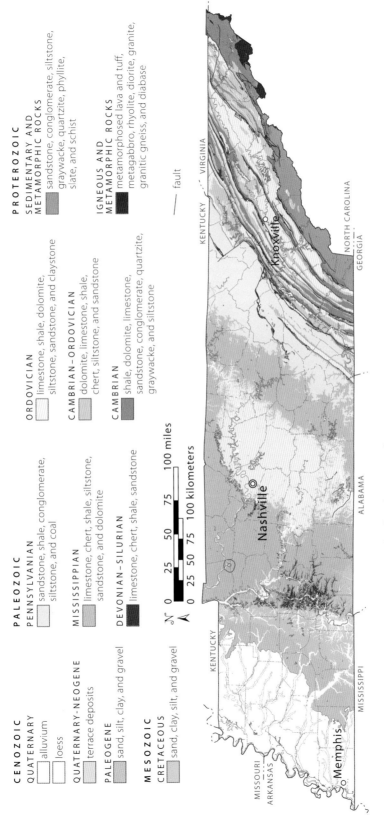

CENOZOIC

QUATERNARY
alluvium
loess

QUATERNARY–NEOGENE
terrace deposits

PALEOGENE
sand, silt, clay, and gravel

MESOZOIC

CRETACEOUS
sand, clay, silt, and gravel

PALEOZOIC

PENNSYLVANIAN
sandstone, shale, conglomerate, siltstone, and coal

MISSISSIPPIAN
limestone, chert, shale, siltstone, sandstone, and dolomite

DEVONIAN–SILURIAN
limestone, chert, shale, sandstone

ORDOVICIAN
limestone, shale, dolomite, siltstone, sandstone, and claystone

CAMBRIAN–ORDOVICIAN
dolomite, limestone, shale, chert, siltstone, and sandstone

CAMBRIAN
shale, dolomite, limestone, sandstone, conglomerate, quartzite, graywacke, and siltstone

PROTEROZOIC

SEDIMENTARY AND METAMORPHIC ROCKS
sandstone, conglomerate, siltstone, graywacke, quartzite, phyllite, slate, and schist

IGNEOUS AND METAMORPHIC ROCKS
metamorphosed lava and tuff, metagabbro, rhyolite, diorite, granite, granitic gneiss, and diabase

—— fault

N

0   25   50   75   100 miles

0   25   50   75   100 kilometers

Generalized geologic map of Tennessee. —Modified from the Tennessee Geological Survey

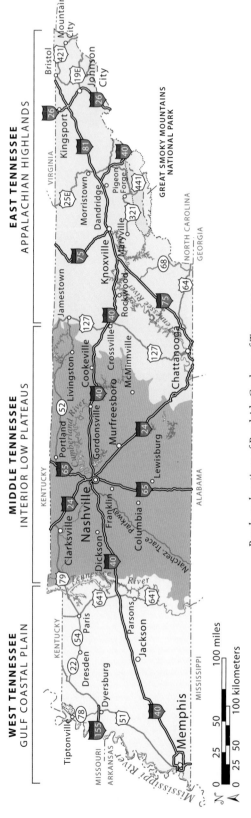

Roads and sections of Roadside Geology of Tennessee.

CONTENTS

The thinly bedded Anakeesta Formation, part of the Great Smoky Group, is well exposed along many popular trails in Great Smoky Mountains National Park. It is pictured here at Cliff Top overlook on Mt. LeConte, the park's third-highest peak. —Bob Carr photo

PREFACE

If you live in Tennessee or are a visitor to the Volunteer State and have an interest in why the landscape looks like it does, then this book is written for you. Tennessee's geologic story is deliberately streamlined here, so don't worry if you have little or no geologic training. A list of cited references, suggestions for further reading, and a glossary of geologic terms can be found in the back of the book. These resources will clarify and elaborate upon the text. There is also a list of Tennessee museums that focus partly on natural history and Earth science.

Those with geologic training may find this book useful as an introduction to Tennessee's geology. Academic and professional geologists will recognize the many sources on which I've relied—field trip guidebooks, peer-reviewed publications, special papers and maps from the United States and Tennessee Geological Surveys, student theses and dissertations, and books on Tennessee's geologic history. A tremendous number of geologists have contributed to our understanding of Tennessee's geologic past. The highlights of this broad body of work are distilled and summarized here; there are simply too many publications to reference in a book of this scope. I hope that I have done their work justice and that they will find this book useful.

This book is organized at three levels. The introduction explains important geologic concepts that will impart to the reader a greater understanding and appreciation of earth science. It also contains an overview of Tennessee's geologic history. The three subsequent chapters, divided according to Tennessee's three Grand Divisions (East, Middle, and West Tennessee), explore Tennessee's geology in more detail. Each chapter contains an introduction to the area that provides geologic context for the road guides.

Road guides highlight the interesting geologic and geographic features you are likely to see during your travels. Interstates are listed first, US highways

The three stars on Tennessee's flag represent the state's three Grand Divisions: East Tennessee, Middle Tennessee, and West Tennessee. Legally defined in the state constitution and under state law, the Grand Divisions highlight Tennessee's three distinct physiographic regions. The flags pictured here are at the Tennessee Map Plaza at Bicentennial Capitol Mall State Park in Nashville. The park has installations that provide information about Tennessee's Grand Divisions and waterways.
—Marcy Davis photo

next, and, finally, Tennessee state routes. All are listed in numeric order. Roads with multiple numeric assignments are listed by their most common designation. I frequently refer to mile markers and exit numbers in the text. This book also covers parkways, scenic roads maintained by the National Park Service or by the state, and byways, federally or state-maintained scenic roads. I mention the Cumberland and Appalachian Trails where they are relevant. Some of Tennessee's best geology is located off major highways. If you are traveling a road that is not covered in the book, look for one close by that parallels your route. Often you can extrapolate the geology from it. A good example is US 70, which roughly parallels I-40.

I used the geologic time periods from version 4 of the Geologic Society of America time chart.

In Tennessee rocks and strata, layers of sedimentary rock, are sometimes well exposed and sometimes not. Exposures tend to be better during winter months when there is less vegetation. During summer months, the best exposures are limited to highway roadcuts, but even they can change over time with erosion, vegetation, or grading. Tennessee's welcome centers, rest stops, and overlooks are often at very scenic locations and can be good places to stretch both your legs and your mind. Some have informational placards that describe the natural history.

This book pays special attention to Great Smoky Mountains National Park, several notable state parks (Tennessee has fifty-six, and only a handful are mentioned in this book), national historical parks, state historic parks, and the Big South Fork National River and Recreation Area, as well as the larger cities of Chattanooga, Knoxville, Memphis, and Nashville.

This book's maps were largely extracted from geologic maps published by the Tennessee Division of Geology (Hardeman et al., 1966). Digital versions of these maps are available through the United States Geological Survey (USGS) website. Quadrangle maps produced by the Tennessee Geological Survey and the USGS were also used as reference. Maps from various other scientific publications were used in some of the figures and are referenced appropriately. The geologic map of Great Smoky Mountains National Park was modified from the National Park Service's digital geologic compilation published in 2006. Road guide maps include a horizontal scale in miles. Miles are used for horizontal reference and feet for vertical reference unless otherwise noted.

Latitude and longitude coordinates, using the WGS84 datum, appear with many of the photographs. You can type these numbers directly into geographic apps, such as Google Maps, and find the location where the photo was taken.

Collecting, Safety, and Etiquette

Collecting rocks, minerals, and fossils is fun! You are welcome to take natural treasures home provided that your collecting is done safely and legally. Please remember that stopping at roadcuts is not only dangerous but also illegal along interstates. Please be respectful of private property and ask landowners for permission prior to collecting on their land. Active mines and quarries may grant you access to their properties, but call in advance so they can plan ahead for your visit (usually they will provide a chaperone). Be sure to have proper safety equipment as mandated by the Mine Safety and Health Administration (MSHA) when visiting active mines—mines are not obligated to supply this gear, but you will likely be denied entrance if you don't have it. Remember, collecting without a permit is illegal in all state and national parks.

Please contact the state or federal government, local museums, or a local university geology department to consult a specialist should you find human remains, animal fossils, or meteorites. Excavation of vertebrate fossils is prohibited on all federal lands without appropriate permits. Excavation of human remains requires a permit from the state archaeologist and must be done by qualified individuals. In select federal areas, such as Big South Fork National River and Recreation Area, surface collecting of artifacts is prohibited. Meteorites found on any federal land are under the stewardship of the Smithsonian Institution and should be properly reported.

Museums, universities, and gem and mineral clubs often organize collecting trips that are open to the public. Such excursions are a great way to meet people with similar interests and to learn about local geology. Trip leaders will provide participants with necessary permission, liability insurance, and access while also considering hazards and safety. This type of oversight is especially important for abandoned mines, caves, and quarries. For a list of Tennessee gem and mineral clubs visit the Southeast Federation of Mineralogical Societies, Inc. website.

Caving, or spelunking, is quite popular in Tennessee. Caves can be dangerous and are often located on private property, so visiting one of Tennessee's many show caves is generally the best option. Remember that cave environments are fragile and that cave formations take thousands of years to develop, so please do not collect in caves. Entry into caves on National Park lands is generally restricted, although certain caves have guided tours. Adventurous sorts who wish to visit a cave that's off the beaten track should contact one of Tennessee's grottoes (caving clubs), which regularly host trips and safety-training events. They will also have information on caves and the status and regulation of white nose syndrome, a disease that has decimated bat populations. For a list of Tennessee grottoes visit the National Speleological Society website.

ACKNOWLEDGMENTS

Material for this book comes from more than 150 years of published scientific literature, much of which was written by professional geologists from the Tennessee Division of Geology, the United States Geological Survey, the Tennessee Department of Transportation, and by the faculty and students of state colleges and universities. I reserve a great deal of respect and gratitude for these geoscientists, many of whom shared their time and knowledge with me.

Many people helped make this book a reality. I give special thanks to Michael Gibson who read several versions of the manuscript, made helpful additions to the West Tennessee text, provided photos, and answered many questions. Cliff Frohlich and Sheryl Harris also read multiple versions of the manuscript and provided thoughtful suggestions for streamlining the text for Roadside Geology readers. Ron Brister generously provided access to his West Tennessee geologic library and reviewed sections of the manuscript.

Alan Barber, Stacie Knight, Nicole LeRoux, and John Ward patiently navigated thousands of miles of road in all conditions and endured countless hours of field work. I am grateful for their patience and for their willingness to pull off highways with a few second's notice.

Many experts, including Malcolm Cleaveland, Randel Cox, William Cupples, Ian Dalziel, William Deane, Sandy Ebersole, Richard Finch, Jana Ruth Ford, Clay Harris, Susan Knowles, Larry Knox, Richard Kyle, Peter Lemiszki, Staci Loewy, Jonathan Mies, Arthur Merschat, Robert Milici, Barry Miller, Robert Miller, Albert Ogden, Travis Paris, Ryan Parish, Bran Potter, Ken Rush, Steve Smail, Scott Southworth, Roy Van Arsdale, Robert Wilson, and Jeannette Wolak, gave helpful reviews of sections of the manuscript. Their comments and suggestions greatly improved the text.

Many people listed above also shared their time with me both in and out of the field, as did Marvin Berwind, Steven Driese, Jonathan Evenick, Robert Hatcher, Martin Kohl, Molly Miller, Harry Moore, Eugene Schweig, Seth Stein, and Nancy Stetten. Others, including David Anderson, Robert Lauf, Kirk McIntosh, David Moecher, Terry Moxon, Gary Pinkerton, Michael Reedy, Phyllis Steckel, Jesse Tune, Martitia Tuttle, helpfully responded to my inquiries.

I am deeply indebted to Chuck Sutherland who generously provided most of the book's photographs. Many others, including some listed above, contributed photographs and illustrations. They are appropriately credited in individual figure captions.

My sincere thanks to the staff at Mountain Press Publishing. Jennifer Carey showed incredible patience over many years and provided invaluable guidance through the manuscript editing process. Her spot-on judgement and input, along with Chelsea Feeney's beautiful illustrations and maps, brought the book to life. I also thank Jeannie Painter, who designed the book.

Many thanks to my husband, Dan Duncan, family, friends, and colleagues for their support and patience with a project that, at times, seemed endless. Many others, not named here, helped in ways big and small, and I apologize for not including all of them here—there are simply too many! I could not have done it without you. Thank you! I have done my best to summarize the abundance of information about the geology of Tennessee and am solely responsible for any misinterpretations or errors.

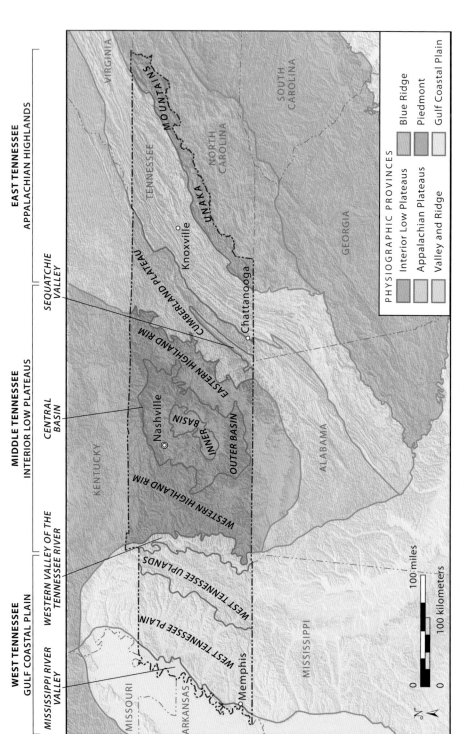

Tennessee's physiographic provinces and subprovinces. —Province boundaries from a number of sources

WEST TENNESSEE
GULF COASTAL PLAIN

MISSISSIPPI RIVER VALLEY

WESTERN VALLEY OF THE TENNESSEE RIVER

MIDDLE TENNESSEE
INTERIOR LOW PLATEAUS

CENTRAL BASIN

SEQUATCHIE VALLEY

EAST TENNESSEE
APPALACHIAN HIGHLANDS

WEST TENNESSEE UPLANDS

WEST TENNESSEE PLAIN

WESTERN HIGHLAND RIM

INNER BASIN

OUTER BASIN

EASTERN HIGHLAND RIM

CUMBERLAND PLATEAU

UNAKA MOUNTAINS

PHYSIOGRAPHIC PROVINCES

Interior Low Plateaus

Appalachian Plateaus

Valley and Ridge

Blue Ridge

Piedmont

Gulf Coastal Plain

Province boundaries from a number of sources

MISSOURI

ARKANSAS

Memphis

MISSISSIPPI

ALABAMA

KENTUCKY

Nashville

TENNESSEE

Chattanooga

Knoxville

GEORGIA

NORTH CAROLINA

SOUTH CAROLINA

VIRGINIA

N

0   100 miles

0   100 kilometers

TENNESSEE'S LANDSCAPE

*Like the Dachshund that is a dog-and-a-half long and half a
dog high, the state of Tennessee has peculiar proportions.*

—MADELINE KNEBERG, 1952

As American anthropologist Madeline Kneberg observed, Tennessee is long
and narrow, like a parallelogram, with 500 diagonal miles between Bristol and
Memphis and only about 120 miles from north to south through Nashville. It
shares borders with eight states, including North Carolina on the east, Mississippi in the South, and Missouri in the Midwest. Visitors will immediately
notice the rich diversity, both cultural and natural, inherent to the different
regions of the state. Not only are these differences reflected in the landscape,
but in the resources, economy, and character of the people.

The three stars on Tennessee's state flag reference the state's three Grand
Divisions: East, Middle, and West Tennessee. These divisions correspond to
physiographic regions. Major physiographic regions of eastern North America
were first described in 1938 by American geographer Nevin M. Fenneman,
who recognized that areas with similar landforms could be grouped and classified. Tennessee includes parts of Fenneman's Appalachian Highlands, Interior
Plains, and Atlantic Coastal Plain physiographic regions, which are subdivided into provinces and sections. The underlying geology, in combination
with millions of years of erosion, has given each physiographic region a distinct
physical character. In Tennessee, plateaus and mountains are typically formed
by more resistant rock types, such as sandstone and conglomerate, while valleys
are formed of less resistant rock types, such as limestone and shale.

The Appalachian Highlands region extends along the east coast of North
America from southeastern Canada to central Alabama. East Tennessee
includes three physiographic provinces that are associated with the Appalachian Highlands: the Blue Ridge, Valley and Ridge, and Cumberland Plateau.
The Blue Ridge province, along Tennessee's eastern border with North Carolina, contains some of the highest mountains in eastern North America, with a
handful of peaks over 6,000 feet high. Rugged ridges, steep-walled canyons, and
narrow valleys create a dramatic landscape in this part of the state. Tennessee's
oldest rocks, some more than 1 billion years old, are found in the Blue Ridge.

A regional fault, called the Great Smoky fault, marks the topographic and
geologic boundary between the Blue Ridge and the rolling hills of Tennessee's
Valley and Ridge physiographic province. The Valley and Ridge is made up of
eroded folded and faulted sedimentary strata. The province name comes from
the northeast-trending, linear valleys and ridges that parallel the Blue Ridge.
The Tennessee section of the Valley and Ridge is often referred to locally as the
Great Valley of East Tennessee because the topography is relatively low when

compared to the neighboring Blue Ridge and Cumberland Plateau. A steep, up to 1,000-foot-high escarpment defines the western edge of the Valley and Ridge where it meets the Cumberland Plateau, a flat-topped highland with elevations consistently between about 1,600 and 2,000 feet above sea level. The Cumberland Plateau features flat-lying sedimentary rocks that contain most of Tennessee's minable coal.

Middle Tennessee lies within the Interior Low Plateaus physiographic province of the Interior Plains region. The province has two sections in Tennessee: a flat area known as the Highland Rim that surrounds a great bowl-shaped depression called the Central (or Nashville) Basin. Most of Middle Tennessee's interesting relief is located at the transition between the basin and rim, where elevations abruptly change as much as several hundred feet. The Highland Rim is several hundred feet lower than the neighboring Cumberland Plateau.

West Tennessee, a low area located between the Tennessee and Mississippi Rivers, is part of the Gulf Coastal Plain physiographic province of the Atlantic Coastal Plain region. The province is characterized by fertile soils, slow-moving streams, and murky, forested bottomlands. Tennessee's Gulf Coastal Plain can be separated into three sections: the West Tennessee Uplands, which separate the watersheds of the Tennessee and Mississippi Rivers; the low-lying West Tennessee Plain; and the Mississippi River Valley.

Earth's Layers and the Formation of Continents

Earth originated from the gradual coming together of dense gas and dust ejected from the Big Bang at the birth of our universe more than 13 billion years ago. Bits of space rocks and dust collided and combined to form a slowly spinning disk of cosmic debris. Heat produced from gravitational forces, friction, and natural radioactive decay melted the disk's interior and caused materials to separate into layers. Earth cooled over time and formed a solid outer crust. Gases and liquid released by volcanoes helped create the atmosphere and oceans.

At Earth's center is the core, made of iron and nickel. It is surrounded by the mantle, which makes up more than 80 percent of Earth's volume. The mantle is rich in iron, magnesium, silicon, and oxygen. Surrounding the mantle is a shell called the crust. There are two types of crust: oceanic and continental crust. A dark, volcanic rock called basalt forms the relatively thin (3-to-5-mile-thick) oceanic crust. Basalt is similar in composition to the underlying mantle. Continental crust, the rocky material on which we live, is made up of mostly lighter-colored granitic and sedimentary rocks that contain far less iron and much more silica and aluminum than basalt. Continental crust is less dense and thicker (about 15 to 40 miles) than oceanic crust.

Incredible pressures combined with heat generated by the natural radioactive decay of mineral isotopes make Earth's interior very hot. This heat is distributed unevenly, so different parts of Earth behave differently in terms of mechanical properties. Earth's core has a solid inner part and a liquid outer part, for example. The upper part of the mantle, called the asthenosphere, behaves plastically. It flows very slowly via convective currents that transfer heat from Earth's interior to the surface. Volcanoes, earthquakes, and mountain building all occur above the places where these currents ascend or descend in the asthenosphere.

The topmost mechanical layer, called the lithosphere, includes the uppermost solid part of the mantle and the crust. It is rigid and broken up into tectonic plates that move continuously over Earth's surface about as fast as fingernails grow, 1 to 2 inches per year. Tectonic plates may be made of oceanic or continental crust, or both. They move independently, pushed and pulled by mantle convection currents in the asthenosphere. The interactions between plates, a process called plate tectonics, are ultimately responsible for both creating and destroying lithosphere. The motions of plates help to explain the jigsaw fit of the continents, the periodic opening and closing of ocean basins, and the genesis of mountains and volcanoes.

Whether plates bump into, pull apart from, or slide past each other partly determines the resulting surface landforms. Convergent plate boundaries are where two tectonic plates come together. Continents grow at these boundaries as new continental material, such as island arcs and continental fragments, becomes welded to the continents during continental collisions. Where two plates containing continental lithosphere collide, massive mountain ranges,

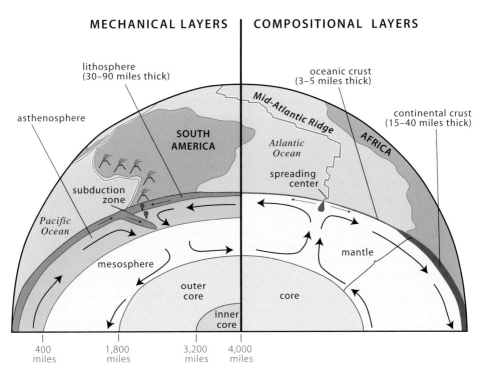

Earth consists of three main compositional layers: the core, mantle, and crust. The behavior of Earth's mechanical layers—the inner and outer cores, mesosphere, asthenosphere, and lithosphere—are responsible for plate tectonics. —US Geological Survey image

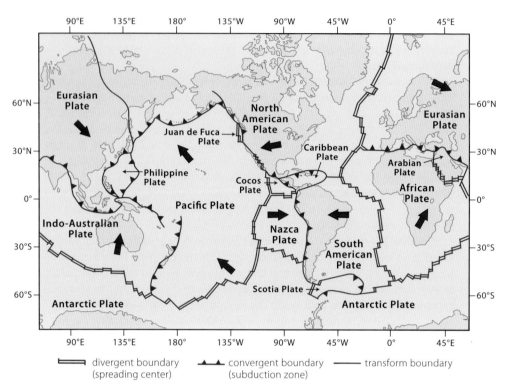

Earth's crust is broken into several major and many smaller tectonic plates. The number of plates and their boundaries change over time as ocean basins open and close. The three main types of tectonic plate boundaries—divergent, convergent, and transform—are often marked by volcanoes and earthquakes. The interaction of these plates produces mountains and ocean basins. Arrows show relative motion along present plate boundaries. —Modified from US Geological Survey

such as the Himalayas, are pushed up. When a plate containing oceanic lithosphere collides with a plate containing continental lithosphere, the plate containing continental lithosphere overrides the other, denser plate, which descends into the asthenosphere; this process, called subduction, often generates earthquakes. At depths of 60 miles or so, the increase in pressure and temperature causes some crustal rocks to melt. Volcanoes form on the overriding plate where molten material reaches the surface via faults and fractures. Oceanic lithosphere is destroyed as it descends into the asthenosphere. The process of subduction created the Andes Mountains of South America and the Cascade Mountains of the western United States.

At divergent plate boundaries, two tectonic plates move apart. Mantle material fills the void to create new oceanic lithosphere. The break in the crust will widen to form an ocean basin so long as rifting continues. The Earth is not expanding, however, so the creation and destruction of plates is balanced. The amount of lithosphere being destroyed at subduction zones equals that created at oceanic rifts.

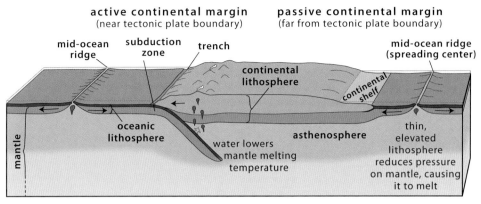

Subduction zones form along active continental margins where oceanic plates collide with continental plates. New ocean crust forms at mid-ocean ridges. Sediments accumulate on continental shelves of a passive continental margin. —Modified from US Geological Survey

Two tectonic plates slide past each other along transform plate boundaries. Movement along transform plate boundaries, such as California's San Andreas fault, often produces large earthquakes but does not typically result in the formation of large mountains or ocean basins.

Both the eastern and western margins of Tennessee were once ancient plate boundaries. Consequently, Tennessee's geologic history records episodic rifting, subduction, volcanism, and the formation of several mountain ranges.

Tennessee is presently located near the center of the North American tectonic plate, which stretches from the Arctic Ocean to the Caribbean Sea, and from the San Andreas fault in California to the Mid-Atlantic rift, a mid-ocean ridge that runs up the center of the Atlantic Ocean. Tennessee's central location means that the state is currently far from the influence of plate boundary forces, but this was not always the case. Divergent plate boundaries once existed on both the western and eastern sides of Tennessee, and ancient convergent plate boundaries are responsible for the Appalachian Mountains of East Tennessee.

Minerals and Rocks

Minerals are naturally occurring, inorganic solids that have a definite crystalline structure and chemical composition. At Earth's surface, minerals are most commonly made of combinations of oxygen, silicon, aluminum, iron, calcium, sodium, potassium, and magnesium. A mineral's hardness, general form, tendency to break into certain shapes, luster, magnetism, and color are all important in mineral identification.

Rocks are mineral aggregates. The group of minerals present in a rock can tell us about the environment in which the rock formed. In general terms, rocks that contain a group of minerals relatively high in iron and magnesium more commonly form in oceanic crust. Rocks with minerals high in aluminum, silicon, and oxygen usually point to a continental genesis. The distribution of rock types on Earth's surface is controlled by plate tectonics and other processes.

When geologists identify rock type, they employ the Principle of Uniformitarianism. This concept, one of the central tenets of geology, says that the present is the key to the past; geologic processes occurring on Earth today are the same as those that occurred long ago. Therefore, each rock is a record of a specific environment at a specific place and time. All three rock types—igneous, metamorphic, and sedimentary—are present in Tennessee. Igneous and metamorphic rocks are found in East Tennessee's Blue Ridge, whereas sedimentary rocks are exposed at the surface throughout the state.

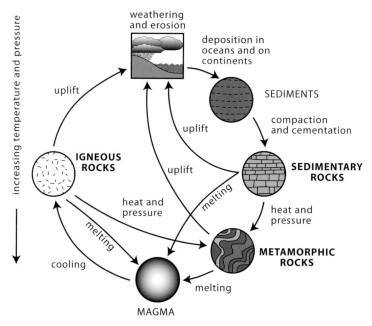

The basic concept of the rock cycle is that any one rock type can become another rock type as the environment changes through geologic time.

Igneous rocks form as molten rock material, called magma, cools and crystallizes above or below Earth's surface. The size and shape of mineral crystals indicates how quickly the material cooled and solidified. Intrusive igneous rocks, such as granite and gabbro, form within Earth's interior, where they cool slowly and crystals grow larger. Extrusive igneous rocks, such as basalt and rhyolite, form where magma is erupted onto Earth's surface from a volcano and cools quickly forming microscopic crystals or even glass (which doesn't have a crystalline structure). A mix of crystal sizes indicates a more complex history.

Igneous rocks typically form where tectonic plates collide or separate. Such environments are conducive to the high temperatures required for molten rock to develop. Igneous rocks more than 1 billion years old lie beneath most of Tennessee, but they are exposed only in Tennessee's Blue Ridge province. Younger igneous rocks, including volcanic ash and kimberlite, occur at rare locations in East Tennessee and in the subsurface of Middle and West Tennessee. Altered volcanic ash layers are also present within carbonate layers in Middle and East Tennessee.

Metamorphic rocks result from changes in pressure and/or temperature conditions, usually due to burial or during mountain building events, called orogenies. It is for this reason that metamorphic rocks are often found close to igneous rocks. Rocks may be heated and squeezed to the point they look nothing like the original. They may melt and become a completely new igneous rock. If the pressures and temperatures are not that high, geologists can determine the original rock type, attaching the prefix *meta* to its name (for example, metasandstone, metasiltstone, and so forth). Metasedimentary rocks, such as slate, may form as mud and silt are buried and compacted over time. Metasedimentary rocks make up most of Tennessee's Blue Ridge.

Metamorphic rocks are named on the basis of the original rock type and the degree of deformation. To determine how much the rocks have been deformed, geologists consider the size and type of minerals that form during metamorphism. They also examine metamorphic fabric, which refers to the tendency for minerals to align in a preferred orientation. The most common types of metamorphic fabric are lineation and foliation. Lineation refers to the favored orientation of relatively long, skinny minerals. Foliation is the tendency for flat

The rocks that form Charlies Bunion in Great Smoky Mountains National Park are made of metasedimentary rocks of the Ocoee Supergroup. These rocks were subjected to heat and pressure, but not so much that their original sedimentary structures were greatly altered. —Bob Carr photo

minerals to be aligned and layered, thereby creating planes of weakness along which the rock splits. Foliation gives a rock a layered look and is common in rocks that originally contained lots of mud, clay, and silt. With metamorphism, clay minerals, which are flat and platy to begin with, become mica minerals, a family of thin, platy minerals.

West of the Blue Ridge, most rocks found at the surface in Tennessee are sedimentary, made of the weathered, eroded, and deposited pieces, or grains, of other rocks, collectively called sediment. Sedimentary rocks are, essentially, made of recycled bits, or clasts, of older igneous, metamorphic, and sedimentary rocks. The sandstone and conglomerate that form the resistant cap of the Cumberland Plateau are clastic sedimentary rocks.

Wind, water, ice, and gravity erode and transport sediment. The farther sediment grains are from their source rocks, the more rounded, the smaller, and the more uniformly sorted by size they become. Rivers, streams, and wind generally carry sand-, silt-, and clay-sized particles. Larger rivers, such as the Mississippi, may transport gravel and sand along their bottoms where currents are strong. They also carry clay-sized particles and fine sand suspended in the water column. In mountainous areas, heavy rains may temporarily increase stream power and move larger cobbles and boulders downstream to where they concentrate at the foot of a mountain. Ocean currents transport sand along beaches. Winds can blow dust thousands of miles from its source. *Alluvium* refers to loose sediments, usually gravel-sized and smaller, deposited relatively recently in a lake, river, or glacial setting. Alluvium is being deposited right now along Tennessee's many rivers and streams.

Eventually, sediment settles and accumulates in horizontal layers. The resulting clastic sedimentary rocks are named for the size and type of sediment they contain. Minerals found in groundwater, including calcium carbonate and silica, cement grains together as sediment is buried and compacted.

Sedimentary rocks help geologists reconstruct former ecosystems and piece together a region's ancient landscape. Fragments of rock may tell us where the

Crossbeds in the Rockcastle Conglomerate formed in an ancient river channel that flowed southward across Tennessee more than 300 million years ago. (about 36.551289N, 84.796679W)
—Chuck Sutherland photo

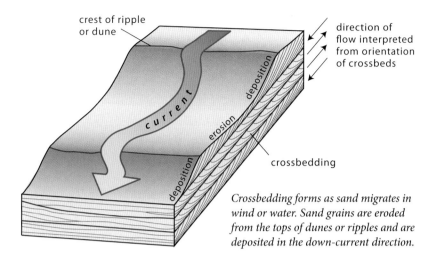

Crossbedding forms as sand migrates in wind or water. Sand grains are eroded from the tops of dunes or ripples and are deposited in the down-current direction.

sediments came from. We can deduce how fast and how much water moved through a river system and how far sediment traveled based on the size and roundness of sediment grains. Fine-grained sediments, such as those that make up mudstone, siltstone, shale, and fine-grained limestone, are deposited in quiet water where particles settle to the bottom and accumulated very slowly. Boulders, gravel, and large volumes of sand indicate a higher-energy environment. Sometimes sedimentary rocks contain structures such as mud cracks, ripple marks, and rain drops, all of which help us better understand the former environment. Sedimentary rocks commonly form where plants and animals lived and died, so they may contain fossils. Coal is made from compressed plant material.

Chalk and some kinds of limestone formed from shell material that collected over time at the bottom of ancient oceans. Most of Tennessee's limestone is made up of fossil clasts, or grains, that were cemented together with crystalline calcite. Some limestones formed from calcium carbonate ooze that precipitated directly from seawater. There are various chemical processes by which magnesium may be substituted for some of the calcium in limestone. When the rock contains more magnesium than calcium, it's called dolomite, or dolostone. *Carbonates* is a collective term that includes both limestone and dolomite.

Evaporites remain after water evaporates from a mineral-saturated solution, usually in a closed basin in an arid environment. Evaporites, such as salt and gypsum, are not found in great quantities in Tennessee but may form thin layers within larger rock formations.

Water's Role in Weathering and Erosion

Water, both above and below Earth's surface, has played a big role in shaping Tennessee's landscape throughout geologic time. Tennessee's current climate, like all southern states, is humid subtropical with hot summers and relatively mild winters. Rainfall is consistent throughout the year, but spring storms often

West Blackburn Fork cascades over resistant rocks of the Highland Rim and into the Central Basin at Cummins Falls. (36.249500N, 85.571700W) —Chuck Sutherland photo

cause flooding, especially in West and Middle Tennessee. Rainfall makes for lush, green foliage and beautiful waterfalls, lakes, and rivers with fertile floodplains—all things that make Tennessee a great place to live and visit. Several large rivers flow through Tennessee, including the Mississippi, Tennessee, and Cumberland, and most of the state's smaller rivers and streams eventually join one of these.

Differential weathering of rocks creates the landscape we see at Earth's surface. Many waterways, particularly in East Tennessee, follow the traces of joints, faults, fractures, and other geologic structures imparted by tectonic events. Stream channels often show patterns that are diagnostic of underlying geology. The most common drainage pattern in Tennessee, called dendritic drainage, forms a treelike pattern where underlying rock is relatively homogeneous and flat-lying. Trellis drainage is common in Tennessee's Great Valley, where strata are heavily folded and faulted. There, streams flow down long, linear valleys. When one stream joins another, it flows into it in a perpendicular direction, having broken through a resistant ridge nearby.

Rocks are broken down into smaller pieces through physical and chemical processes that occur at Earth's surface. This is known as weathering. With physical or mechanical weathering, rocks are simply broken down into smaller pieces without undergoing any chemical change. There are numerous ways that rocks mechanically weather. For example, newly exposed rocks often expand

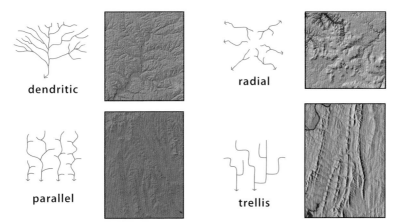

Surface drainage reflects underlying geologic structure. Parallel drainage is common in West Tennessee where strata are flat-lying to gently dipping. Dendritic, parallel, and radial drainage patterns are all present in Middle Tennessee. Trellis drainage patterns are most common in East Tennessee's Valley and Ridge.

Mushroom rocks are pedestals created by differential erosion. Here, wind and water preferentially eroded finer-grained sandstone that is less resistant than the overlying conglomeratic sandstone. This mushroom rock is located on the Cumberland Trail in Prentice Cooper State Forest off TN 27. —Michael Hicks photo

and crack as overlying materials are eroded and pressure is reduced. Temperature and humidity fluctuations may cause expansion, contraction, and eventual breakage. When water, wind, or ice containing sediment scours underlying rock, it is physically abraded. Water from rain, dew, and melting snow can flow into and fill cracks during the day. When temperatures drop at night the water freezes, expanding by about 10 percent and prying rock apart like a wedge. This type of weathering is typical at higher elevations and in colder climates. Lastly, plant roots and burrowing organisms can contribute to physical weathering, pushing rocks apart like a crowbar. (See the following section for a discussion on chemical weathering.)

Erosion is the process by which wind, water, ice, and gravity entrain weathered earth materials and deposit them elsewhere. Sustained periods of erosion are preserved in the geologic record by unconformities, erosional surfaces that represent short to long gaps in the depositional record. In Tennessee, there are several major unconformities, each of which represents a regional environmental change, such as rises or drops in sea level or new tectonic environments, that lasted tens of millions of years. There are also many smaller unconformities representing relatively short periods of erosion. Geologists have used these to reconstruct local environments.

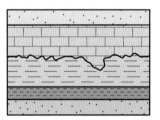 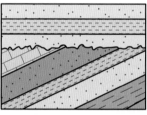 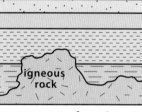

disconformity   **angular unconformity**   **nonconformity**

Unconformities are erosional surfaces that represent sustained periods of erosion. A disconformity is an unconformable surface between horizontal strata. An angular unconformity separates strata that were deformed by tectonic processes from overlying horizontal strata. A nonconformity separates crystalline rocks from overlying horizontally bedded sedimentary strata.

Caves and Springs

Tennessee's state rock is limestone, and with good reason—there's lots of it, and it's a valuable economic resource. The relatively soluble rock also hosts caves and springs in Middle and East Tennessee. Caves and springs are features of karst topography, a distinctive landscape that forms in humid temperate climates where carbonate bedrock is at the surface. In Middle and East Tennessee, ancient karst topography hosts ore mineralization and aquifers.

Caves may form through erosion, whereby sand entrained in water abrades surrounding rock, but more commonly they form through dissolution, a weathering process that breaks down rock through chemical means. The chemical means for dissolution begins in the atmosphere, where falling precipitation

Delicate and beautiful cave formations such as stalactites, stalagmites, and flowstone form as calcium carbonate precipitates from water seeping into a cave. Secret Cave in Putnam County is known for its high density of decorations. —Chuck Sutherland photo

Caves form mainly through a chemical weathering process called dissolution. Water combines with carbon dioxide in the air and soil to produce a weak acid that dissolves rock. When the water table drops, empty spaces, now caves, remain.

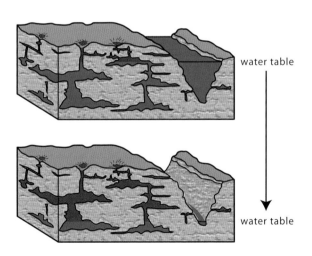

incorporates carbon dioxide from the air, becoming slightly acidic. The water becomes even more acidic as it absorbs additional carbon dioxide from decaying organic matter on the ground. The water, now a weak acid, dissolves limestone while flowing through cracks and joints or along bedding planes. Channels become interconnected with time, and over thousands of years caves form below the water table where freely flowing groundwater dissolves the rock it flows through. When the water table drops due to erosion or tectonic processes, water drains from the passages and caves. Tennessee has many privately owned show caves open to the public for tours.

Sinkholes develop where cave ceilings collapse. Sinkholes aren't necessarily an issue in rural areas, but in urban areas they can be problematic. In 2014, for example, a small sinkhole developed between the football field and track at Governors Stadium at Austin Peay State University. The school had to enlarge the sinkhole, making it 40 feet wide by 40 feet deep, which they then filled and resurfaced. Sinkholes commonly develop under roadways in Middle and East Tennessee and are a constant challenge for the Tennessee Department of Transportation.

In Middle Tennessee karst has developed widely in the flat, laterally continuous carbonate strata. Cave development is concentrated between the outer and inner parts of the Central Basin and along the Highland Rim's eastern edge. In both cases, dissolution is aided by gravity as stream waters flow from higher elevation to lower elevation. The gradient difference increases erosive power which, in addition to dissolution, enhances cave development. Cumberland Caverns, located near McMinnville, is a good example of this type of cave development. In East Tennessee's Valley and Ridge physiographic province, groundwater is channeled in folded and faulted carbonate rocks, so caves develop in parallel, linear belts.

Montlake is a 150-to-200-foot-deep, nearly 400-foot-diameter sinkhole in Hamilton County. It's unusual because it's walled by sandstone at the surface. Montlake is likely the result of a large cave that collapsed in the underlying limestone more than 800 feet below the sandstone. (35.240843N, 85.226410W)
—Chuck Sutherland photo

Springs, where groundwater comes to the surface, may form in any rock type but are quite common in carbonate rocks. The amount of water discharged from a spring depends on a number of factors, including water pressure and the amount of rainfall. Springs may flow continuously or stop during dry parts of the year or droughts, when water tables drop. Some springs flow intermittently for short periods, such as Ebbing and Flowing Spring near Rogersville, which increases from a dribble to a 500-gallon-per-minute flow in a 3-hour cycle. Most of Tennessee's earliest resorts were developed at natural mineral springs, particularly in Middle and East Tennessee. In the eighteenth and nineteenth centuries physicians even prescribed certain springs based on their chemistry, such as Epperson Springs, located near the Sumner-Macon county line. Springs have been important sources of Tennessee's drinking water, and many are popular swimming holes.

Mapping Tennessee

The New Madrid earthquakes of 1811–1812 brought a great deal of geologic interest to Tennessee, and geologic mapping began in earnest soon after the earthquakes. Dutch-born geologist Gerard Troost (1776–1850) became the first Tennessee state geologist in 1831. His report to the legislature in 1841 included the state's first geologic map. Troost also taught geology at the University of Nashville (now Vanderbilt University). Tennessee state geologist and Vanderbilt University professor James M. Safford (1822–1907) published *Geology of Tennessee* in 1869, Tennessee's first geologic compendium with maps. The Tennessee Geological Survey, established in 1909, continues the geologic work of these pioneers, along with private companies, universities, and students.

As with all scientific disciplines, geology comes with its own jargon and conventions. For example, most minerals are named by the person who discovers and publishes a study of the mineral's physical and chemical properties. The mineral Coskrenite was named by and for its discoverer, T. Dennis Coskren, who found the mineral at Alum Cave Bluff in Great Smoky Mountains National Park.

Most of Tennessee's surface rocks are sedimentary and form distinctive layers. Geologists informally refer to sedimentary layers as *beds* or *stratum*; collectively they are called strata. Layer thicknesses vary depending on how quickly deposition occurred and how much the sediment was compacted during burial.

To map sedimentary strata, geologists follow an outcrop, a place where rocks are exposed. They describe the rocks and trace their lateral extent, grouping similar rocks and giving them formal names as geologic formations. Some formations are made of one rock type, whereas others are a combination of rock types. Geologists usually name formations for the place where they were first described, or for the best exposure location, known as the stratigraphic unit's *type section*. For example, Tennessee's Cretaceous-age Coffee Sand is named for exposures at Coffee Landing, on the Tennessee River in Hardin County, where it was first described. The Knox Group was first described at an outcrop in Knox County in East Tennessee. Names help geologists correlate rocks of

Geologists of the US Geological Survey Great Smoky Mountains field-mapping party (1946–1955). Left to right: Richard Goldsmith, Willis Nelson, Robert Neuman, Jarvis Hadley, and Phillip King. Warren Hamilton, also a member of the field party, took the photo in 1953. —US Geological Survey photo

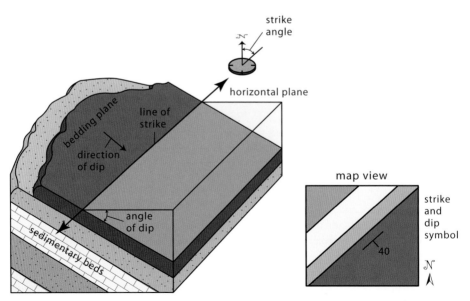

Geologists take a number of field measurements in order to create a geologic map. Color, pattern, and standard geologic symbols communicate rock type, age, and three-dimensional orientation on a two-dimensional map.

similar age across a region. When making a geologic map, geologists add the surface extent of a formation, along with rock descriptions, to a topographic map base. Each formation is distinguished by its own color and pattern, which reflects age and rock type. Symbols describe the three-dimensional orientation of strata, as well as structural features, such as faults and folds.

In this book I use the US Geological Survey's formal formation names for Tennessee. Sometimes I use group names (collections of formations) or super-groups (collections of groups). Occasionally, I reference formation members, a smaller subset of a formation with distinctive characteristics. In general, super-groups represent hundreds of millions of years, groups tens of millions of years, and formations up to several million years.

Geologic Structures

Regional tectonic activity deforms rocks, sometimes creating complex struc-tures. Faults, folds, domes, basins, and joints are some of the most common types of structures that develop, and examples of all can be found in Tennessee.

Faults are fractures in rocks along which displacement occurs, and they form when rocks are pushed or pulled from opposite directions. With force and time, rocks on either side of a fracture will break and slide past each other, forming a fault. The size of a fault reflects the scale of the forces at work. Large faults rarely occur alone. Rather, many smaller associated faults help accommo-date the complex motion that occurs within what's called a fault zone. Thrust faults are widespread in East Tennessee and are the result of the compressional forces that were associated with Appalachian mountain building. These faults are no longer active. The earthquakes that shake East Tennessee occur on a mix of fault types deep in the crust. Earthquakes in West Tennessee are thought to occur on buried normal and strike-slip faults.

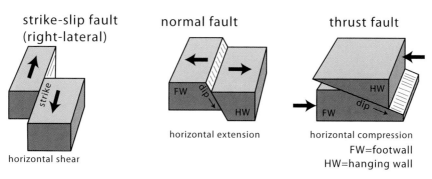

Geologists recognize three basic fault types that differ with respect to how rocks move relative to each other on either side of the fault. Rocks appear to move past each other laterally in a strike-slip fault. Strike slip faults are classified as right-lateral or left-lateral. If you stand on one side of the fault and the other side of the fault slips to the right, it is a right-lateral strike-slip fault. Normal faults are the result of tensional, or stretching, forces. Rocks on top of the fault appear to slide down the fault relative to the rocks on the other side. Thrust faults are the result of compressional forces that produce the opposite motion of normal faults.

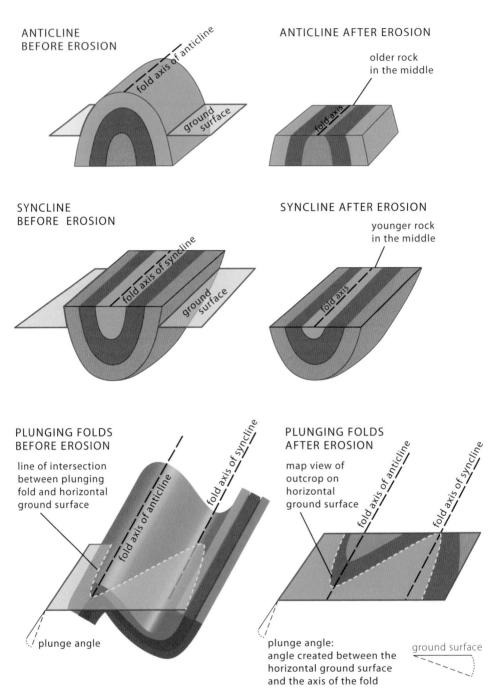

ANTICLINE
BEFORE EROSION

fold axis of anticline

ground surface

ANTICLINE AFTER EROSION

older rock in the middle

fold axis

SYNCLINE
BEFORE EROSION

fold axis of syncline

ground surface

SYNCLINE AFTER EROSION

younger rock in the middle

fold axis

PLUNGING FOLDS
BEFORE EROSION

line of intersection between plunging fold and horizontal ground surface

fold axis of anticline

fold axis of syncline

plunge angle

PLUNGING FOLDS
AFTER EROSION

map view of outcrop on horizontal ground surface

fold axis of anticline

fold axis of syncline

plunge angle: angle created between the horizontal ground surface and the axis of the fold

ground surface

Strata may be folded into anticlines and synclines. Folds are described as "plunging" if the fold axis is tilted. Plunging folds create a zigzag pattern on a geologic map, while nonplunging folds create stripes. In both cases, differential weathering often results in topographic inversion, whereby anticlines become valleys and synclines remain ridges. In Middle and West Tennessee, strata are typically deformed into very broad folds, whereas in East Tennessee folding occurs at many scales.

The Principle of Horizontality is a core tenet of geology. It proposes that beds of sedimentary rock were originally horizontal. Compressional forces squeeze sedimentary strata into folds during orogenies, so folding is easiest to see in sedimentary strata because rocks that were originally flat are tilted or folded. Folds exist at all scales. Some are microscopic features, whereas others are regional in scale and mappable over long distances. Some are shaped like arches (anticlines) and others like troughs (synclines). Strata may also be downwarped in a three-dimensional basin or upwarped as a dome. Both result in circular surface patterns, as seen in the area surrounding Nashville.

Joints are sets of parallel cracks that develop in solid, brittle rocks that were strained to their breaking point, and they can form in several ways. Some are the result of tectonic activity, and they develop perpendicular to the direction of either tension or compression. Often, rocks contain several joint sets that are oriented in different directions as a result of multiple tectonic events. Joints may also form as rocks shrink and swell with changing temperature. Some form as volcanic rock cools and contracts, for example. Most jointing in Tennessee resulted from the tectonic stresses associated with Appalachian mountain building. In addition to providing clues about an area's geologic history, joints create paths for groundwater, thereby aiding weathering, erosion, karst development, and mineralization. Breakage along joints may create steep bluffs or cliffs, as is the case along the margins of the Cumberland Plateau.

A folded ridge of sandstone is exposed at the north end of the Sequatchie Valley anticline in Cumberland County. Sequatchie Valley formed from the erosion of the Sequatchie Valley anticline. (35.787161N, 85.021324W) —Chuck Sutherland photo

GEOLOGIC TIME SCALE

EON	ERA	PERIOD / EPOCH		AGE (millions of years)	MAJOR EVENTS IN THE HISTORY OF LIFE	MAJOR GEOLOGIC EVENTS IN TENNESSEE
PHANEROZOIC	CENOZOIC	QUATERNARY	HOLOCENE			stream and river erosion continues across Tennessee; Mississippi River becomes a meandering river and karst expands
				0.01		
			PLEISTOCENE		modern humans	12,000 years ago humans arrive in Tennessee
						Mississippi River delivers sand, gravel, and loess to West Tennessee; mastodons and mammoths preserved in sediments
					North American ice ages	spruce-forested mountain scree and talus slopes develop in Tennessee Blue Ridge
				2.6		
		NEOGENE	PLIOCENE			extensive erosion continues across most of Tennessee; rivers deposit gravel in Mississippi Embayment
				5.3		
			MIOCENE			diverse flora and fauna preserved in sinkhole sediments at Gray Fossil Site
				23		
		PALEOGENE	OLIGOCENE			ocean withdraws from Mississippi Embayment for last time
				34		
			EOCENE			shoreline fluctuates; marine and nonmarine sedimentation in the Mississippi Embayment; ancestral Mississippi River forms; erosion throughout Middle and East Tennessee
				56		
			PALEOCENE			
				66		
	MESOZOIC	CRETACEOUS			great extinction / earliest flowers	Mississippi Embayment forms as North America passes over the Bermuda hot spot; marine deposition in Mississippi Embayment; erosion throughout Middle and East Tennessee
				145		
		JURASSIC				no rock record in Tennessee — Pangea breaks up and continents move toward present-day locations; east coast of North America becomes a passive margin as Atlantic Ocean forms
				201		
		TRIASSIC			dinosaurs and first mammals	
				252		
	PALEOZOIC	PERMIAN			greatest extinction	
				299		
		PENNSYLVANIAN			first reptiles	Alleghanian orogeny (330–240 million years ago) occurs with formation of Pangea; ancestral Appalachian Mountains form; faulting, deformation, and metamorphism in East Tennessee; growing mountains become sediment source; abundant forests and coal swamps preserved in Cumberland Plateau region
				323		
		MISSISSIPPIAN			abundant crinoids	a warm, shallow sea and carbonate platform are widespread across Tennessee until the end of the period, when deposition changes from marine to terrestrial as Laurentia and Africa collide
				359		
		DEVONIAN			treelike plants	organic black shale deposited across East and Middle Tennessee
					first land vertebrates	Acadian orogeny (390–350 million years ago) occurs in northeast Laurentia; uplift and erosion in East Tennessee
				419		
		SILURIAN			first land plants	marine deposition continues in Middle and West Tennessee as Nashville Dome is intermittently above and below sea level; lagoons, barrier islands, and shallow marine conditions develop in East Tennessee
				444		
		ORDOVICIAN			many marine groups evolve	Iapetus Ocean closes; Taconic orogeny (480–440 million years ago) occurs; volcanism and uplift along eastern Laurentian margin; subsidence occurs and a shallow sea transgresses across Tennessee
						karst develops on exposed carbonate rocks as ocean regresses; stable carbonate platform persists until Middle Ordovician time
				485		
		CAMBRIAN			first fossil shells / stromatolites	eastern passive margin develops and sea level rises; sediment erodes from continental interior
				541		
PRECAMBRIAN	PROTEROZOIC	LATE (NEOPROTEROZOIC)			algae and jellyfish	Rodinia breaks up and rift basins form along eastern continental margin; Iapetus Ocean begins to form; Reelfoot rift develops and fails in West Tennessee
				1,000		
		MIDDLE (MESOPROTEROZOIC)				supercontinent Rodinia forms and Grenville orogeny (1,200–900 million years ago) creates basement rocks that are exposed in East Tennessee
				1,600		
		EARLY (PALEOPROTEROZOIC)				
				2,500		
	ARCHEAN				first life (bacteria)	no rock record in Tennessee
				4,000		
	HADEAN				Earth forms	
				4,600		

Events in Tennessee through geologic time with numbers in millions of years.

TENNESSEE'S GEOLOGIC HISTORY

No Himalayan-scale mountains exist in Tennessee today, but they did several times in Tennessee's geologic past! The geologic history of Tennessee includes not millions, but billions of years. Some geologic processes happen relatively quickly—earthquakes, landslides, volcanic eruptions, hurricanes, and floods—but most happen very, very slowly. The rocks and sediments we see at the surface in Tennessee today provide clues about the environments that existed in the distant past, such as those very tall mountains that no longer exist. In general, geologists know more about younger rocks than older rocks because older rocks are often covered by younger rocks and may have been subjected to millennia of deformation and erosion. As a general rule, the rocks under your feet are younger as you travel from east to west across Tennessee.

Geologic time is a tough concept to wrap one's mind around, so compressing Earth's 4.6 billion years of history into one calendar year, a quantity of time with which we are far more familiar, can serve as a useful metaphor. In doing so, one day represents 12,300,000 years of geologic time, one hour represents 512,000 years, one minute represents 8,550 years, and one second represents 142 years. By this scale, the first fossils, which appear in the fossil record about 3.5 billion years ago, appear on March 22, just 81 days into the year, and Homo sapiens appears just 10 minutes before the end of the year.

In the late 1600s, pioneering geologists figured out that the oldest layers of sedimentary strata are at the bottom, and the younger layers at the top. Consequently, geologists typically describe the order of events through time from oldest to youngest, and from the bottom upward. They also noticed that fossils preserved in sedimentary rock record evolutionary change through time. These two fundamental observations, called the Principle of Superposition and the Principle of Faunal Succession, respectively, are the tenets on which the geologic time scale is based. This system allows geologists to correlate more than 4 billion years of Earth history across the globe.

Major units of time are divided into supereons, eons, eras, periods, and epochs. The names of time units within the geologic time scale come from locations where rocks of a certain age were first described. The boundaries between time units mark major Earth history events, but units do not include the same amount of time. Boundaries are typically determined by a major extinction event that resulted in the end of one life-form and the subsequent emergence of another. The first approximately 4 billion years of Earth history are the exception, because there was little to no life on the planet. For rocks this old, absolute ages, measured through chemical means, are used.

The geologic time scale helps geologists determine whether a geologic formation is older or younger than another, thereby creating a relative order of events. For absolute ages, which provide a narrow time range, geologists utilize dating methods that rely on radioactive elements, such as uranium, potassium,

Jeletzkytes nodosus, *a fast-moving predator in Tennessee's Cretaceous-age seas, is from a family of extinct marine animals called ammonites that were related to nautiloids, octopuses, and squids.* Jeletzkytes nodosus *is also an index fossil, a species that lived over a broad area for a relatively restricted period of time. Its presence in the Coon Creek Formation helps date the unit as 70 to 71 million years old. The scale is in centimeters.* —Tammy Braithwaite, Pink Palace Museum photo

argon, beryllium, and carbon, that occur naturally in rocks. Over time, these elements break down and turn into other elements at a known rate. Therefore, the ratio of the original, or "parent," element to the new, or "daughter," element can be used to determine when the rock formed. Radiometric dating techniques are most useful for igneous and metamorphic rocks but not sedimentary rocks. Most minerals containing radioactive elements do not form during sedimentary processes.

PRECAMBRIAN

The first 4 billion years of Earth history, nearly 90 percent of it, is included in the Precambrian Supereon. The Precambrian Supereon includes the Hadean, Archean, and Proterozoic Eons. Some of Earth's oldest rocks were formed during the Hadean Eon, more than 4 billion years ago. These rocks, located in northwest Canada, were part of a stable continental craton called Laurentia. Through geologic time, younger rocks were added to Laurentia's margins as tectonic plates bumped into, moved away from, and slid past the ancient craton.

PROTEROZOIC EON
2,500 TO 541 MILLION YEARS AGO

Tennessee's geologic story begins more than 1 billion years ago during the middle and late eras of the Proterozoic Eon. (It undoubtedly began earlier; however, no rocks older than those of the Proterozoic Eon are exposed at the surface in Tennessee). Geologists refer to the rocks of this age as basement rocks because they are the oldest crystalline rocks of the continent, on which thousands of feet of younger sedimentary strata were deposited. The basement that underlies Tennessee is made of more than 1-billion-year-old, silica-rich igneous and metamorphic rocks. These rocks are buried beneath Paleozoic,

Mesozoic, and Cenozoic strata throughout most of Tennessee, and often they can only be sampled and studied from drill cores. They are exposed in a few places in northeastern Tennessee.

By about 1 billion years ago, the southern and eastern sides of Laurentia had collided with continental fragments that would eventually become South America, Europe, and Africa. A major mountain building event, known as the Grenville orogeny, was the result of the formation of the supercontinent called Rodinia, which was the amalgamation of most of Earth's landmasses. The mountain chain created during the collisions of these continents, called the Grenville Mountains, extended more than 3,000 miles, between what are now Mexico, Texas, and Newfoundland. They were located approximately where today's Ouachita and Appalachian Mountains are. The range also extended onto other cratons, thereby forming a suture between several landmasses. The Grenville Mountains were likely comparable to the Alps and possibly the Himalayas. Rocks that formed during the Grenville orogeny underlie much of East Tennessee but are exposed only in the northeastern part of the state. These igneous and metamorphic rocks include the Max Patch Granite, Cranberry Gneiss, and Carvers Gap/Cloudland Gneiss.

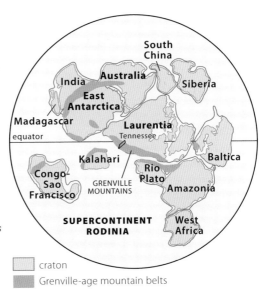

The supercontinent Rodinia formed about 1 billion years ago as most of Earth's landmasses collided. These continental collisions resulted in the formation of long, linear mountain chains, including the Grenville Mountains. These mountains extended the length of eastern Laurentia, from Texas to Newfoundland and onto neighboring cratons, acting as sutures between the landmasses.

At about 760 million years ago, tectonic plate motions changed and Rodinia began to break into continent-size fragments. In the area that is now West Tennessee, the crust thinned and stretched as it began to separate. A linear rift valley, called the Reelfoot rift, formed between what are now southern Illinois and southern Arkansas. At New Madrid, Missouri, the Reelfoot rift split into three segments that extended into Missouri, Indiana, and Kentucky. Steeply dipping normal faults defined the rift valley margins. These faults vertically displaced basement rock up to nearly 2 miles. In some areas, molten rock

The Cloudland/Carvers Gap Gneisses, exposed in the Roan Highlands of northeast Tennessee, formed during the Grenville orogeny. —Arthur Merschat photo

worked its way to the surface along faults, penetrating zones of weakened rock. Movement along these faults has continued periodically.

For reasons not well understood, the Reelfoot rift ceased to open by the end of the Cambrian Period, and Laurentia did not break apart along the rift. The failed rift remains an important area of crustal weakness that has influenced the location of the Mississippi Embayment, the Mississippi River, and intraplate earthquakes in the New Madrid Seismic Zone, located at the northern end of the Reelfoot rift.

In southeast Laurentia, most of the rifting occurred near the Grenville Mountains, including the area of East Tennessee. Igneous dikes and sills were emplaced along faults within the basement rocks as the crust stretched and thinned. These intrusions, known as the Bakersville Gabbro and Beech Granite, are present within the crystalline basement rocks of northeast Tennessee.

Several disconnected, fault-bounded rift basins formed during Rodinia's early rifting phase about 750 million years ago. The basins were not completely open to the ocean but did have some marine influence. A variety of sedimentary rock types, their sediment eroded from highlands located to the northwest, west, and southeast, accumulated in the Mount Rogers Basin of northeast Tennessee, southwest Virginia, and northwest North Carolina. These rocks, which include the Konnarock and Mount Rogers Formations, record nearby volcanic activity (rhyolite and basalt) as well as stream and lake environments

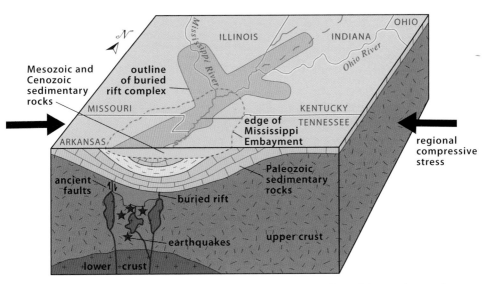

The Reelfoot rift is an important regional crustal feature that formed during the initial rifting of the supercontinent Rodinia. The rift is buried under thousands of feet of Phanerozoic-age sediment but has influenced the location of the Mississippi Embayment and the Mississippi River. Movement on the ancient faults generates small earthquakes and sometimes creates surface deformation on associated younger faults. Larger earthquakes, such as the New Madrid earthquakes of 1811 and 1812, occur on a time frame of a few hundred to thousands of years. —Modified from Braile and others, 1986

The Konnarock Formation contains diamictite, a conglomeratic rock that includes clasts of a variety of shapes and sizes embedded within mudstone and sandstone. The rock type, age, and provenance of the clasts vary. Many are dominated by pink feldspar crystals and were derived from the 1.2-billion-year-old Cranberry Gneiss. The diamictite formed as alpine glaciers delivered sediment to a local lake. Larger rocks dropped out of floating glacial ice and into finer sediments on the lake bottom. Hammer head for scale. —James St. John photo

that were adjacent to the glaciated Grenville Mountains. The Konnarock and Mount Rogers Formations are exposed in Tennessee only in northeastern Johnson County.

A second basin, called the Ocoee Basin, formed between northeastern Tennessee and northern Georgia. More than 30,000 feet of marine and non-marine sedimentary rocks of the Ocoee Supergroup accumulated in the basin. These rocks were also made from sediments eroded from the Grenville Mountains. Ocoee Supergroup rocks are exposed throughout Tennessee's Blue Ridge physiographic province. East of the Mount Rogers and Ocoee Basins, the rifted edge of the Laurentian craton widened to form the Iapetus Ocean, a predecessor of the Atlantic.

The global record of Precambrian life for the first 4 billion years is mainly limited to single-celled organisms such as bacteria and algae; however, multicellular, soft-bodied animals such as jellyfish have been found around the world in the youngest Proterozoic-age rocks. They were first discovered and are best preserved in the Flinders Range of South Australia. Questionable Precambrian-age fossils have been found in Tennessee in the Sandsuck Formation at the top of the Walden Creek Group, the youngest of the Ocoee Supergroup units.

PALEOZOIC TIME

Laurentia was located about 20 degrees south of the equator during most of Paleozoic time. During the Cambrian Period, the first of seven periods of the Paleozoic Era, a surge in evolution produced nearly all modern animal groups. A similar swell in biodiversity occurred during the Ordovician Period. Marine invertebrates flourished early in the Paleozoic Era, and marine vertebrates, especially fishes and sharks, amphibians, reptiles, insects, fungi and primitive plants became well-established by the end of the era.

The supercontinent Pangea formed at the end of the Paleozoic Era. As eastern Laurentia and Africa slowly smashed together during its formation, their collision created a continuous mountain chain along today's eastern edge of North America. The Appalachian Mountains we see today are the eroded remnants of these mountains. The mountain building event, known as the Alleghanian orogeny, was one of four orogenies ultimately responsible for the formation of the Appalachians. The others are the Grenville orogeny of the Proterozoic Eon, and the Taconic and Acadian orogenies of the Paleozic Era.

The Paleozoic Era ended with the Great Dying, the most severe mass extinction in Earth history. As much as 96 percent of all marine species may have gone extinct. Massive volcanic eruptions in Siberia, and possibly one or more asteroid impacts off the coast of northwest Australia, Brazil, and East Antarctica, occurred during the same time frame and may have been responsible for the extinction event.

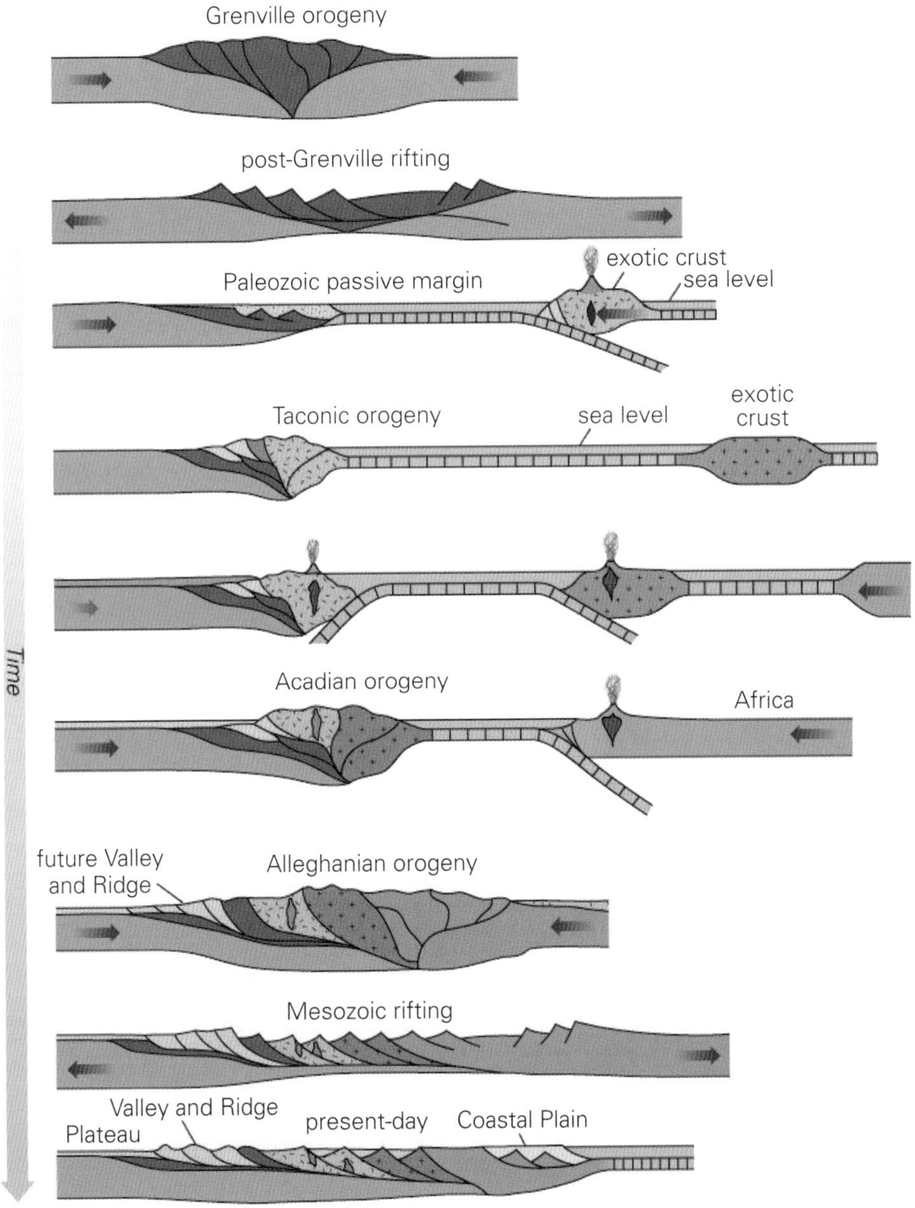

Grenville orogeny

post-Grenville rifting

Paleozoic passive margin — exotic crust — sea level

Taconic orogeny — sea level — exotic crust

Acadian orogeny — Africa

future Valley and Ridge — Alleghanian orogeny

Mesozoic rifting

Valley and Ridge — present-day — Coastal Plain
Plateau

Time

The rocks of the Appalachian Mountains are the result of four main mountain building events that affected eastern Laurentia. Three occurred during the Paleozoic Era. The mountains we see today are the eroded remnants of a Himalaya-scale mountain range that sutured together eastern Laurentia and Africa during the formation of Pangea. —

Figure 11.32, from *Earth: Portrait of a Planet*, Fifth Edition by Stephen Marshak. Copyright © 2015, 2012, 2008, 2005, 2001 by W.W. Norton & Company, Inc. Used by permission of W. W. Norton & Company, Inc.

CAMBRIAN PERIOD
541 TO 485 MILLION YEARS AGO

By about 550 million years ago, Laurentia had drifted from other continental masses as a result of the breakup of Rodinia, and the Grenville Mountains had eroded to near sea level. Most of the southeastern Laurentian margin was low relief. Sea level rose during Cambrian time as a warming climate caused glaciers to melt all over the world. The Iapetus coastline began to shift inland in one of the first major marine transgressions of the Paleozoic Era. Warm, shallow tropical seas covered much of the continent by the end of the Cambrian Period and persisted in the southeastern part of the continent through the Early Ordovician Period.

The Cambrian-age ocean teemed with life. Cyanobacteria built mounds, called stromatolites, that are preserved in Cambrian-age carbonates in East Tennessee. Trilobites, an early group of marine scavengers, are preserved in Tennessee's Cambrian-age rocks, as are many types of trace fossils, such as the burrows, borings, tracks, and trails of marine invertebrate animals. The fossils of shelled animals are more common in late Cambrian rocks.

Modern-day stromatolites, pictured here at low tide in Shark Bay, Australia, are often referred to as "living fossils" because they represent one of Earth's earliest life-forms. These rock-like structures are colonies of single-celled microbes that thrive in warm, coastal areas just as they did in Tennessee's Cambrian ocean. Fossilized stromatolites are preserved in several of the state's Cambrian-age formations, including the Copper Ridge Dolomite of East Tennessee. —Hans Arne Nakrem photo

A. initial sea level

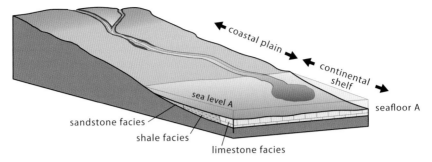

coastal plain

continental shelf

sea level A

seafloor A

sandstone facies

shale facies

limestone facies

B. marine transgression: rising sea level

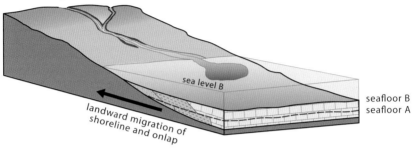

sea level B

seafloor B
seafloor A

landward migration of shoreline and onlap

C. marine transgression: rising sea level—coastal plain submergence

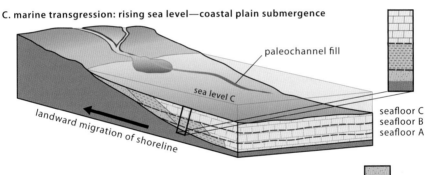

paleochannel fill

sea level C

landward migration of shoreline

seafloor C
seafloor B
seafloor A

D. marine regression: lowered sea level—coastal plain emergence

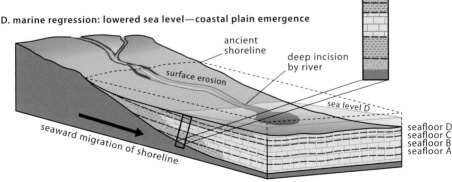

ancient shoreline

deep incision by river

surface erosion

sea level D

seaward migration of shoreline

seafloor D
seafloor C
seafloor B
seafloor A

During a marine transgression, sea level rises and the shoreline moves inland, while the opposite occurs during a marine regression. Tectonic events and severe climate changes may cause transgressions and regressions. Each cycle results in a characteristic stratigraphy that geologists use to reconstruct sea level history. Marine transgressions are identified in a stratigraphic section as a change from nearshore rocks, such as sandstone, to offshore rocks, such as shale and limestone. A marine regression has the opposite pattern. Tennessee's Paleozoic-age rocks record several major transgressions and regressions as well as many minor ones.

Sediments eroded from the stable continental interior were deposited on the Konnarock Formation, Ocoee Supergroup, and Grenville basement rocks. These sediments became the sedimentary rocks of the Chilhowee Group, including marine and nonmarine sandstone, siltstone, and shale. Basalts, which likely migrated upward along faults during the final stages of rifting, are layered with the earliest Chilhowee Group sediments. The Chilhowee Group was deposited during the transition from the active continental rifting of Rodinia to a tectonically quiet environment. The latter, known to geologists as a passive margin, became the norm along the coast of Laurentia for the next tens of millions of years. Chilhowee Group rocks are found between Newfoundland and Alabama and are exposed in a series of long, linear ridges. In Tennessee, they're found primarily in Polk, Blount, and Sevier Counties, including on Chilhowee Mountain, Buffalo Mountain, Holston Mountain, and the Iron Mountains.

The land inland of the eroded Grenville Mountains began to subside, and continued to do so throughout the Paleozoic Era, becoming the Appalachian Basin. A carbonate bank developed along the eastern part of the basin as the marine transgression continued. The bank faced the open ocean, and 1,300 to 2,000 feet of dolomite and limestone of the Shady Dolomite were deposited on it.

A broad tidal flat connected the carbonate bank and mainland Laurentia. Sand, siltstone, and shale derived from the continental interior were deposited across the flats and eventually covered the carbonate bank. The environment is preserved in the distinctive red, brown, and green sandstones, siltstones, shales, limestones, and evaporites of the Rome Formation. The Rome Formation is not exposed at the surface in Middle and West Tennessee, but it is present in the subsurface at least as far west as Nashville. It plays a major role in the structural geology of Tennessee's Valley and Ridge.

The marine transgression continued through middle and late Cambrian time. Carbonates were deposited across a shallow eastern bank while sand and mud eroded from the continental interior were deposited along western tidal flats. The boundary of the two environments oscillated in between. The result of this oscillation is the 2,000-foot-thick Conasauga Group, a sequence of alternating carbonate and shale layers. Cambrian-age strata are exposed at the surface in East Tennessee but are covered by younger strata in Middle and West Tennessee.

ORDOVICIAN PERIOD
485 TO 444 MILLION YEARS AGO

The Iapetus Ocean widened to its maximum width during Early Ordovician time, and Tennessee looked very similar to today's Bahama Islands and Florida Keys. The sea supported a rich diversity and abundance of invertebrate marine animals, including trilobites, mollusks, sponges, cephalopods, and echinoderms. Fossils of these animals are preserved throughout Tennessee's Ordovician strata. Corals and bryozoans, which first appear in the fossil record during Ordovician time, are often found together because both animals built reefs in Tennessee's shallow waters. Much of Tennessee's Ordovician-age strata are composed of limestone that formed almost entirely from the accumulation of shells that were broken into small fragments by southeasterly storms, waves, and strong currents.

From Cambrian into Early Ordovician time, the sea covered a broad carbonate platform that extended across much of North America. In Tennessee, 3,000 to 5,000 feet of carbonates were deposited across the platform, which deepened westward. These strata, known collectively as the Knox Group, are exposed throughout Tennessee's Valley and Ridge and are buried beneath younger strata in Middle and West Tennessee. The Knox Group thickens westward into Middle Tennessee, differing from older carbonate strata that thin westward.

Global sea level fell about 470 million years ago, following the deposition of the Knox Group. The seas regressed from Laurentia, and Knox Group strata were exposed for about 10 million years over a broad area of the continent as far west as the present-day Rocky Mountains. River erosion and groundwater dissolution created a karst landscape, with an average of up to 250 feet of topographic relief in Tennessee and up to 400 feet in other areas. Geologists recognize this widespread erosional surface, an important time marker for the geology of North America, as the post-Knox or Middle Ordovician unconformity. It's also economically important in Tennessee. Zinc and barite deposits in Middle and East Tennessee are concentrated within the rubble of sinkholes that lie below the unconformity, and the ancient karst surface itself is also a target for petroleum exploration because hydrocarbons can become trapped in carbonates.

The cause of such a widespread unconformity remains somewhat controversial. It's unlikely that the tectonic events that occurred along the eastern Laurentian margin would cause sea level to lower over an area as broad as all of Laurentia; however, this tectonism may have been, at least partly, responsible for localized uplift along the eastern Laurentian margin.

Much of Tennessee's Ordovician-age limestone is made from densely packed shell fragments that accumulated in warm, shallow seas. The fossils of numerous animals, including brachiopods, crinoids, and bryozoans, are preserved in this sample from the Carters Limestone of Middle Tennessee. Note hammer head for scale.
—Steve Smail photo

The post-Knox unconformity is exposed at Dandridge Municipal Park, located off TN 92. The irregular erosional surface is near the top of the staff (marked in decimeters). Brecciated limestone and chert clasts lie in low areas of the ancient karst surface at the top of the Knox Group strata. The Lenoir Limestone overlies the unconformity. —John T. Haynes photo

In Middle Ordovician time, the Iapetus Ocean began to close, and eastern Laurentia changed from a passive to an active tectonic margin—the beginning of the Taconic orogeny. An eastward-dipping subduction zone partially melted overlying crust, and an island arc developed on the overriding tectonic plate. Small intervening ocean basins closed as subduction continued, and the islands collided with eastern Laurentia. Compressional forces, along with the weight of new continental material, caused the Laurentian crust to downwarp west of the rising Taconic Mountains. Rapid subsidence created a foreland basin there, a structural basin that develops adjacent and parallel to an actively forming mountain belt. Foreland basins are wedge shaped: deeper close to the mountains and shallower inland. Clastic sediments eroded off neighboring highlands accumulated in the foreland basin as it subsided.

The foreland basin, still part of the Appalachian Basin, extended along the western front of the new mountains between Alabama and New York. During Middle and Late Ordovician time, both submarine landslides and west-flowing rivers brought sediments to the eastern part of the basin that became shales, siltstones, and sandstones. Carbonates were deposited in the shallow, western part of the basin, which was closer to the continental interior and farther from the eroding Taconic Mountains. Corals and bryozoans and other organisms constructed reef complexes in shallower areas. The carbonate and clastic sediments overlapped in the middle of the basin. Collectively, these sedimentary rocks make up the Chickamauga Group.

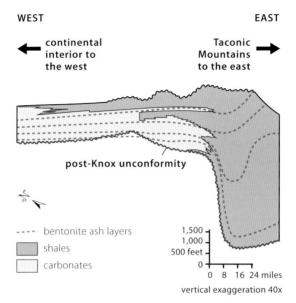

WEST

EAST

continental
interior to
the west

Taconic
Mountains
to the east

post-Knox unconformity

- - - - bentonite ash layers

shales

carbonates

1,500
1,000
500 feet

0

0   8   16 24 miles

vertical exaggeration 40x

Cross-sectional reconstruction of the asymmetrical Appalachian Basin during Middle and Late Ordovician time. The asymmetrical shape is characteristic of foreland basins, which are deeper close to the mountain range and shallower toward the continental interior. Erosion of the Taconic highlands created a thick sequence of shales, siltstones, sandstones, and conglomerates that filled the eastern part of the basin. Carbonates formed in the shallower western part. The facies interfingered in the central part of the basin where depositional environments overlapped and oscillated. Volcanic ash layers (dashed lines) are also preserved in these strata. These sedimentary rocks make up the Middle and Late Ordovician Chickamauga Group and the Juniata Formation. —Modified from Walker and others, 1983; Lemiszki and Kohl, 2006

Clastic sedimentation persisted in Late Ordovician time in the eastern part of the basin. Broad tidal flats and shallow marine environments, which received sediments from the eroding upland to the east, are preserved in the Bays Formation and Martinsburg Shale of the Chickamauga Group, and the Juniata Formation. These rocks are exposed in Tennessee's Valley and Ridge physiographic province.

Clastic sedimentary rocks of the Chickamauga Group grade westward into the carbonate-dominated strata of the Stones River and Nashville Groups of Middle Tennessee. These strata formed in the shallow, western extension of the sea at the same time the clastic sediments were deposited in East Tennessee. Although they are well exposed in Middle Tennessee, they are mostly covered by younger sediments of the Cumberland Plateau in East Tennessee, except in Sequatchie Valley, where erosion has exposed them.

Geologists have mapped several disconformities and preserved stream channels in Middle Tennessee's Middle Ordovician rocks. These surfaces suggest that the Nashville Dome, a structural uplift in Middle Tennessee, was periodically exposed as an island during Middle Ordovician time. When submerged, sedimentation was continuous across the basin. When exposed, the dome was eroded.

Several layers of rhyolite ash ejected from island arc volcanoes are preserved in Tennessee's Middle Ordovician strata. The volcanic eruptions occurred as the volcanic island arcs and continental fragments collided with eastern Laurentia. The eruptions are, both in areal extent and volume, comparable to some of the largest eruptions in the geologic record. Wind and ocean currents redeposited the volcanic ash over the eastern and central United States, carrying it as far west as Oklahoma, south to Alabama, and north to southern Ontario. In the shallow ocean the ash mixed with calcium carbonate. Over time the calcareous ash was chemically altered to a potassium-rich clay called bentonite. Each ash bed is chemically unique—a property that makes them relatively easy to correlate over a broad area. Ash layers also make good time markers because they are deposited over a very short period of time, geologically speaking, so they can provide very detailed age information for the formations in which they are found.

The Carters Limestone contains layers of bentonite clay (dashed white lines) that started as volcanic ash that settled to the bottom of Tennessee's oceans during the Taconic orogeny. The ash beds are relatively easy to identify; both their color and texture contrast with the carbonate rocks above and below. Bentonite erodes more easily than limestone and dolomite, so it forms recesses in the rock face. This outcrop is on I-840 between Lebanon and Gladeville. (36.139301N, 86.382175W) —Steve Smail photo

Red calcareous shales, siltstones, and sandstones of the Bays Formation are well exposed at Dodson Mountain, along TN 70 southeast of Rogersville. Oxidation of iron-rich minerals found in the deltaic and shallow marine sediments caused the red color. The Bays Formation is near vertical here as a result of folding and thrust faulting during late Paleozoic time. (36.342182N, 82.949730W) —John T. Haynes photo

SILURIAN PERIOD
444 TO 419 MILLION YEARS AGO

High-latitude glaciers that formed during Ordovician time began to melt during the Silurian Period, and global sea level rose. Sediments continued to erode off the Taconic Mountains into the Appalachian Basin, and west- and south-flowing rivers deposited sand along the basin's eastern beaches. This well-sorted, white sandstone, the Clinch Sandstone, is well exposed at Clinch Mountain. Farther south and west, the finer-grained Rockwood Formation was deposited on the continental shelf. These calcareous marine sandstones, silt-stones, and shales are exposed along the eastern Cumberland escarpment and on White Oak Mountain. The Rockwood Formation was an important source of Tennessee iron during the late nineteenth and early twentieth centuries.

Silurian-age strata in Middle and West Tennessee are very different from equivalent units in East Tennessee. The Rockwood Formation grades westward into calcareous shale and limestone units that are exposed in the Sequatchie Valley and Middle and West Tennessee. These areas were far from the sediment source of the Taconic Mountains and, therefore, more susceptible to sea level fluctuations and midcontinent tectonic activity. The Nashville Dome, along with several other regional structural features that were located west and north of Tennessee, was sometimes above and sometimes below sea level during the Silurian Period. This resulted in the erosion of older strata as well as areas

Strata of the Silurian-age Brownsport Group were deposited in a shallow sea along the western edge of the Nashville Dome. They are pictured here on US 641/TN 69 in Decatur County. (35.442306N, 88.064877W) —Chuck Sutherland photo

of complexly overlapping depositional environments. Alternating layers of highly fossiliferous calcareous shale and limestone were deposited on a mixed carbonate-clastic shelf on the west side of the Nashville Dome at the end of Silurian time and the beginning of Devonian time. These strata, including the Decatur Limestone and the Brownsport and Wayne Groups, are exposed in the Western Valley of the Tennessee River, and along larger stream valleys of the western Highland Rim.

DEVONIAN PERIOD
419 to 359 million years ago

Sea level began to drop at the end of the Silurian Period, and the shallow sea regressed westward. The area between the Nashville Dome and the Reelfoot rift remained submerged during Early Devonian time. Highly fossiliferous silt-stones and limestones of the Ross Formation and chert of the Harriman and Camden Formations preserve this period of deposition in West Tennessee. These units are exposed along the Western Valley of the Tennessee River.

The sea regressed from West Tennessee following the deposition of the Camden Formation, and erosion of the exposed seabed formed the first of two major unconformities of the Devonian Period. Sea level rose again, and the Pegram Formation was deposited. Then, in Middle Devonian time, the sea regressed once more, and another period of extensive erosion across Tennessee followed. In some areas of East Tennessee, strata as old as Middle Ordovician age were removed. It is unclear which erosional period is responsible for this erosion because much of the Pegram Formation was removed from its original area of deposition.

By the end of the Devonian Period, much of the interior eastern United States and Canada was again covered by a shallow sea that remained into the Early Mississippian Period. The Acadian orogeny, the second of eastern Laurentia's Paleozoic mountain building events, occurred at this time. The Acadian orogeny affected the New England area more intensely than Tennessee. There, microcontinents and islands collided with Laurentia as the Iapetus Ocean continued to close, forming mountains. Sediments eroded from the mountains were carried southward and westward as part of large delta systems. Over a period of about 14 million years, organic-rich black shales and fine sands blanketed the Appalachian Basin and the continental shelf. The shale covered much of interior Laurentia, including Canada. In Tennessee and other places, this distinctive black shale is called the Chattanooga Shale.

Exposures of Chattanooga Shale are fairly limited because it erodes into soils that support heavy vegetation. Geologists first described the Chattanooga Shale from exposures in downtown Chattanooga on the north side of Cameron Hill. The unit is visible along the eastern Cumberland escarpment and in many locations throughout the Valley and Ridge physiographic province. It is also exposed along the margins of the Central Basin, in the Flynn Creek impact structure in

The Chattanooga Shale, a distinctive black and finely laminated marker bed, can be traced throughout Middle and East Tennessee. Oxidization of the iron sulfide minerals pyrite and marcasite give weathered surfaces a rusty red and yellow color. The unit is pictured here at the Flynn Creek impact structure near Gainesboro. (36.280006N, 85.668889W) —Chuck Sutherland photo

Middle Tennessee, and in the Western Valley of the Tennessee River. The Chattanooga Shale is nearly 2,000 feet thick in northeastern Tennessee but nearly absent near Hohenwald and completely absent in areas of Middle Tennessee, where part of the Nashville Dome was likely above sea level as the clay was being deposited. Across Tennessee, surface exposures of the Chattanooga Shale average 20 to 30 feet thick. An exception is in the Flynn Creek impact structure, where the shale is 200 feet thick. A Late Devonian meteor impact deformed and thickened the lower part of the shale before the upper part of the unit was deposited. Although scarce, spores from Tennessee's first land plants and bones and scales of Tennessee's first fish are fossilized in the Chattanooga Shale.

Similar black shale beds were deposited in many locations around the world when the Chattanooga Shale was being deposited. For many years geologists thought that black shales formed only in deep, stagnant, oxygen-depleted waters, but it would be highly unusual for such conditions to exist over widespread areas of the world simultaneously. New research indicates that many of these black shales formed in shallower water, perhaps only a few hundred feet deep at most. The Chattanooga Shale contains thin beds of siltstone and sandstone, which are not ordinarily found in deep, stagnant waters, and sedimentary structures indicate the Chattanooga Shale was subjected to energetic storm surges and erosive bottom currents. In addition, evidence of sediment reworked by animals means the basin was not oxygen depleted. The shale contains few macroscopic fossils, with only low numbers of small brachiopods, conodonts, crinoids, and some plant material. Much of the organic matter that makes the shale black came from dense mats of floating algae and other microscopic animals that lived in the water column. In large die-offs, similar to the algal blooms that happen today in the Gulf Coast region, the algal mats sank to the ocean bottom where they were eventually buried and compacted.

In many areas of the world black shales are economically important as a source for hydrocarbons. The Chattanooga Shale is so organic rich that fresh surfaces smell like petroleum. The shale also contains small amounts of low-grade uranium, which decays to radon gas. People living in houses on top of the Chattanooga Shale need to monitor for this gas. The secret World War II effort at Oak Ridge, where factories separated uranium ore for the Manhattan Project, considered using uranium from the Chattanooga Shale. Ultimately, it was not used because extracting the disseminated element wasn't cost-effective.

MISSISSIPPIAN PERIOD
359 TO 323 MILLION YEARS AGO

A warm, shallow sea covered much of Laurentia throughout Mississippian time, the last time in Tennessee's geologic history that a sea covered the entire state. Deposition of the Chattanooga Shale continued, while the Acadian Mountains continued to erode in northeastern Laurentia. The Chattanooga Shale grades upward into the Maury Formation, an easy-to-recognize, 1-to-4-foot-thick green mudstone that owes its color to the mineral glauconite. It forms a sharp visual contrast to the underlying black Chattanooga Shale and the overlying yellowish-gray, chert-rich carbonates and siltstones of the Fort

Payne Formation. Fish bone fragments and microfossils can be found in the Maury Formation, often concentrated in phosphate nodules that are up to 1 foot in diameter.

Following the deposition of the Fort Payne Formation, a thick sequence of chert-rich carbonate rocks was deposited across Tennessee. Periodic influxes of mud, silt, and sand came from uplands to the north and east. The thickness of Mississippian-age strata totals more than 700 feet in Middle Tennessee and up to 5,000 feet in East Tennessee. These rocks record the transition from a deep, subsiding basin to a shallow carbonate platform that was stable for nearly 30 million years. Erosion has largely removed the Mississippian-age rocks that once extended across Tennessee, but they do form the resistant cap of Middle Tennessee's Highland Rim. They are also exposed in several areas of the Valley and Ridge and along the base of the Cumberland Plateau and Lookout Mountain in East Tennessee. Tennessee's largest caves are found within Mississippian-age limestones.

Great numbers of marine invertebrates, as well as fish, sharks, and rays, flourished in the Mississippian seas. The Mississippian Period is nicknamed the Age of Crinoids because these animals diversified then. They thrived along the sloped margins of Tennessee's carbonate ramps, where they built reefs with other animals, such as bryozoans. Tennessee's Mississippian-age limestones are highly fossiliferous and, in many areas, are made up of the shells of reef-builders and other marine invertebrates, such as corals and mollusks. The ancient reefs, called bioherms, are an important source of hydrocarbons in Middle and East Tennessee.

Ordovician- to Mississippian-age strata are exposed throughout Middle Tennessee, particularly where highways cut through erosional remnants of the Highland Rim. Limestone of the Ordovician-age Fernvale Member is exposed at the base of the roadcut, and the Mississippian-age Fort Payne Formation caps the hill at this exposure on Old Hickory Boulevard west of Nashville. (36.0923897N, 86.922884W) —Chuck Sutherland photo

Crinoid fossils are a common find in Tennessee's Mississippian-age rocks, especially the plates that make up their stems and arms. These samples from White County include calyxes, a much rarer find. —Chuck Sutherland photo

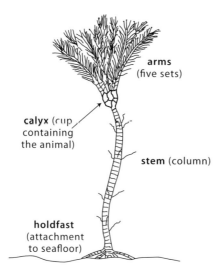

arms
(five sets)

calyx (cup
containing
the animal)

stem (column)

holdfast
(attachment
to seafloor)

Crinoids attached to the ocean bottom with a column and holdfast. Feather-like appendages filtered and steered the food to the animal's mouth in the calyx. The animals' resemblance to plants earned them the nickname "sea lilies."

A pronounced tectonic change took place at the end of the Mississippian Period and continued to affect Laurentia through the Permian Period. As Africa approached Laurentia, the Iapetus Ocean closed and the Alleghanian orogeny developed as the continents collided. The extensive deformation that occurred overprinted that of the older orogenies that had affected Tennessee. The Alleghanian orogeny, which culminated in the development of the Appalachian Mountains we know today, was the last mountain building event to affect the eastern margin of North America.

In Tennessee, the onset of this orogeny is preserved in rocks of the Mississippian-age Pennington Formation. Its red and green shales, along with siltstone, sandstone, and thin beds of limestone and dolomite, were deposited in tidal flats and offshore sandbars along the edge of the closing Iapetus Ocean. The Pennington Formation is considered a transitional unit; it separates a thick sequence of underlying Mississippian-age marine carbonate rocks from a thick overlying sequence of nonmarine Pennsylvanian-age clastic rocks eroded from the rising Appalachian Mountains.

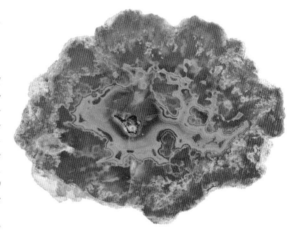

The Tennessee state mineral is the paint rock agate, a semi-precious variety of colorful, banded, fine-grained quartz. Paint Rock agate can be found in Franklin and Grundy Counties at the contact of the Bangor Limestone and the overlying Pennington Formation on the western side of the Cumberland Plateau, between elevations of 1,200 and 1,600 feet. This hand-sized sample was found outside Pelham.
—Will Smith photo

The Pennington Formation's distinctive red and green shales formed in tidal flats at the interface between land and sea. The unit is pictured along US 70 east of Sparta. (35.920874N, 85.398253W)
—Chuck Sutherland photo

PENNSYLVANIAN PERIOD
323 TO 299 MILLION YEARS AGO

The Alleghanian orogeny continued during the Pennsylvanian Period. A large thrust sheet of crystalline basement became detached from the Laurentian crust. Westward-directed forces pushed the thrust sheet inland, where it acted like a bulldozer, shoving Proterozoic- and Paleozoic-age rocks of the Appalachian Basin inland ahead of it along regional-scale, low-angle thrust faults. This movement created the foreland fold-and-thrust belt, mountainous foothills that formed as stacked thrust sheets repeated the same sections of sedimentary strata. Unlike strata located closer to the mountain core, sedimentary strata of fold-and-thrust belts are typically unmetamorphosed. The deeply eroded Alleghanian fold-and-thrust belt is preserved in the Valley and Ridge physiographic province. Regional-scale thrust faulting also affected the Cumberland Plateau, although faults occur in much younger rocks and are spaced much farther apart than those in the Valley and Ridge.

Tennessee was above sea level during the continental collision. Rivers similar in scale to the modern-day Amazon scoured underlying Mississippian-age limestones and carried large volumes of sediments from the mountains into the foreland basin. Pennsylvanian-age conglomerates and sandstones preserve braided and meandering river channels. The coastline, mainly southwest of

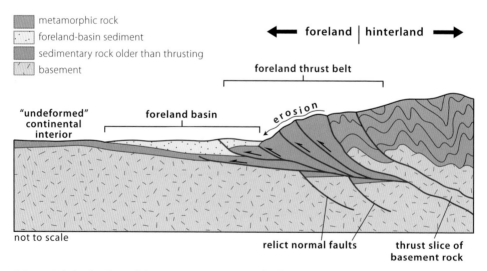

Mountain belts that formed during a major continental collision exhibit a distinctive geometry. Crystalline igneous and metamorphic rocks form the core of the mountain range, where the crust was thickened, deformed, and intensely metamorphosed. Older sedimentary strata were pushed ahead of the range where faulting produced stacked thrust sheets in the foreland fold-and-thrust belt. The weight of the new mountains and the fold-and-thrust belt depressed the continental margin, and a wedge-shaped foreland basin formed ahead of the mountain front. Sediments eroded from the adjacent highlands accumulated in the basin. —Adapted from "Figure 18.2a", from *Earth Structure, Second Edition* by Ben A. van der Pluijm and Stephen Marshak. Copyright © 2004 by W. W. Norton & Company, Inc. Used by permission of W. W. Norton & Company, Inc.

The Town Knobs thrust fault, exposed on TN 11W southwest of Rogersville, thrust Pumpkin Valley Shale over Conasauga Group carbonates, all of Cambrian age. This style of thrust faulting is typical of the Tennessee Valley and Ridge. (36.3788N, 83.0686W) —Marcy Davis photo

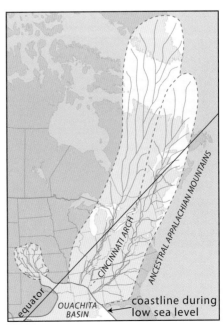

An Amazon-scale river system transported sediments eroded from the ancient Appalachian Mountains over vast floodplains and coastal swamplands to a southern sea. The headwaters of the rivers, located in the northern Appalachian Mountains, were 4,000 miles inland of the coastline. The river system is preserved in the Pennsylvanian-age strata of the Cumberland Plateau. Tennessee is outlined in green.
—Modified from Archer and Greb, 1995

Tennessee, was a dynamic place with coastal swamps, lagoons, tidal flats, large deltas, and migrating barrier islands.

Tennessee was close to the equator in Pennsylvanian time and its climate was tropical. Primitive plant fossils are common in rocks of this age. Roots, stems, bark, and leaves of plants related to modern club mosses, scale trees, ferns, horsetails, and rushes are preserved in coal seams and as casts and imprints in sandstones and shales. Fish scales, amphibian tracks, and invertebrate body and trace fossils are also well preserved in sedimentary rocks that were deposited in brackish areas along the coast.

Pennsylvanian-age strata contain casts, molds, and carbonized impressions of fossilized leaves, stems, roots, trunks, and bark. Pictured here are two modern tree trunks and three fossilized trunks of Lepidodendron, *a treelike plant that grew up to 100 feet tall and had a 3-foot-diameter trunk with a branching crown. The bark of the tree is known for its scaly, diamond-shaped pattern, a cast of which is pictured in inset. These fossils are from the Pennsylvanian-age strata in Morgan County.*
—Chuck Sutherland photos

Pennsylvanian-age rocks once extended across Tennessee but have been mostly eroded. In addition to the Cumberland Plateau, rocks of this age are found at Short Mountain in Cannon County, and at Grindstone Mountain, located in Hamilton County.

PERMIAN PERIOD
299 TO 252 MILLION YEARS AGO

By about 270 million years ago, most of the world's existing continents collided to form the supercontinent Pangea. Parts of what are now Europe, Africa, and South America collided with southern and eastern Laurentia, and the Iapetus Ocean closed. A continuous, Himalayan-scale mountain range extended from eastern Canada to Alabama, and southwest to Oklahoma, Texas, and Mexico. Most of the eastern United States, including Tennessee, was uplifted as part of the Pangea interior. Erosion during the following several hundred million years stripped Tennessee of its Permian geologic record, as well as that of most of the Mesozoic Era, and helped shape the physiographic provinces we see today.

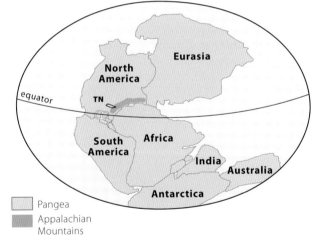

At the end of the Paleozoic Era, North America was part of the super-continent Pangea. The Appalachian Mountains formed during the convergence of Africa and Laurentia.

───────── **MESOZOIC TIME** ─────────

The Mesozoic Era, from 252 to 66 million years ago, is also known as the Age of Reptiles. It is divided into the Triassic, Jurassic, and Creta-ceous Periods. After remaining a supercontinent for about 100 million years, Pangea began to break apart late in the Triassic Period, and the modern continents began to drift toward their present-day locations. The Atlantic Ocean and Gulf of Mexico formed as Africa and South America rifted from eastern and southeastern North America. Pangea split along the suture of the ancient Appalachian Mountains, so parts of the range are found in Africa and Europe.

With the exception of West Tennessee, the state has been above sea level since the breakup of Pangea. Consequently, erosion has been the main surface process in Tennessee for roughly the last 200 million years. By the end of the Mesozoic Era, the Appalachian Mountains had eroded to an almost flat plain. All sedimentary rocks of Triassic and Jurassic age were stripped from Tennessee. Rivers breached the Nashville Dome and Sequatchie Valley anticline, removing Pennsylvanian-age strata and exposing the underlying Mississippian-age carbonate rocks to further erosion and karst development. West Tennessee developed as a low-relief coastal plain on Mississippian-age limestones until the Cretaceous Period, when the region was inundated by the sea. Marine and nonmarine sediments from this time are found in West Tennessee.

CRETACEOUS PERIOD
145 TO 66 MILLION YEARS AGO

Hot spots are intense, stationary heat sources located at the base of Earth's mantle. The North American tectonic plate drifted over one called the Bermuda hot spot about 100 million years ago. Igneous material rising from the mantle was injected into the crust below the Reelfoot rift and into faults along the rift's margin. The intrusions are not visible at the surface; however, drill holes in West Tennessee have intersected these igneous rocks.

The hot spot heated the crust beneath the Reelfoot rift and caused it to expand and rise as a structural and topographic arch that was nearly 2 miles high and 60 miles wide. This arch, called the Mississippi Embayment arch, extended from southern Illinois to Louisiana, superimposed over the old rift.

Erosion had worn the arch down to near sea level by about 85 million years ago. The North American tectonic plate drifted westward off the hot spot, and by about 80 million years ago the crust under the Reelfoot rift was cooling and subsiding. The subsidence and extensive erosion along the top of the arch formed a low-lying depression called the Mississippi Embayment. This erosional trough tilts gently southward and crosses parts of Illinois, Kentucky, Missouri, Tennessee, Arkansas, Alabama, and Louisiana. It is 200 miles wide and 300 miles long. An arm of the Western Interior Seaway, an inland sea that stretched between the Gulf of Mexico and the Arctic Ocean, filled the embayment at the end of the Cretaceous Period. Global sea level was more than 550 feet higher than today, inundating large areas of North America. With the exception of a couple of minor pulses of sea level rise during the Cenozoic Era, this was the last time that any part of Tennessee would be under marine waters.

By about 40 million years ago, the crust of the embayment had subsided to more than 1 mile below sea level at its southernmost point. The modern Mississippi River flows through the embayment today. The embayment contains up to nearly 4 miles of Phanerozoic sediments. Cretaceous- and Cenozoic-age marine and nonmarine units, which are relatively unconsolidated, are exposed around its edge like bathtub rings. On the northeast side of the bathtub, these strata are exposed in northeast-trending swaths across West Tennessee.

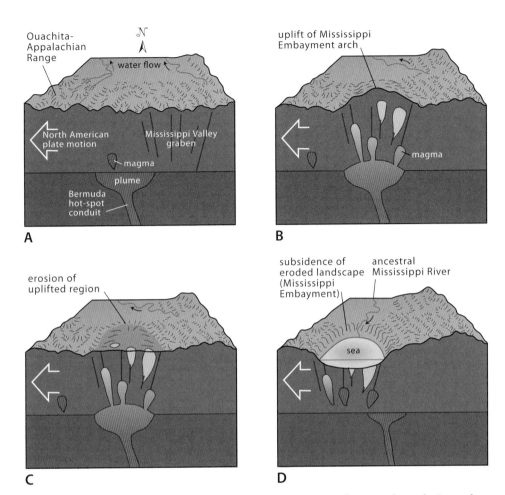

The Mississippi Embayment formed as the North American tectonic plate passed over the Bermuda hot spot during the Cretaceous Period. (a) The hot spot heated the crust in the area of the Reelfoot rift, (b) causing the crust to expand and rise as a structural and topographic arch called the Mississippi Embayment arch. Igneous material was injected into the crust along preexisting faults. (c) The arch was eroded to near sea level, and (d) the plate moved off the hot spot and the crust cooled and subsided. The extensive erosion along the top of the arch created a low spot that waters from the Gulf of Mexico filled, extending into the interior of the continent in Late Cretaceous and Cenozoic time. —From Van Arsdale and Cox, 2007

    The sediments eroded from the arch make up Tennessee's oldest Cretaceous unit, the Tuscaloosa Formation. Derived in part from underlying Paleozoic-age units, the coarse gravels of the Tuscaloosa are preserved in sinkholes and low areas of eroded Paleozoic-age limestone along the Western Valley of the Tennessee River, and on scattered hilltops of the western Highland Rim in Middle Tennessee. The most extensive exposures of Tuscaloosa Formation are south of Hohenwald in Wayne and Hardin Counties, and near Kentucky Lake in northwesternmost Middle Tennessee.

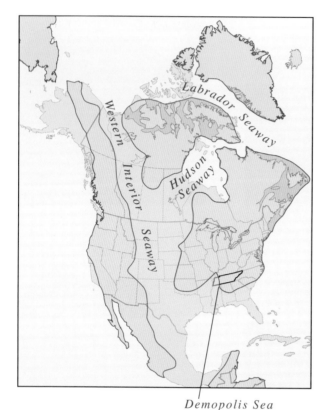

During the latter half of Cretaceous time, a large inland seaway split North America into two landmasses. It stretched from the Gulf of Mexico, through the central and western United States and Canada, to the Arctic Ocean. The Demopolis Sea, a bay on the east side of the Mississippi Embayment, covered parts of West Tennessee.

Demopolis Sea

Tennessee's oldest Cretaceous-age sedimentary rocks are conglomerates of the Tuscaloosa Formation, which contains coarse, cherty gravels with boulders up to 6 inches in diameter. —Roy Van Arsdale photo

Marine sediments were deposited in the embayment throughout Late Cretaceous time. Sand, silt, and clay were deposited in river deltas, lagoons, coastal swamps, tidal channels, and bays across the northern Mississippi Embayment, in a setting similar to the modern Gulf Coast. Many animals, including crabs, snails, clams, fish, sharks, and nautiluses, lived in these waters and are preserved in rocks in West Tennessee. The Coon Creek Formation, known the world over for exceptional fossil preservation, is perhaps the most famous unit of this age in Tennessee. These marine sediments make up the West Tennessee Uplands, where they lie on eroded Cambrian-to-Mississippian-age carbonates and cherts and dip gently westward under younger units.

A few dinosaur bones have been found in Cretaceous-age units of West Tennessee. The bones belong to a hadrosaur, a duck-billed dinosaur called *Edmontosaurus* (first identified and described in Alberta, Canada). Despite being an herbivore, the animal weighed a hefty 4 tons and was up to 40 feet long. Scientists also found a pterosaur vertebra in nearshore marine sediments of the Coon Creek Formation near Selmer in 2016. Pterosaurs are winged reptiles that are thought to be the earliest flying vertebrates.

The end of the Cretaceous Period is marked by the global extinction of many plants and animals, namely the dinosaurs. Several explanations have been put forward for the devastation of global ecosystems, including one or more meteorite impacts, extreme marine regression, and increased volcanism.

A skeletal reconstruction of Edmontosaurus *"Monty"* annectens *is on permanent display in front of the McClung Museum of Natural History and Culture on the University of Tennessee at Knoxville campus. The animal comes from a family of herbivorous duck-billed dinosaurs that roamed Tennessee in small herds during the Cretaceous Period. (35.952379N, 83.927127W)* —Travis Paris photo

CENOZOIC TIME

We live in the Cenozoic Era. It is divided into three periods and seven epochs, including the Holocene Epoch of today. The Cenozoic Era is referred to as the Age of Mammals and is defined largely by the evolutionary boom of mammals (including humans), birds, and flowering plants. The first flowering plants evolved during the Mesozoic Era, but by the Cenozoic Era they became the dominant type of land plant—a fact that is still true today. Fossilized mammals and flowering plants from the Cenozoic Era are found in East, Middle, and West Tennessee.

With the exception of West Tennessee, erosion continued throughout the state into the Cenozoic Era, and the modern landscape has developed over the last several million years. In West Tennessee, the situation remained very similar to late Cretaceous time. During times of sea level rise, the Gulf of Mexico extended into the northern Mississippi Embayment, where deep and shallow marine and nearshore sedimentary rocks were deposited. When sea level dropped, rivers grew southward.

PALEOGENE PERIOD
66 TO 23 MILLION YEARS AGO

Marine sedimentary rocks of the Midway Group were deposited during the Paleocene Epoch as a shallow sea entered the northern Mississippi Embayment. The group consists of relatively unconsolidated sand, silt, and clay. It also contains a high amount of kaolinite, a type of absorbent clay used for cat litter, oil spill products, and a number of other purposes.

Rocks overlying the Midway Group were deposited in the ancestral Mississippi River, which was well-established by about 40 million years ago in the Eocene Epoch. Streams and rivers meandered across a broad, forested, coastal floodplain. Ancient oxbow lakes and backswamps are preserved as clay lenses within layers of silt and sand. These clays, called ball clays, are mined in northern West Tennessee. Other clay bodies contain spectacular impressions of Eocene-age subtropical plants that were deposited in quiet water, probably a lagoon. These units also contain seams of lignite coal. The coal has not been

This leaf fossil is from the Claiborne Group of Eocene age. The scale is in millimeters.
—Hongshan Wang, Paleobotany and Palynology, Florida Museum of Natural History photo

mined because it is not economically viable. Eocene-age sands are important aquifers for West Tennessee and areas of neighboring states.

At the end of the Eocene Epoch and early Oligocene Epoch, the sea briefly returned to the northern Mississippi Embayment and West Tennessee one last time. Geologic evidence of this marine pulse is limited to siltstone, coal, and ancient soils of the Jackson Formation. It is poorly exposed in a narrow outcrop in the bluffs along the Mississippi River Valley. Following deposition of the Jackson Formation, the sea retreated southward, and Tennessee has been above sea level ever since.

NEOGENE PERIOD
23 TO 2.6 MILLION YEARS AGO

There is increasing evidence that the present-day topography of the southern Appalachian Mountains may have formed as recently as 7 million years ago. The ancient Appalachian Mountains had been eroded to low relief by the end of the Mesozoic Era, following the removal of thousands of feet of rock and sediment. The crust adjusted by moving upward during the Miocene Epoch, rejuvenating streams that rapidly cut into bedrock. New drainages overprinted older drainages that had developed when there was less relief. By some estimates, the relief of the southern Appalachian Mountains has increased by more than 150 percent since Miocene time.

A gap in Tennessee's Cenozoic sedimentary record occurs between the Oligocene and Pliocene Epochs, with the exception of the Gray Fossil Site in Washington County. There, Miocene-age plants and animals are fossilized in clays that accumulated in a sinkhole pond. The site includes many unique vertebrate fossils, including a rare species of red-faced panda. Tennessee contains no other Miocene-age strata.

Early in the Pliocene Epoch, the ancient Mississippi River Valley began to look very similar to the modern river valley, with a broad floodplain more than 60 miles wide at Memphis. The ancient Mississippi River followed a course

Red gravels of the Pliocene-to-Pleistocene-age Upland Complex were deposited by the ancient Mississippi River and its tributaries. Pleistocene-age loess overlies the Upland Complex. The contact between the two is near the top of the photo.
—Will Cupples photo

similar to the modern river's but drained a larger part of North America and had six to eight times the water discharge. The ancient floodplain was about 230 feet higher in elevation than the modern floodplain. Patches of red gravel, sand, silt, and clay up to 300 feet thick, deposited by the ancient river, are preserved on the tops of hills adjacent the modern river valley. These discontinuous remnants of river floodplain terraces, the Upland Complex, are an important source of commercial sand and gravel in West Tennessee.

Sea level dropped during late Pliocene and Pleistocene time with the onset of the ice ages. The river cut downward, in some areas into strata as old as Eocene age, to meet the new sea level, thereby abandoning the old floodplain, which is why the modern Mississippi River is at a lower elevation than the ancient river. Tennessee's current landscape was well established by the end of the Neogene Period.

QUATERNARY PERIOD
2.6 MILLION YEARS AGO TO PRESENT DAY

The Quaternary Period is most known for the Pleistocene ice ages, when continental glaciers expanded and contracted across the world. Contrary to popular belief, the "ice age" was not one single event but rather a series of cooler glacial periods interrupted by warmer interglacial periods. We are living in an interglacial period that began at the end of the Pleistocene Epoch, about 10,000 years ago.

The last significant glacial period was between about 95,000 and 20,000 years ago. About half of North America was covered by the 2-mile-thick Laurentide ice sheet. It reached as far south as the Ohio River valley, about 200 miles north of Tennessee. The ice sheet was susceptible to climate oscillations. During colder periods the ice sheet advanced, scouring and grinding up underlying material. Rocks and sediments of all sizes became entrained in the ice sheet and were transported to its margins. When the ice sheet retreated during warmer periods, the edge melted and left behind piles of rock and sediment. Massive braided rivers, which form in areas with a high sediment load, carried gravel, sand, silt, and clay downstream. The braided rivers' networks of interconnecting channels were tens of miles wide, and their sediments are preserved along the margins of the modern Mississippi River Valley.

Large volumes of glacial meltwater flowed down the Mississippi River drainage system through the northern Mississippi Embayment to the Gulf of Mexico. Pulverized rock, called glacial flour, washed over riverbanks and onto the floodplain, where it dried out. Strong winds entrained and redeposited the glacial flour over 20,000 square miles of the lower Mississippi River Valley, between western Kentucky and Louisiana. The yellowish-gray silt, called *loess* (a German word that is typically pronounced "luss" in the United States), forms a blanket up to 100 feet thick over much of West Tennessee. Loess is thickest along West Tennessee's Chickasaw Bluffs and decreases eastward to near the longitude of Jackson, where it is minimal.

During the Pleistocene Epoch, Tennessee's climate was cold, dry, and similar to today's interior Alaska. Imagine, tundra conditions existed in the highlands

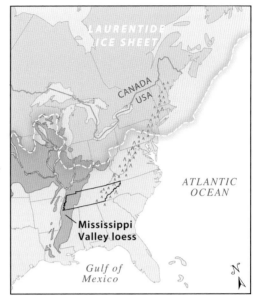

Evidence for the Pleisto-cene ice ages can be seen in the glacially derived windblown silt called loess, which covered much of the midcontinent and the Mississippi Embayment, including West Tennessee. This figure shows the maximum coverage of the loess, which in places has been eroded.
—Modified from Muhs, 2017

of the Tennessee Blue Ridge! Block fields found at the base of many Blue Ridge mountain slopes record the intense physical weathering that took place during the Pleistocene ice ages. Landslides and other talus deposits of this age are also common along the Chickasaw Bluffs in West Tennessee and along the Cumberland Plateau escarpment. Open spruce forests grew along the Mississippi River Valley and in the Appalachian Mountains. Remnants of these forests remain along the crest line of the Great Smoky Mountains at Clingmans Dome and other nearby 6,000-foot-high peaks.

Giant ground sloths, beavers, and armadillos, as well as camels, llamas, saber-toothed cats, panthers, jaguars, and mammoths lived in Tennessee, and *Homo sapiens* evolved during the Pleistocene Epoch. Herds of foraging mastodons migrated along the bluffs above the Mississippi River. Teeth and bones of these animals and the humans who hunted them are found in caves, rock shelters, sinkholes, and stream deposits throughout Tennessee.

At the end of the Pleistocene Epoch, North American glaciers retreated, and the Mississippi River's sediment load stabilized. Loess deposition stopped as the braided river valley system changed to the meandering system of the early modern Mississippi River about 12,000 years ago. Once the Laurentide ice sheet had completely retreated, spruce forests followed in its footsteps. A humid temperate climate developed during the Holocene Epoch, and a deciduous forest took hold in Tennessee.

Erosion has remained the dominant geologic process of the Holocene Epoch. Aggressive stream development has expanded the Central Basin, eroded the edges of the Cumberland Plateau, and created the extensive cave systems found on the Highland Rim and in the Valley and Ridge. The Mississippi River and its tributaries continue to deposit sediments in West Tennessee.

Pleistocene-age footprints of the North American jaguar are preserved in Blue Spring Cave in White County. The animal is related to the modern jaguar but was larger. —Chuck Sutherland photo

Geology and Humans in Tennessee

Geology played an important role in the human history of Tennessee. The state's first human inhabitants no doubt enjoyed and relied upon Tennessee's clear spring waters, took shelter in natural rock overhangs and caves, capitalized on its rocks for making tools, and reaped the benefits of an abundant diversity of plants and animals.

The Midsouth region, between northern Alabama and the Ohio River, has the greatest numbers of Paleo-Indian fluted points of any region in the Americas. A lot of the artifacts are found along and near the Tennessee and Cumberland Rivers. Nomadic Paleo-Indians came to Tennessee at the end of Pleistocene time more than 12,000 years ago and migrated through the state exploiting its abundant natural resources. Rivers and streams provided easy access to water, fertile floodplains, and travel corridors. Paleo-Indians used a multitude of Tennessee's igneous, metamorphic, and sedimentary rocks to make a variety of tools, including weapons they used to hunt ice age animals, such as mastodons.

The last of Tennessee's prehistoric peoples were seminomadic. They prospered in Tennessee for thousands of years prior to the arrival of Spanish conquistador Hernando de Soto in the sixteenth century. These peoples earned the nickname "mound builders" for the flat-topped earthen mounds on which they constructed houses, burial sites, and temples for chiefs and shamans. These mounds are accessible in many areas of West and Middle Tennessee, including

This adze, a woodworking tool used like a hoe by Tennessee's earliest humans, was made from Mississippian-age chert. The adze was found at the Brigham quarry site, one of four prehistoric rock quarries near Dover on the western Highland Rim in Stewart County. —Ryan Parish photo

Tennessee's prehistoric peoples became increasingly less nomadic. New hunting technologies and the farming of the rich alluvial soils along river trade routes and in tributary valleys encouraged more permanent settlements. Pottery, such as the 5.5-inch-tall Sinti Bottle found at the Chucalissa village site near Memphis, was made from local clays and could be used for food storage.
—Katie Maish, C. H. Nash Museum at Chucalissa photo

the C. H. Nash Museum at Chucalissa in Memphis, Pinson Mounds State Archaeological Park southeast of Jackson, and Mound Bottom in Cheatham County.

By the sixteenth and seventeenth centuries the Cherokee were the only tribal group living permanently in Tennessee. The Chickasaw controlled western Tennessee, but they only used the area for hunting. These tribes traded with early European settlers, mainly of British and French descent, who came to Tennessee during the mid-1700 and 1800s, exploring the frontier and taking advantage of inexpensive land. These adventurous people often came in groups, following animal and Native American trails through mountain passes. They settled small, topographically isolated agricultural communities.

During the Civil War, Tennessee officially sided with the Confederacy. However, state physiography coupled with the proximity of a Union state along the northern border, meant that many Tennessee soldiers fought for the Union. The wide, open spaces and rich soils of West and Middle Tennessee were conducive to large plantations, while East Tennessee farms were small and developed on rocky soil and steep hillsides. Different labor requirements in these areas influenced philosophical differences across the state.

Many battles were won or lost, in part, because of local geology. The Mississippi River provided an important communications and supply corridor that was defended from overlooks on the loess bluffs or from strategic positions along the river's many meanders. Higher elevations in Middle Tennessee, formed of resistant sandstone or silica-rich carbonates, for example, became important lookouts and strongholds. Rugged terrain, especially of the Cumberland Plateau and Appalachian Mountains, hindered a marching army's progress, as did areas with well-developed karst topography. Iron mined on the Highland Rim and near Chattanooga became cannonballs. Saltpeter from East Tennessee caves became gunpowder.

Tennessee's rich natural resources fed developing industries, many of which began during and right after the Civil War. Coal, copper, gold, iron, lead, phosphate, clay, and zinc mining all began in the eighteenth and nineteenth centuries. Their success resulted from the proximity of lumber, coal fuel, water, the developing railroads. Many of Tennessee's original, resource-based industries continue to thrive in the twenty-first century. For example, chert, limestone, and sandstone are quarried for construction materials, and sand, gravel, and limestone for aggregates and concrete. Bricks and ceramics are manufactured from locally quarried clays in the eastern and western parts of the state.

One modern human endeavor that is often overlooked in the sense of geologic influence is viticulture. Tennesseans established vineyards during the late 1800s, primarily in areas deemed unfit for other crops. Most vineyards failed and lay fallow in the early twentieth century with Prohibition and did not begin to recover until fairly recently. Although Tennessee is not widely known for its wine, viticulture has grown in popularity since Tennessee's first commercial winery was licensed in 1982. Nowadays Tennessee is home to more than fifty commercial wineries, most of which are located in Middle and East

The Mississippian-age Monteagle Limestone is quarried in Algood. Limestone is one of Tennessee's most important economic resources and is the state rock. (36.198344N, 85.434592W) —Chuck Sutherland photo

Tennessee. If you visit one of Tennessee's wineries, give some thought to the rocks and sediment that underlie the vineyard and the consequent soil acidity, mineral composition, drainage, and topography. All these factors and more contribute to the wine's uniqueness.

Terroir (pronounced "tare-wah") is a French word describing the specific and unique geographic, climatic, and geologic characteristics that impart distinctive regional personality to products like cheese, meat, butter, coffee, and wine. American Viticultural Areas (AVA), based on geographical location and the distinctive physical qualities of an area—the terroir—distinguish officially sanctioned growing regions. At least 85 percent of grapes used in a wine produced in a given AVA must be grown within the AVA. Tennessee is currently part of the Mississippi Delta AVA.

Many of Tennessee's viticulturists experiment with growing French and other varietals, but traditionally muscadine grapes are used in Tennessee wine. Native to the American South, muscadine grapes can withstand Tennessee's humid temperate climate. Tennessee's muscadine wines are often sweet, in part due to the grape, but also because vintners traditionally add sugar during wine making. Many people enjoy muscadine wines as dessert wines. Several wineries also experiment with fruit wines and tomato wines made from Ripley's famous tomatoes. These wines speak to southern culture and nostalgia as much as terroir!

Named for the bluish color of the mountains when seen from a distance, the Blue Ridge physiographic province includes several rugged subranges that consist mainly of metasedimentary rocks of the Ocoee Supergroup of Neoproterozoic age. —Bob Carr photo

EAST TENNESSEE
Appalachian Highlands

Most of the East Tennessee landscape we see today is a reflection of the Alleghanian orogeny and the subsequent erosion of the ancient Appalachian Mountains; however, faulting, folding, and metamorphism from earlier orogenies are present, especially in the Tennessee Blue Ridge. Each orogeny left a geologic imprint that affected all preexisting rocks, and many of East Tennessee's stratigraphic units contain evidence of more than one tectonic event. However, much of East Tennessee's terrain is rugged and remote, and ample rainfall encourages the development of thick soil and dense vegetation that obscure the underlying bedrock. Sorting out East Tennessee's geologic history takes hard work, unique skills, an open mind, and a good imagination. Despite the many challenges, more than two hundred years of scientific work in Tennessee and neighboring states has greatly advanced our understanding of how large mountain belts form, as well as our understanding of the history of the Earth.

Together, the Cumberland Plateau, Valley and Ridge, and western Blue Ridge physiographic provinces form the southern Appalachian Mountains of

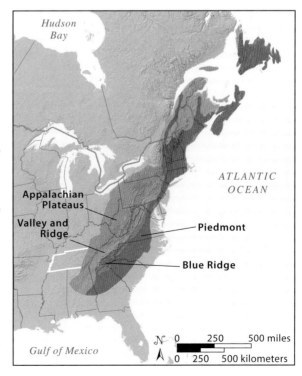

The Appalachian Highlands extend the length of eastern North America, from northern Alabama and Georgia to Newfoundland. This system of mountains includes the Piedmont, Blue Ridge, Valley and Ridge, and Appalachian Plateaus physiographic provinces. (The Cumberland Plateau is part of the Appalachian Plateaus.) In Tennessee, all provinces are present except for the Piedmont.

East Tennessee. Tectonic forces during the Paleozoic Era created these physiographic provinces at roughly the same time. Differences of rock type and deformation across the Appalachian Basin make the provinces distinct.

Blue Ridge

The Blue Ridge physiographic province includes mountainous parts of Alabama, Georgia, Tennessee, South Carolina, North Carolina, and Virginia. The Blue Ridge is often discussed in terms of eastern and western sections because of significant geologic differences in the basement rocks of the two areas. The boundary between the eastern and western Blue Ridge roughly corresponds to the Tennessee–North Carolina state line.

The basement rocks of the western Blue Ridge were originally part of Amazonia, the main South American craton. During the amalgamation of Rodinia that culminated in the Grenville orogeny, eastern Laurentia collided with Amazonia. As Rodinia later split apart, fragments of Amazonia that were embedded in Laurentia were left behind. Collectively called granitoids, these coarse-grained, silica-rich crystalline rocks are more than 1 billion years old. Igneous rocks intruded the Grenville rocks during the initial rifting of Rodinia and also form part of the western Blue Ridge basement. All of the basement rocks were further metamorphosed and deformed during mountain building in Paleozoic time. Basement rocks of the western Blue Ridge are exposed in northeastern Tennessee.

EAST TENNESSEE: APPALACHIAN HIGHLANDS

Five subranges make up the Blue Ridge physiographic province in Tennessee. From north to south these are the Iron, Unaka, Bald, Great Smoky, and Unicoi Mountains. The shaded relief base emphasizes the topographic differences between the relatively flat tableland of the Cumberland Plateau, the linear relief of the Valley and Ridge, and the rugged highlands of the western Blue Ridge.

STRATIGRAPHIC COLUMN FOR THE TENNESSEE BLUE RIDGE

EON	ERA	PERIOD / EPOCH	GROUP	FORMATION	DESCRIPTION	DEPOSITIONAL ENVIRONMENT
PHANEROZOIC	CEN.	QUATERNARY / HOLOCENE		alluvial and colluvial deposits	silt, clay, sand, conglomerate	deposited along rivers and streams and at the base of mountain slopes
PHANEROZOIC	PALEOZOIC	ORDOVICIAN	Knox Group	Jonesboro Limestone	limestone, dolomite	shallow carbonate shelf; exposed in tectonic windows of the western Blue Ridge
PHANEROZOIC	PALEOZOIC	CAMBRIAN	Conasauga Group	Maynardville Limestone; Nolichucky Shale; Maryville Limestone; Rogersville Shale; Rutledge Limestone; Pumpkin Valley Shale; Honaker Dolomite	shale, siltstone, limestone, dolomite	western tidal flats, shallow marine, and eastern carbonate platform
PHANEROZOIC	PALEOZOIC	CAMBRIAN		Rome Formation	shale, siltstone, sandstone, limestone, dolomite	tidal flat and lagoon
PHANEROZOIC	PALEOZOIC	CAMBRIAN		Shady Dolomite	dolomite	carbonate bank or reef
PHANEROZOIC	PALEOZOIC	CAMBRIAN	Chilhowee Group	Erwin Formation (Hesse Sandstone, Murray Shale, Nebo Sandstone)	quartzite, sandstone, siltstone, shale	rivers, nearshore, and shelf record a change from an active to passive continental margin; basalts are layered with other sediments within the Unicoi Formation; the Murray Shale contains oldest trilobite in eastern North America
PHANEROZOIC	PALEOZOIC	CAMBRIAN	Chilhowee Group	Hampton Formation (Nichols Shale)	shale, siltstone	
PHANEROZOIC	PALEOZOIC	CAMBRIAN	Chilhowee Group	Unicoi Formation (Cochran Formation)	conglomerate, siltstone, sandstone, shale	
PROTEROZOIC	LATE (NEOPROTEROZOIC)		Ocoee Supergroup — Walden Creek Group	Sandsuck Formation; Wilhite Formation; Shields Formation; Licklog Formation	conglomerate, quartzite, metasandstone, metasiltstone, slate, sandstone, shale, siltstone, phyllite	rift basin, shallow shelf
PROTEROZOIC	LATE (NEOPROTEROZOIC)		Ocoee Supergroup — Great Smoky Group	Copperhill Formation; Anakeesta Formation; Cades Sandstone; Thunderhead Sandstone; Elkmont Sandstone	conglomerate, metasandstone, metasiltstone, slate, phyllite	turbidites in a deep, asymmetric basin
PROTEROZOIC	LATE (NEOPROTEROZOIC)		Ocoee Supergroup — Snowbird Group	Rich Butt Sandstone; Metcalf Phyllite; Pigeon Siltstone; Roaring Fork Sandstone; Longarm Quartzite; Wading Branch Formation	conglomerate, quartzite, metasandstone, metasiltstone, slate, phyllite, schist	river, delta and offshore environments associated with an asymmetric basin that developed near the eastern Laurentian margin during the initial rifting of the Alleghanian orogeny
PROTEROZOIC	LATE (NEOPROTEROZOIC)			Konnorock Formation	siltstone, sandstone, diamictite	glacial, lake deposits; contains clasts of basement rocks, rift basin
PROTEROZOIC	LATE (NEOPROTEROZOIC)			Mount Rogers Formation	rhyolite, conglomerate, sandstone	volcanic and sedimentary, rift basin
PROTEROZOIC	LATE (NEOPROTEROZOIC)			Bakersville Gabbro; Beech Granite	gabbro, metagabbro, granite, mylonite	intruded older basement rocks during the initial rifting of the supercontinent Rodinia
PROTEROZOIC	MIDDLE (MESO.)		basement rocks	Max Patch Granite; Cranberry Gneiss; Carvers Gap/Cloudland Gneiss	granite, gneiss, mylonite	formed during the Grenville orogeny; exposed in northeastern Tennessee

The western Blue Ridge also includes low-grade metamorphic rocks of the Ocoee Supergroup, a thick section of clastic metasedimentary rocks that rests unconformably on the crystalline basement. The Ocoee rocks were deposited in extensional rift valleys in Neoproterozoic time during the breakup of Rodinia. They were metamorphosed during the Taconic orogeny and again during the Alleghanian orogeny when they were shoved northwestward along thrust faults. Ocoee Supergroup strata form the highlands of the Tennessee Blue Ridge and, along with metasedimentary rocks of the Cambrian-age Chilhowee Group, also rift related, form the western foothills.

Eastern Blue Ridge basement rocks were originally mafic volcanic rocks and passive-margin sediments that were deposited in the early Iapetus Ocean as it opened during the breakup of Rodinia. These volcanic and sedimentary rocks were metamorphosed to medium to high grade during the Taconic and Acadian orogenies as the Iapetus Ocean closed. They were finally pushed to their present location during the Alleghanian orogeny. Fragments of other continents and island arcs, collectively called suspect terranes or alien terranes, were added to the Laurentian continental margin east of the Blue Ridge during Paleozoic Era mountain building. In Tennessee, eastern Blue Ridge rocks are exposed at the surface in eastern Johnson County.

Valley and Ridge

Tennessee's Valley and Ridge physiographic province is a hilly zone, up to 90 miles wide, of narrow, parallel, northeast-trending valleys and ridges. Cambrian-to-Pennsylvanian-age sedimentary rocks, including limestone, dolomite, shale, and sandstone, originally covered the Valley and Ridge; however, Mississippian- and Pennsylvanian-age strata have been mostly eroded away. Today's topography, with elevation differences of up to several hundred feet, results from the differential weathering and erosion of mainly Cambrian-to-Ordovician-age strata that were originally deposited in relatively shallow marine and nearshore environments along the Laurentian margin. These rocks were transported to their current location by faulting in the Alleghanian fold-and-thrust belt.

The Valley and Ridge contains numerous thrust faults, most of which have been inactive for hundreds of millions of years. Some are relatively short in length, whereas others are regional-scale features that can be traced for hundreds of miles across the surface of eastern Tennessee and into neighboring states. Valley and Ridge thrust faults strike northeastward, and the planar surfaces of the faults mostly dip southeastward. These faults typically dip more steeply at the surface than at depth, where they become low-angle faults, subparallel to bedding. A thrust fault with this special geometry is called a detachment thrust fault. Most major Valley and Ridge detachment thrust faults originate in sedimentary layers that more easily assist fracture and movement, such as shale or coal layers that are mechanically weak. Detachment faulting is typical in fold-and-thrust belts throughout the world.

In Tennessee's Valley and Ridge, detachment thrust faults commonly originate from a master detachment fault that is confined to a bedding plane in the

STRATIGRAPHIC COLUMN FOR THE TENNESSEE VALLEY AND RIDGE

EON	ERA	PERIOD / EPOCH	GROUP	FORMATION	DESCRIPTION	DEPOSITIONAL ENVIRONMENT
PHANEROZOIC	CEN.	QUATERNARY / HOLOCENE		alluvial and colluvial deposits	silt, clay, sand, conglomerate	sediments deposited along rivers and streams and at the base of ridge slopes
PHANEROZOIC	PALEOZOIC	MISSISSIPPIAN		Pennington Formation	shale, siltstone, limestone	tidal flats, delta, shallow shoreface with barrier islands and sandbars distinctive red and green shales; represents the transition between marine and terrestrial sedimentation as the Alleghanian orogeny began
				Newman Limestone / Greasy Cove Formation	limestone	shallow marine shelf with a carbonate ramp or platform that persisted throughout the Mississippian Period
				Fort Payne Formation / Grainger Formation	chert, silicastone, limestone	
		DEVONIAN		Chattanooga Shale	black shale	shallow sea, oxygen-poor environment, highly organic
		SILURIAN		Brassfield Limestone / Rockwood Formation / Clinch Sandstone	shale, sandstone, siltstone, limestone	barrier islands, lagoons, shallow marine; the Rockwood Formation contains hematite
		ORDOVICIAN		Sequatchie Formation / Juniata Formation	sandstone, siltstone, shale, limestone	tidal flats to very shallow subtidal; distinctive red beds
				Martinsburg Shale	shale, limestone	
			Chickamauga Group	Moccasin Formation / Bays Formation	shale, siltstone, limestone	western carbonate platform with patch reefs; deltaic sediments and turbidites accumulated in an eastern subsiding basin; strata contain layers of bentonite that were once volcanic ash generated by the Taconic orogeny
				Ottosee Shale / Holston Formation / Lenoir Limestone / Athens Shale — Sevier Shale — Tellico Formation	shale, limestone, conglomerate	
				Newala Formation — Jonesboro Limestone	limestone, dolomite, shale, chert	post-Knox unconformity
			Knox Group	Mascot Dolomite / Kingsport Formation	limestone, dolomite, shale, chert	broad carbonate platform; the Mascot Dolomite and the Kingsport Formation are rich in zinc and lead minerals; the Copper Ridge Dolomite contains stromatolites
				Longview Dolomite / Chepultepec Dolomite		
		CAMBRIAN		Copper Ridge Dolomite	dolomite, chert	
				Conococheague Limestone	dolomite, chert	
				Maynardville Limestone		
				Nolichucky Shale		
			Conasauga Group	Maryville Limestone / Rogersville Shale / Rutledge Limestone / Pumpkin Valley Shale	shale, siltstone, limestone, dolomite, chert	western tidal flats, shallow marine, and eastern carbonate platform
				Rome Formation	shale, siltstone, sandstone, limestone, dolomite	tidal flat and lagoon; shales are distinctive variegated maroon, brown, and green; fossiliferous
				Shady Dolomite	dolomite	carbonate bank

Generalized stratigraphic section of the Valley and Ridge physiographic province. A squiggly line signifies an unconformity in the rock record. —Compiled from various sources.

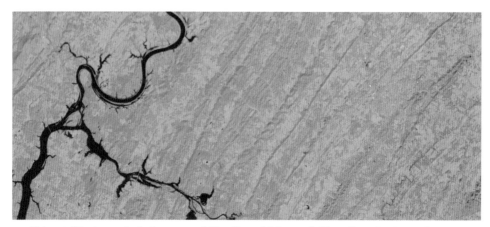

This satellite image includes parts of Hamilton, Meigs, and Rhea Counties in southeastern Tennessee and illustrates the washboard-like texture that characterizes the Valley and Ridge physiographic province. Pictured here are alternating ridges (brown) and valleys (green) near the confluence of the Hiwassee and Tennessee Rivers. —US Geological Survey and NASA, Landsat 8

flat-lying, Cambrian-age Rome Formation, near the contact with the underlying basement. In some areas splay faults branch upward from the master detachment fault through thick, competent carbonates of Cambrian to Ordovician age. The splay faults may return to horizontal in another mechanically weak layer that is within the carbonates, or they may reach the surface. Often, strata above the fault are folded as a result of being pushed up along a ramp. The overriding thrust sheet drapes over the end of the ramp and forms an anticline.

The combination of detachment faulting with northwest-directed force during the Alleghanian orogeny created a series of parallel, overlapping, southeast-dipping thrust sheets. These planar sheets of sedimentary rock are typically 3 to 4 miles thick and were moved northwestward up to 200 miles. Older rocks at the bottom of each thrust sheet were pushed over younger rocks on the tops of underlying thrust sheets. The thrust sheets overlap something like roof shingles, with one stack of sedimentary strata shoved northwestward on top of the next. Thus, stratigraphic sections are repeated in linear, northeast-trending belts across the Valley and Ridge physiographic province. All roads that cut across the Valley and Ridge cross repeated sections of Paleozoic-age strata. This type of deformation is commonly referred to as "thin-skinned" tectonics because deformation was limited to the sedimentary sequence that lies above the basement rocks.

About ten major detachment thrust faults and associated thrust sheets can be grouped into three main fault families in Tennessee's Valley and Ridge: the Kingston, White Oak Mountain–Clinchport, and Saltville. Each fault family consists of major and minor faults, and almost all of these faults bring the Rome Formation to the surface over younger rocks of the Knox or Conasauga Groups. The faults in the White Oak Mountain–Clinchport family merge southward one

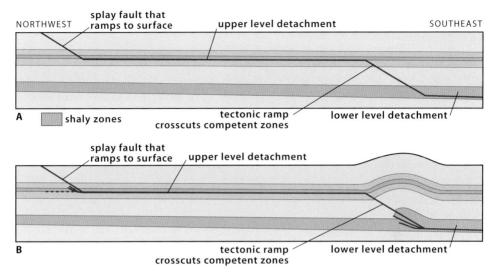

NORTHWEST

splay fault that ramps to surface

upper level detachment

SOUTHEAST

A ▭ shaly zones

tectonic ramp crosscuts competent zones

lower level detachment

splay fault that ramps to surface

upper level detachment

B

tectonic ramp crosscuts competent zones

lower level detachment

(A) Detachment thrust faults lie in mechanically weak rocks above the basement at the base of the sedimentary cover. They are horizontal at depth but ramp up to another weak layer or to the surface. In Tennessee's Valley and Ridge, detachment faults commonly develop in the Rome Formation and Chattanooga Shale. (B) Rocks underlying the fault remain relatively undisturbed, but those above the fault may become deformed as the thrust sheet is pushed over a fault ramp. —Modified from Harris and Milici, 1977

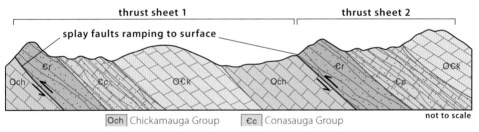

thrust sheet 1

thrust sheet 2

splay faults ramping to surface

Och   Cr   Cc   OCk   Och   Cr   Cc   OCk

not to scale

Och Chickamauga Group   Cc Conasauga Group

Movement along detachment thrust faults and associated splay faults results in stacked, overlapping thrust sheets. This generalized cross section illustrates the relationship between surface topography and underlying geology. Sections of southeast-dipping, mainly Cambrian-to-Ordovician-age strata are repeated across Tennessee's Valley and Ridge. Each unit has a unique weathering profile, which is also repeated across the province. —Modified from Byerly, 2013

by one to eventually become the White Oak Mountain fault. The Saltville fault, one of the largest thrust faults in the Valley and Ridge, extends from Georgia to Virginia and displaced strata more than 60 miles.

Northwest of the Saltville fault, Tennessee's Valley and Ridge is structurally dominated by faulting. Folds are typically relatively small, parallel to larger faults, and located close to fault traces. Southeast of the Saltville fault, folding is more dominant than faulting. Large groups of folds are also more common in this area. In both areas, folds trend northeast-southwest, parallel to faults.

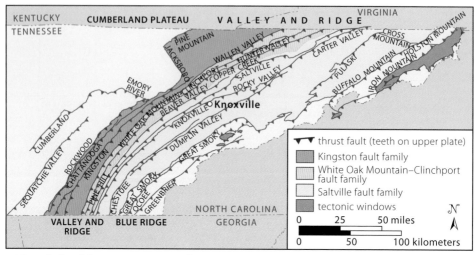

Major faults of the East Tennessee Valley and Ridge may be grouped into three main fault families based on geographic location and faulting style. These faults are mainly detachment thrust faults. Sawteeth indicate fault dip direction, and colors highlight fault families. —Modified from Clark et al., 2005

Anticlines tended to develop near the surface and on the southeast side of large thrust faults, as the rocks were pushed up along the steeper ramps of detachment thrust faults.

Cumberland Plateau

The Cumberland Plateau is the southern part of the Appalachian Plateaus, a flat-topped tableland that extends from Alabama to New York. The Cumberland Plateau is nearly 70 miles wide along the Kentucky border but narrows to about 50 miles where Tennessee borders Alabama and Georgia. Resistant, Pennsylvanian-age conglomerate, sandstone, and siltstone cap the plateau. The rocks that occur in the plateau's subsurface are the same as those at the surface in the Valley and Ridge. These strata, mostly Cambrian to Mississippian in age, are exposed in Sequatchie Valley and in lower slopes and benches of the plateau margins and are relatively undeformed.

The Cumberland Plateau is bounded by steep-sided escarpments that extend northward and southward from Tennessee into neighboring states. Along much of the eastern escarpment, strata dip northwestward or are overturned and have eroded into steep bluffs and pinnacles. Strata are nearly flat along the deeply dissected western escarpment. There, the Cumberland, Duck, and Elk Rivers and their tributaries have incised deeply into the margin of the plateau forming steep-walled canyons that are locally called "gulfs." Most of Tennessee's waterfalls are located along the western escarpment, where high-gradient streams flow over and erode through Pennsylvanian-age sandstone. Streams undercut more soluble and less resistant units composed mostly of limestone and shale; this process causes lower slopes to fail and large blocks of overlying

STRATIGRAPHIC COLUMN FOR THE CUMBERLAND PLATEAU

EON	ERA	PERIOD / EPOCH	GROUP	FORMATION	DESCRIPTION	DEPOSITIONAL ENVIRONMENT
PHANEROZOIC	PALEOZOIC (CEN.)	QUATERNARY / HOLOCENE		alluvial and colluvial deposits	silt, clay, sand, conglomerate	along rivers and streams and at the base of the Cumberland Plateau
		PENNSYLVANIAN		Breathitt Formation: Cross Mountain Formation, Vowell Mountain Formation, Redoak Mountain Formation, Graves Gap Formation, Indian Bluff Formation, Slatestone Formation	shale, sandstone, siltstone, coal	deltas, bays, coastal marshes, plant fossils
			Crooked Fork Group	Wartburg Sandstone, Glenmary Shale, Coalfield Sandstone, Brunt Mill Shale, Crossville Sandstone, Dorton Shale	shale, sandstone, siltstone, coal	marshes, tidal lagoons, deltas, barrier beaches
			Crab Orchard Mountains Group	Rockcastle Conglomerate	conglomerate, sandstone, siltstone, shale, coal	
				Lee Formation / Fentress Formation: Vandever Formation, Newton Sandstone, Whitwell Shale, Sewanee Conglomerate	sandstone, siltstone, shale, coal, conglomerate	coastal streams and rivers, tidal lagoons, marshes, swamps, barrier islands, and deltas, plant fossils
			Gizzard Group	Signal Point Shale, Warren Point Sandstone, Raccoon Mountain Formation	sandstone, siltstone, shale, coal	tidal flat, lagoon, marsh, delta environments, plant fossils
		MISSISSIPPIAN		Pennington Formation	shale, siltstone, limestone	tidal flats, delta, shallow shoreface with barrier islands and sandbars; distinctive red and green shales; represents the transition between marine and terrestrial sedimentation as the Alleghanian orogeny began
				Bangor Limestone	limestone	shallow shelf
				Hartselle Formation	sandstone, shale, limestone	delta, shallow marine
				Monteagle Limestone, St. Louis Limestone, Warsaw Limestone, Fort Payne Formation, Maury Formation / Newman Limestone, Greasy Cove Formation	chert, silicastone, limestone, shale	shallow marine shelf with a carbonate ramp or platform that persisted throughout the Mississippian Period
		DEVONIAN		Chattanooga Shale	black shale	shallow sea, oxygen-poor environment, highly organic
		SILURIAN		Rockwood Formation	siltstone, sandstone	lagoons, tidal, subtidal; contains hematite

Generalized stratigraphic section of the Cumberland Plateau. —Compiled from various sources

sandstone to move downslope. Mass wasting events, such as rockfalls and landslides, are common along both plateau margins, where rock moves downslope in response to gravity. The unconsolidated material, collectively called colluvium, blankets the lower slopes of the Cumberland Plateau.

The Cumberland Plateau is divided into three structurally distinct areas: the Cumberland thrust sheet, the Pine Mountain thrust sheet, and the northern Cumberland Plateau. The Cumberland thrust sheet includes the area south of I-40. It is a relatively thin thrust sheet, not quite 1 mile thick, which moved northwestward along the Cumberland fault, also called the Cumberland overthrust. This low-angle detachment thrust fault lies mainly in the Pennsylvanian-age shales and coals of the Gizzard Group. The Cumberland thrust sheet is bisected by the Sequatchie Valley fault and anticline, both of which have deeper roots in the Valley and Ridge physiographic province. The Sequatchie Valley separates Walden Ridge from the rest of the southern Cumberland Plateau. The southern Cumberland Plateau was folded into a broad, asymmetrical syncline with its axis parallel and close to the west side of Sequatchie Valley. Walden Ridge was also folded into an asymmetrical syncline with its axis parallel and close to the

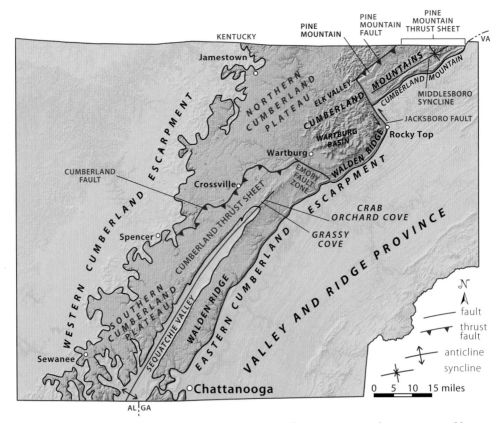

The Cumberland Plateau is broken into three structurally unique regions that are separated by detachment thrust faults and strike-slip faults. —Modified from Wilson and Jewell, 1956; Wilson and Stearns, 1958

eastern Cumberland escarpment. In the interior of the thrust sheet, the western part of Walden Ridge, and the area west of Sequatchie Valley, strata are mostly flat lying. The Cumberland thrust sheet is cut off near I-40 by the Emory River fault zone and by a complex series of faults that are part of the Cumberland fault zone.

The Pine Mountain thrust sheet encompasses a rectangular area about 125 miles long and 10 to 25 miles wide that includes parts of Tennessee, Kentucky, and Virginia. In Tennessee, the Pine Mountain thrust sheet forms the northeastern part of the Cumberland Plateau between Jacksboro and Jellico. Similar to detachment thrust faults in the Valley and Ridge, the Pine Mountain fault begins as a low-angle fault in the Rome Formation. It ramps twice: once from the Rome Formation to the Chattanooga Shale, and again between the Chattanooga Shale and the surface. Rock layers under the detachment thrust fault are nearly horizontal, whereas layers above the detachment are horizontal where the fault is flat and folded where the fault ramps up. Rocks on the Pine Mountain thrust sheet were moved about 10 miles northwestward along the Pine Mountain fault. They were also pushed upward so that the Pennsylvanian-age strata that cap this section of the plateau may be up to 500 feet higher than their equivalents on adjacent parts of the plateau.

The northern Cumberland Plateau separates the Pine Mountain and Cumberland thrusts sheets. The eastern part of the northern Cumberland Plateau is more rugged and mountainous than other parts of the plateau and includes part of the Cumberland Mountains. Although this area is topographically high, it is a structural low called the Wartburg Basin. Beds dip gently into the basin at less than 2 degrees, except along the edge where they may dip at greater than 50 degrees. Strata are relatively flat-lying on the northwest part of the plateau.

Tennessee's Coal, Oil, and Natural Gas

The nearly 4,000 feet of Pennsylvanian-age clastic sedimentary rocks that cap the Cumberland Plateau were deposited by a large and dynamic river system that carried sediments eroded from the rising Appalachian Mountains southwestward across Tennessee to the sea. It is difficult to correlate rock layers of this age across Tennessee because many depositional environments existed at the same time and because rocks look similar. North of I-40, strata of the Crab Orchard Mountains and Crooked Fork Groups and younger units generally comprise sediments deposited in river channels, floodplains, natural levees, and oxbow lakes. These strata generally consist of relatively thin sandstone beds that contain more shale and siltstone layers than the southern units. They also include many layers of coal. Fossilized plants are abundant in these layers, and many are preserved intact and in growth positions.

South of I-40, the Gizzard and Crab Orchard Mountains Groups contain sediments deposited in other parts of the same system, including tidal lagoons, marshes, beaches, barrier islands, sandbars, and deltas. Most southern plateau strata consist of thickly bedded sandstone with shale interbeds. There are also many layers of well-rounded, relatively pure quartz sand, indicating that these

A variety of Pennsylvanian-age plants are preserved in the Crab Orchard Mountains Group. This sample contains the wood of the conifer-like Cordaites *(middle), primitive ferns, and a seed pod.*
—Wayne K. Williams photo

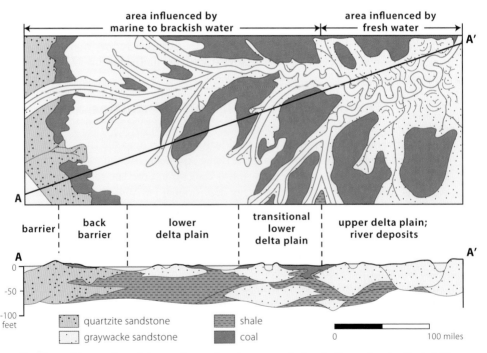

Coal formed in a variety of river and coastal environments during the Pennsylvanian Period. The top figure shows a map view of a river and delta system similar to that which existed in Tennessee. The bottom figure illustrates the complexity of these environments, which overlapped as the river's course and the sea's shoreline changed through time. —Modified from Horne et al., 1978

sediments traveled far enough to be sorted and rounded. These units also contain coal beds that formed in marshes on the coastal plain, although plant fossils tend to be fragments rather than large specimens, reflecting the longer transport and higher-energy depositional environments.

Tennessee's coal formed from the accumulation and compression of organic matter in tropical wetland environments, including swamps, coastal plains, and broad river floodplains that were close to sea level. Black bituminous coal seams are visible in Pennsylvanian-age strata throughout the Cumberland Plateau.

For more than two hundred years, coal has been mined from Pennsylvanian-age strata on the Cumberland Plateau. Although Tennessee's coalfields are not as rich in quality or quantity as equivalent areas in Kentucky, Pennsylvania, and West Virginia, they remain commercially viable, with more than forty named coal seams. Coal mining began near Rockwood but did not develop commercially until railroads expanded across the plateau's rugged terrain. Coal mining prospered all over the plateau following the Civil War, and evidence of the early industry remains throughout East Tennessee.

Coal miners extracted mainly bituminous coal, a soft, high-quality coal that supplied blacksmiths and the iron industry during the late nineteenth and early twentieth centuries. Bituminous coal is still mined on the Cumberland Plateau and mainly supplies utility companies in Tennessee and neighboring states, although some high-grade coal is exported to other countries to fuel steel and iron mills. Today, coal is extracted by underground mining, open-pit mining, and contour strip mining. Augers are often used to extract coal from thin seams along contour strip mines. Mountaintop removal is currently not allowed in Tennessee, although it has occurred in the past. Various remediation projects such as reforestation and highwall reduction have successfully hidden old coal mine scars and rehabilitated the land.

Coal grade increases with pressure, heat, and time through the compression and dewatering of organic material. Tennessee's coal is mainly bituminous and lignitic.

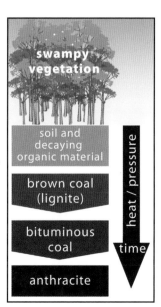

At the Richland Mine, located near Dayton, coal was extracted from underground mines developed in the Raccoon Mountain Formation. A 3-foot-thick coal layer is located in the upper part of the mine adit. The coal was hauled by railcars to local coke ovens, and the finished coke was sent by rail to a foundry in Dayton. The Richland Mine is one of several coal mines now protected in the Laurel-Snow State Natural Area. Many of the park trails were paths created by mine workers during the late 1800s and early 1900s. —Alan Cressler photo

Tennessee produces small amounts of crude oil and natural gas mainly from eleven counties on the northern Cumberland Plateau and eastern Highland Rim. Small pump jacks are fairly common in fields and pasturelands on the northern Cumberland Plateau, but gone are the days of the gushers. Most oil wells are small and produce less than 10 barrels per day. Many are mom-and-pop operations operated by local farmers and townspeople.

Oil and gas develop from plankton, algae, and other marine organisms that accumulate and are buried in an oxygen-deprived environment. This organic material must be subjected to heat to become fluid hydrocarbons that pool in a porous reservoir rock, such as sandstone and limestone. The oil must then be trapped and sealed by shale or another impermeable rock, or by geologic structures, such as folds, faults, and salt domes.

The Wartburg Basin, on the northern Cumberland Plateau, is the highest oil-producing area in Tennessee. Oil and gas are extracted from Ordovician-age carbonates, Devonian- and-Mississippian-age shale and limestone, and Pennsylvanian-age sandstone, shale, and coal. Relatively shallow (2,000 to 6,000 feet) wells are used in Ordovician and Mississippian limestones, whereas horizontal wells are typically used to extract hydrocarbons from isolated reef limestones in the Mississippian Fort Payne Formation. In addition to the oil and gas produced from the northern Cumberland Plateau and eastern Highland Rim, the Swan Creek field, located in the northern Valley and Ridge east of Kingsport, produces oil from Ordovician-age carbonate and shale units.

GREAT SMOKY MOUNTAINS NATIONAL PARK

Great Smoky Mountains National Park is the largest federally protected area east of the Mississippi River. Many park overlooks, trails, and landforms are named for the civic leaders, professionals, and conservationists who supported the creation of the park for both recreation and to protect the remaining old-growth forests from logging. With one foot in Tennessee and the other in North Carolina, President Franklin Roosevelt officially dedicated Great Smoky Mountains National Park in September 1940 at the Rockefeller Memorial at Newfound Gap on US 441. More than 10 million people visit Great Smoky Mountains National Park each year—more than any other US national park!

Named for the rugged Great Smoky Mountains, the park is part of the western Blue Ridge physiographic province. The highest peaks in the Appalachian Mountains are found in the Great Smoky Mountains, with sixteen summits rising above 6,000 feet, including the 6,643-foot Clingmans Dome. Great Smoky Mountains National Park also includes the foothills of the western Blue Ridge Mountains, a 6-to-8-mile-wide zone that ranges from about 900 to 4,000 feet in elevation.

Most rocks exposed in the highlands of the Great Smoky Mountains are fine-to-coarse-grained formations of the Neoproterozoic-age Ocoee Supergroup. These sedimentary rocks lie on the eroded surface of metamorphic and igneous basement rocks, which are exposed in a few places in the eastern part of the park. The Ocoee Supergroup was deposited in a series of interconnected nonmarine

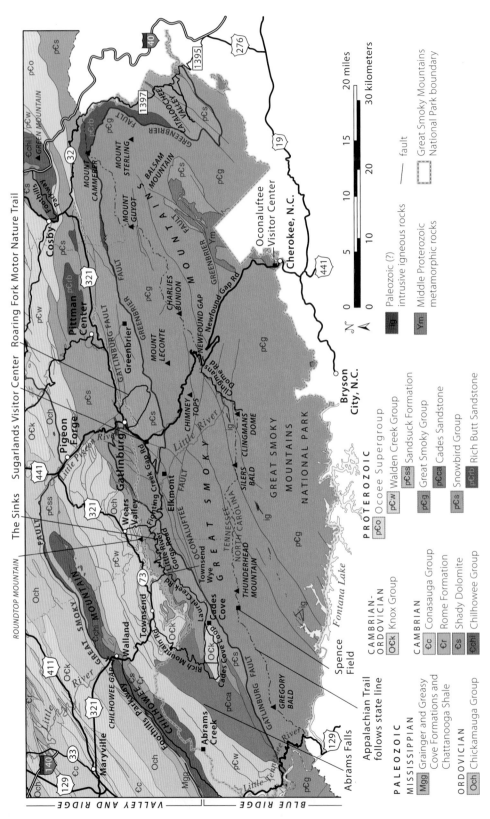

Generalized geologic map of Great Smoky Mountains National Park.

PALEOZOIC

MISSISSIPPIAN

Mgg — Grainger and Greasy Cove Formations and Chattanooga Shale

ORDOVICIAN

Och — Chickamauga Group

CAMBRIAN–ORDOVICIAN

OCk — Knox Group

CAMBRIAN

Cc — Conasauga Group
Cr — Rome Formation
Cs — Shady Dolomite
Cchi — Chilhowee Group

PROTEROZOIC

pCo — Ocoee Supergroup

pCw — Walden Creek Group
pCss — Sandsuck Formation

pCg — Great Smoky Group
pCca — Cades Sandstone

pCs — Snowbird Group
pCrb — Rich Butt Sandstone

ig — Paleozoic (?) intrusive igneous rocks

Ym — Middle Proterozoic metamorphic rocks

— fault

Great Smoky Mountains National Park boundary

N

0   5   10   15   20 miles

0   10   20   30 kilometers

Appalachian Trail follows state line

The Sinks   Sugarlands Visitor Center   Roaring Fork Motor Nature Trail

Abrams Falls

basins that formed along the Laurentian margin during the initial rifting of supercontinent Rodinia, during late Proterozoic time. Ocoee basins extended more than 175 miles, from near Johnson City, Tennessee, through the western Carolinas to northern Georgia. Large rivers brought massive volumes of poorly sorted gravel, sand, silt, and clay into the basins from neighboring highlands. The total thickness of the Ocoee Supergroup ranges from a few feet at Johnson City to more than 50,000 feet at Great Smoky Mountains National Park.

The Ocoee Supergroup is divided into the Snowbird, Great Smoky, and Walden Creek Groups. The Snowbird Group consists of sandstones and silt-stones that lie upon the crystalline basement rocks. Strata of this group are exposed in northeast sections of the park, including the Cataloochee and Balsam Mountain areas, and in the northwestern foothills, where they were brought to the surface along thrust faults. Look for Snowbird Group rocks in the Cosby and Greenbrier areas of the park and along Laurel Creek Road.

Great Smoky Group strata underlie the highlands and are well exposed along US 441 and Clingmans Dome Road. This sequence of sedimentary rocks formed from sediments eroded from mountains that were nearby and includes massive sandstone and shale that were metamorphosed to slate and phyllite.

Strata of the Walden Creek Group underlie the central and southwest foot-hills and are exposed in areas outside the park near Walland, Pigeon Forge, and Cosby. This group includes sandstone, siltstone, and conglomerate, and minor amounts of limestone and dolomite. Ocoee Supergroup rocks were lightly metamorphosed during the Taconic orogeny and again during the Alleghanian orogeny, so they are generally referred to as metasedimentary rocks.

Cambrian-age strata of the Chilhowee Group form a linear ridge along the western margin of the Blue Ridge and along nearly the entire length of the Appalachian Mountains. This group overlies the Ocoee Supergroup and consists of conglomerates, sandstones, siltstones, and shales that formed from sediments eroded from western highlands. They reflect a change in eastern North America's paleogeography, from an active tectonic margin to a drifting and stable passive margin. Chilhowee Group strata are exposed along Foot-hills Parkway on Chilhowee Mountain, southwest of Walland, and northeast of Cosby on Green Mountain.

Ocoee Supergroup and Chilhowee Group strata were carried in the hanging wall of the Great Smoky fault northwestward about 250 miles and placed on Ordovician-to-Mississippian-age strata of the Valley and Ridge. The Great Smoky fault is an Alleghanian age thrust fault that extends several hundred miles into Virginia, Georgia, and Alabama and is one of three major faults in the Great Smoky Mountains. The fault marks the abrupt geologic and topo-graphic boundary between the Blue Ridge and Valley and Ridge physiographic provinces. The fault surfaces at both Chilhowee and Green Mountains. Where the Great Smoky thrust sheet has been eroded through, Ordovician-age carbonate rocks below the fault are exposed in oval-shaped, steep-sided valleys called tectonic windows. The Great Smoky fault is exposed along the margins of these tectonic windows. Cades Cove is a tectonic window, as are Wears and Tuckaleechee Coves, both located outside of the park.

The Anakeesta Formation, part of the Great Smoky Group, forms the backbone of Chimney Tops. —Bob Carr photo

The other two major faults are the Gatlinburg and Greenbrier. The Gatlinburg fault, actually collection of faults that formed during the Alleghanian orogeny, contains many small faults that together form a transitional boundary between the foothills and highlands of the Great Smoky Mountains. This group of faults trends northeasterly along the north side of the mountains in the southern foothills area. The Gatlinburg fault system separates the Walden Creek and Snowbird Groups, and rocks along its faults are highly fractured. In general, faults of the Gatlinburg system dip steeply and have relatively linear surface traces. Stream valleys and eroded gaps in foothill ridges are often the eroded topographic expression of Gatlinburg faults.

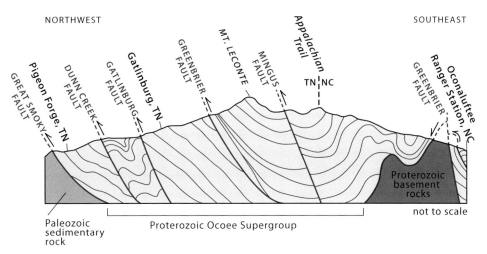

Generalized geologic cross section through central Great Smoky Mountains National Park oriented roughly along Newfound Gap Road/US 441. —Adapted from Harry L. Moore's *A Roadside Guide to the Geology of Great Smoky Mountains National Park.* Copyright © 1988 by The University of Tennessee Press. Reprinted by permission.

The Greenbrier fault, which formed during the Taconic orogeny, extends along the west side of the Great Smoky Mountains between the Little Tennessee and Pigeon Rivers and separates the Great Smoky and Snowbird Groups. Great Smoky Group rocks, located above the Greenbrier fault, are folded into a broad, bowl-shaped structure called the Alum Cave synclinorium—a broad syncline on which many smaller folds are superimposed. The Alum Cave synclinorium forms the highlands of the Great Smoky Mountains with the Anakeesta Formation at its center.

CADES COVE LOOP ROAD
16 miles

The Cades Cove Loop Road, a one-way loop that begins and ends near Cades Cove Campground, allows visitors to explore the human, natural, and geologic history preserved in the beautiful Cades Cove valley. Sparks and Hyatt Lanes provide shortcuts across the loop for those with a compressed schedule. A morning or two out of the week, the loop is closed to motorized traffic; only cyclists and hikers are allowed in, so check with the visitor center before you make the trip.

In southern Appalachian vernacular, a "cove" is a local, steep-sided valley, and Cades Cove fits the bill. It's a 10-square-mile flat spot, about 5 miles long and 2 miles wide, surrounded by high peaks of the Great Smoky Mountains. The Cherokee Indians used Cades Cove as a hunting ground until Europeans arrived in the early 1800s. Settlers found the protected and fertile valley conducive to farming, an anomaly in the otherwise steep and rocky slopes of the southern Appalachian Mountains.

Geologically speaking, the cove is a tectonic window, where erosion has cut through the Great Smoky thrust sheet to reveal the strata that underlie it. During the Alleghanian orogeny, Ocoee Supergroup metasedimentary rocks were transported more than 200 miles northwestward along the Great Smoky fault. These strata were pushed up and over younger Paleozoic-age carbonate rocks. In Cades Cove, erosion has exposed the Ordovician-age Jonesboro Limestone, part of the Knox Group, which underlies much of Tennessee's Valley and Ridge physiographic province.

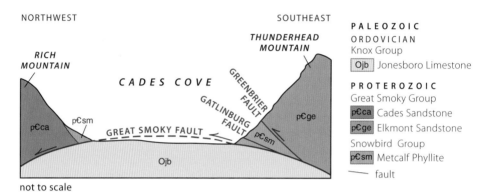

Cades Coves is a tectonic window eroded through the Great Smoky thrust sheet. Strata of the Ocoee Supergroup, part of the thrust sheet, form the surrounding mountains, whereas the underlying Ordovician-age Jonesboro Limestone is exposed in the cove. —Modified from Southworth, S., et. al., 1999

Cades Cove Loop Road roughly parallels the Great Smoky fault around the margin of Cades Cove. The road crosses the fault in several places, but it is covered by younger soil and alluvium. The fault is exposed at Gregory's Cave where the Metcalf Phyllite, part of the Snowbird Group, was thrust over the Jonesboro Limestone.

For the first 5 miles, the road follows the base of Cades Cove and Rich Mountains along the northern side of Cades Cove. Both mountains are formed of the Cades Sandstone. The Metcalf Phyllite is present along the base of the ridge to Rich Mountain Road.

Surficial debris flow material and modern stream alluvium are exposed throughout Cades Cove. Older stream terrace deposits are exposed at about 1,800 feet in elevation. They were left behind as rivers incised deeper into the valley. Younger alluvial deposits on the valley floor may be as thick as 300 feet. Settlers dug a few pits between the Primitive Baptist Church and Hyatt Lane to extract nodules of the iron oxide minerals limonite and hematite from the younger terrace deposits for use as iron ore, but they were not very successful. They had more success finding iron in older rocks on Rich Mountain. A forge was located near the Cable Mill.

The Cades Sandstone, part of the Great Smoky Group, is present on the west side of the cove. The coarse-grained sandstone is well exposed along the Abrams

The Ordovician-age Jonesboro Limestone is exposed along the road near the John Oliver cabin. Karst features such as Gregory's Cave and Bull Cave, along with several sinkholes, have developed in Cades Cove through continued erosion of the limestone.
—James St. John photo

Falls trail and in the bed of Abrams Creek. You may notice beds of conglomerate that contain pebbles of quartzite, gneiss, and granite. The sandstone is folded at Abrams Falls. The thick beds of sand were folded during deposition, before the unit became rock, probably due to gravity and the pressure of overlying strata rather than tectonic forces. Abrams Creek drains out the western end of Cades Cove and flows southward to Chilhowee Lake.

Gregory Bald is located on the ridge south of Cades Cove Visitor Center. Balds, treeless domes that form between 4,000 and 6,000 feet of elevation, contain distinctive plant communities, mainly composed of native grasses and shrubs. How balds form is unclear; there seems to be no direct correlation between bald distribution and underlying rock type. Soils at many balds are quite acidic, perhaps due to lightning strikes or clearing by early settlers, both of which may have changed the original soil chemistry. Creeping soil acidity may expand balds by poisoning the surrounding forest.

From Cades Cove Visitor Center, the road follows the south side of the cove, where the Gatlinburg fault, a steeply dipping thrust fault, forms a linear escarpment at the base of the mountains. About halfway up the mountainside Elkmont Sandstone was placed on top of Metcalf Phyllite along the Greenbrier fault.

The cove can get a bit swampy as streams coalesce and flow westward to meet Abrams Creek east of the Tipton cabin. Stream terraces underlie the road and surrounding areas. Near the ranger station, picnic area, and campground, boulders of the Elkmont Sandstone wash out of old stream terraces.

In the western part of Cades Cove, Abrams Creek spills 25 feet over the Cades Sandstone. The folds in the sandstone are likely the result of gravitational slumping during deposition. Look for potholes, circular depressions abraded in the rock by pebbles and cobbles carried by eddies in the stream current. —Michael Hicks photo

Gregory Bald is a 14-acre grassy bald underlain by southeast-dipping Elkmont Sandstone, part of the Great Smoky Group. Cades Cove is in the middle-left background. —Bob Carr photo

Cataloochee Valley

Cataloochee Valley, an isolated mountain valley in the northeastern section of the park, was a bustling place from the mid-1800s to the 1930s. At one point the population was 1,200 residents. A robust elk population now inhabits the heavily vegetated valley, where most geologic exposures are in a handful of roadcuts or along creek beds.

The Cataloochee Valley area formed in the eroded Cataloochee anticlinorium, a 5-to-6-mile-wide and 15-mile-long structure on which smaller folds are superimposed. The entire structure is outlined by the trace of the Greenbrier fault; because the fault predated the folding it was incorporated into the final structure during the Alleghanian orogeny. Rocks of the Snowbird Group make up most of the anticlinorium. Strata along the northwestern side of the anticlinorium dip steeply westward, whereas strata along the southeastern side dip southeastward. Mesoproterozoic-age crystalline basement rocks, which form the core of the Cataloochee anticlinorium, are at the surface along fold crests in several remote locations.

Cataloochee Valley is accessible via two primary routes, most directly via I-40 (exit 20 for Waynesville, Maggie Valley, and US 276) near Dellwood, North Carolina. Take Cove Creek Road (NC 1395) for about 8 miles between the interstate and Sal Patch Gap. Roadcuts expose southeast-dipping rocks of the Great Smoky and Snowbird Groups. Turn left on Cataloochee Entrance Road and follow it to the head of the valley. The northern two-thirds of Cataloochee Valley has been eroded out of southeast-dipping rocks of the Longarm Quartzite, part of the Snowbird Group; the Roaring Fork Sandstone forms the surrounding slopes in the southern third of the valley.

The other route in or out of Cataloochee Valley is accessed via TN 32, a pleasant route to take if you're not in a hurry, don't have a recreational vehicle or trailer, and are up for a little adventure. TN 32 is not traveled as much as many of the other park roads, partly because it is narrow and winding for most of its 13 miles. The paved highway follows the national park boundary between Cosby and Davenport Gap, where the road crosses into North Carolina and becomes NC 1397, a mostly gravel road on the North Carolina side.

TN 32 follows Cosby Creek south of Green Mountain. At the turnoff to Cosby Campground, the highway skirts the east side of Turkey Knob and Cammerer Ridge to Davenport Gap. Rocks of the Snowbird Group are exposed intermittently to Davenport Gap. The 7-mile-long Mt. Sterling Ridge separates the Big Creek and Cataloochee Valleys. Metasiltstone and sandstone of the Great Smoky Group form the ridge to the west, and the Snowbird Group is to the east across a minor fault. On the south side of Mt. Sterling Ridge, strata of the Snowbird Group underlies the road to Cataloochee Valley.

CLINGMANS DOME ROAD

7 miles

Clingmans Dome Road begins at the Tennessee–North Carolina state line east of the Newfound Gap parking area at the junction with Newfound Gap Road. The thinly bedded, rust-colored Anakeesta Formation dips southeastward at the junction. The road follows the narrow State Line Ridge southwestward for 7 miles and ends in the Forney Ridge parking area. The entire route is above 5,000 feet, and turnouts and overlooks provide breathtaking panoramas of some of the highest peaks in the Great Smoky Mountains. On clear days, the spectacular views extend tens of miles into Tennessee and North Carolina.

The Anakeesta Formation is visible along the road to Indian Gap, about 1 mile south of the intersection of Newfound Gap Road and Clingmans Dome Road. Prior to the development of Great Smoky Mountains National Park, Indian Gap was considered the lowest point on State Line Ridge (Newfound Gap was surveyed as lower in 1872) and was the pass for Cherokee hunters, pioneers, and the old road over the highlands. The topographic notch is the surface expression of the Oconaluftee fault, a splay of the Gatlinburg fault system. It merges with the Gatlinburg fault on the northwest side of the park. The Oconaluftee Valley follows the Oconaluftee fault.

Look for exposures of the dark-gray Copperhill Formation west of Indian Gap to the Forney Ridge parking area. The Copperhill Formation, which is resistant to erosion due to its high quartz content, forms the ridge and weathers into large gray blocks. About halfway between Indian Gap and the Forney Ridge parking area, the road crosses a series of intrusive rocks, but they are not visible. These metamorphosed, iron-rich rocks intruded bedrock fractures, most likely during crustal extension related to the development of rift basins during the break up of Rodinia.

There are good views of the southwestern Great Smoky Mountains from the Forney Ridge parking area. The spruce forest is a remnant of the cold conditions associated with the last glacial period. Take a closer look at the Copperhill Formation at the trailhead for the Clingmans Dome observation tower. The unit is massively bedded, and the soil cover is thin due to the resistant nature of the metagraywacke and metaconglomerate, which don't easily break down. Clasts of white feldspar and blue and gray quartz make up the coarse-grained unit. These grains were weathered from Mesoproterozoic-age granitic gneiss. Grain size decreases from Tennessee to Georgia, which suggests that the unit was deposited by southeast-flowing rivers.

The Copperhill Formation contains graded bedding, a sedimentary structure wherein sand grains within a sandstone bed grade in size from coarser to finer. Graded bedding is useful for determining which direction of a unit leads to the stratigraphic top. It's also diagnostic of turbidites, a type of submarine gravity flow in which massive amounts of sediment move downslope, typically in deep water on submarine fans at the base of the continental shelf. Graded bedding develops as sediments settle out of the water onto the seafloor. Turbidites found

Some of the best exposures of the Copperhill Formation are located in the Forney Ridge parking area and at the beginning of the paved trail to the Clingmans Dome observation tower. The unit is massive and dense and weathers into large, rounded blocks. Inch-wide joints, filled with quartz and calcite, are common. —Marcy Davis photo

This palm-sized nodule in the Copperhill Formation is a concretion. Concretions form where calcite or quartz cement has nucleated around cobbles and boulders and grown into a hard mass; many in the Copperhill are softball-sized and larger. Concretions weather out of the rock and leave behind oval-shaped holes. (35.557710N, 83.496128W)
—Chuck Sutherland photo

in the Copperhill Formation were deposited in a deepwater basin on Rodinia during its breakup, before oceanic crust had formed in the rift.

At 6,643 feet above sea level, Clingmans Dome is the highest point in Great Smoky Mountains National Park, the highest point in Tennessee, the highest point along the entire 2,144 miles of the Appalachian Trail, and the second-highest point east of the Mississippi River. Get out of the car and walk up the trail, because the view is worth it. On a clear day you can see 100 miles in any direction!

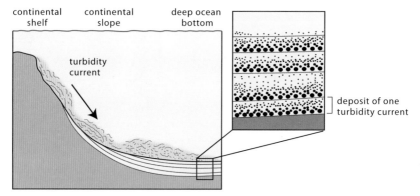

Graded bedding forms in deepwater environments where strong, episodic, short-lived turbidity currents deposit dense slurries of sediment. These currents form in response to gravity, in which sediments slide into deeper water, or they can be triggered by earthquakes. Coarse sediments settle out of the water column first followed by finer sediments. This order is preserved as the sediment turns to stone. Each graded bed represents a separate event. The inset illustrates four events.

FOOTHILLS PARKWAY

The Foothills Parkway was originally conceived as the western equivalent of North Carolina's Blue Ridge Parkway. The plan is for the road to connect US 129, at Chilhowee Lake, and I-40 via Walland, Townsend, Pigeon Forge, and Cosby. Although construction was authorized in 1944, the road remains unfinished. Currently, the Foothills Parkway consists of two segments that are unofficially connected by US 321. The eastern 6-mile segment connects I-40 with TN 32 at Cosby via TN 339. The western segment runs 17 miles between Chilhowee Lake and Walland across Chilhowee Mountain.

Eastern Segment

The eastern segment of the Foothills Parkway, which begins at I-40 south of the bridge over the Pigeon River, crosses Green Mountain. Two scenic overlooks on the north side of the mountain provide views across the eastern Valley and Ridge to English Mountain. The city of Newport is in the valley below. Green and English Mountains are both synclines made of Cambrian-age rocks of

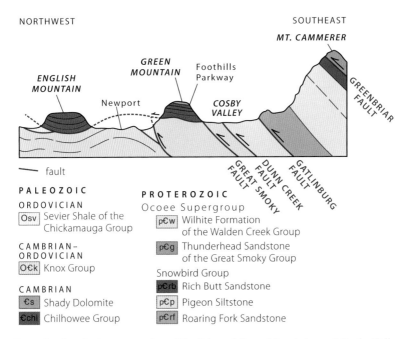

Generalized geologic cross section of English and Green Mountains and Cosby Valley.
—Modified from Moore, 1988

the Chilhowee Group. The intervening valley is a broad, eroded anticline. The Great Smoky fault dips shallowly here but is highly folded so that it surfaces on both the north and south sides of English and Green Mountains. Ordovician-age carbonates of the Knox Group are exposed in the valley where the Great Smoky thrust sheet was eroded through.

The Hesse Sandstone, part of the Chilhowee Group, is exposed at the top of Green Mountain. The heavily weathered sandstone is actually a coarse-grained quartzite. Fresh surfaces of it are nearly white, whereas a reddish-brown patina of iron oxide coats older surfaces. The sandstone is highly fractured as a result of movement along the Great Smoky fault.

The south-facing turnouts along the Foothills Parkway offer views across Cosby Valley toward the central foothills and highlands of the Great Smoky Mountains. The ridge is capped by the resistant, cliff-forming Thunderhead Sandstone, part of the Great Smoky Group. Three thrust faults underlie the clay-rich soils of Cosby Valley. The Great Smoky fault put the Neoproterozoic-age Wilhite Formation, part of the Walden Creek Group, over Cambrian-age Chilhowee Group strata. The fault surfaces along the base of Green Mountain. The Dunn Creek fault, located in the middle of Cosby Valley, put older Pigeon Siltstone, part of the Snowbird Group, on top of the younger Wilhite Formation. The Gatlinburg fault placed older Roaring Fork Sandstone, which lies at the base of the mountains, on top of younger Pigeon Siltstone. Movement on these three faults caused underlying units to fracture and erode more easily, forming Cosby Valley.

South-facing overlooks along the Foothills Parkway provide views across the Cosby Valley of Great Smoky Mountains National Park. Along the ridge you will see two high points: Mt. Cammerer, at 4,928 feet, and Cosby Knob to the southwest, at 5,161 feet. Elevation from Mt. Cammerer decreases northeastward to Davenport Gap and the Pigeon River at the northeastern park boundary. The Greenbrier fault is located near the top of the ridge and placed Thunderhead Sandstone on Rich Butt Sandstone. Both the fault and strata dip away from the view. (35.812640N, 83.223942W) —Bob Carr photo

The Cosby campground is located at the base of Cosby Knob, the high point on the ridge located south across the valley. The campground sits on a large alluvial fan that was built by several streams that flow off Cosby Knob and merge with Caney Creek near the town of Cosby. Alluvial fans, cone-shaped deposits of sediments, are commonly found at the base of cliff-forming sandstone beds throughout the Appalachians. Poorly sorted Pleistocene-age sedimentary deposits are also visible along Cosby Creek. Terraces of these deposits, former floodplains of Cosby Creek, which has since cut down through them, line the Cosby Valley.

Western Segment

The western segment of the Foothills Parkway begins near Walland and follows the crest of Chilhowee Mountain, a narrow, 30-mile-long, northeast-trending ridge that averages about 2,500 feet in elevation and extends from the Little Tennessee River to Pigeon Forge. Some of the best views of the southern foothills and highlands of the Great Smoky Mountains can be had from overlooks on Chilhowee Mountain's southeast side. Four overlooks on the northwest side provide views of the Valley and Ridge and the city of Maryville. Most of the outcrops are at road level, and there are a few larger roadcuts. Sedimentary strata of the Cambrian-age Chilhowee Group make up Chilhowee Mountain. The group was named for exposures first described here by James M. Safford in 1869. In general, the Chilhowee Group includes sandstones, siltstones, and shales that are somewhat metamorphosed.

The small town of Walland lies at a water gap the Little River cut through Chilhowee Mountain. A minor fault that cuts through the gap offsets the Chilhowee Group on either side of US 321/TN 73.

Chilhowee Group rocks do not contain very many fossils, but those they do contain are some of Tennessee's oldest. *Skolithos*, fossilized worm burrows, look like pencils stuck in the Hesse and Nebo Sandstones. Ostracods, tiny shrimp-like animals with bivalve shells up to a half-inch long, are found in the Murray Shale. The oldest trilobite in eastern North America was found in the Murray Shale on Chilhowee Mountain, and fragments of trilobites from the genus *Olenellus* were found in the Helenmode Member of the Erwin Formation, the youngest unit in the Chilhowee Group, near Walland at Little River Gap.

For about 1 mile, Foothills Parkway crosses the northern end of Miller Cove, eroded in the less-resistant Shady Dolomite of Cambrian age. Turnouts on the south side of the road provide beautiful views across Happy Valley to the foothills and highlands of the Great Smoky Mountains. The national park boundary follows Happy and Abrams Ridges, the low ridges south of Happy Valley that are composed of the Walden Creek Group. The trace of Miller Cove fault, a minor thrust fault, is located in Happy Valley and separates Chilhowee Mountain from the southern foothills.

This 2-inch-wide cephalon, or head shield, is from the oldest trilobite in eastern North America, a member of the Nevadiidae family. It was discovered in the Murray Shale on Chilhowee Mountain. —S. J. Hageman photo

Views become more impressive with elevation and culminate in spectacular, nearly 360-degree views from the Look Rock observation tower, the highest point along the western segment of the Foothills Parkway. Make time for the half-mile walk to the tower, where you'll be treated to sweeping views.

Look for the white, medium-to-coarse-grained Hesse Sandstone in turnouts along the ridge crest and at and around the Look Rock observation tower. The Hesse Sandstone consists of 2-to-4-foot-thick beds of quartzite that form cliffs along the top of Chilhowee Mountain. The clean quartz sands that make up the sandstone were deposited in a narrow belt of sand ridges on the continental shelf in Cambrian time. The sandstone was altered to quartzite through metamorphism associated with the development of the Appalachian Mountains. Fresh surfaces are nearly white, whereas weathered surfaces have a rusty patina created by the oxidation of iron minerals.

The Murray Shale underlies the road at Murray Gap, about a quarter mile south of the Look Rock parking area. The thinly bedded, dark-grayish-brown and green shale is rich in organic matter and glauconite, a phosphate-rich, green clay mineral found in marine sands. The shale is easily eroded from the hillside. Samples taken from the Murray Shale on Chilhowee Mountain contain acritarchs, microscopic, roughly circular fossils made of organic material that include a range of structures. Scientists use the term *acritarch* only as a descriptor; once a specimen has been identified and classified, it's taken out of the acritarch classification. The acritarchs found in the Murray Shale were eventually classified as phytoplankton, unicellular marine algae.

The Hesse Sandstone dips southeastward into the road so that the southeast slope of Chilhowee Mountain is relatively gentle compared to the northwest slope. Landslides (and resulting road closures) are common along this section of Foothills Parkway because the road undercuts rock layers in many places. (35.716831N, 83.838044W) —Chuck Sutherland photo

Approximately 4 miles south of the Look Rock observation tower, the road crosses the Miller Cove fault and onto strata of the foothills section of the Blue Ridge. This thrust fault placed strata of the Wilhite Formation, part of the Walden Creek Group, onto strata of the Chilhowee Group.

Thinly bedded phyllite and slate of the Wilhite Formation is exposed along the Foothills Parkway near Chilhowee Lake and along the part of US 129 that follows the shore of the lake. The unit is highly deformed and fractured here due to movement along the Miller Cove fault. (35.572353N, 84.003391W) —Chuck Sutherland photo

LAUREL CREEK ROAD
7.5 miles

Laurel Creek Road connects the Townsend Wye (the junction with the Little River Gorge Road) and Crib Gap, near the junction with Cades Cove Loop Road. The Townsend Wye is named for the Y-shaped confluence of the Little River with two tributary streams.

Laurel Creek Road follows the beautiful, narrow, winding canyon of Laurel Creek. Many turnouts provide opportunities to examine rocks in roadcuts and along the creekbed. For about 1 mile south of the turnoff to the Great Smoky Mountains Institute at Tremont, nearly vertical, brownish-gray Cades Sandstone of the Great Smoky Group is exposed along the east side of the road. Metcalf Phyllite, part of the Snowbird Group, is exposed at and south of the tunnel. The Metcalf Phyllite is a brownish-gray to green metasiltstone with thin beds of fine-grained metasandstone and phyllite. Mica minerals such as muscovite impart a metallic-looking sheen on fresh surfaces. These minerals formed during metamorphism when clay minerals were altered by the heat and pressure within Earth's crust.

South of the Bote Mountain Trailhead, Laurel Creek Road crosses the Great Smoky fault. The fault placed the Metcalf Phyllite over the Ordovician-age

The Metcalf Phyllite is well exposed along Laurel Creek Road, especially between the tunnel and the trailheads to Bote Mountain and Spence Field. The rock was thoroughly sheared and deformed by local thrust faulting. (35.649811N, 83.715190W) —James St. John photo

Jonesboro Limestone. The fault is exposed behind the falls at White Oak Sinks, an interesting karst feature that developed in the Jonesboro Limestone. Short Creek disappears underground here and surfaces again outside the park near Tuckaleechee Caverns southwest of Townsend. Take a hike up the Schoolhouse Gap trail to have a look.

Little River Gorge Road/ Fighting Creek Gap Road
SUGARLANDS VISITOR CENTER ON US 441—TOWNSEND WYE
18 miles

Little River Gorge Road was the route of the Little River Railroad that ran between the lumber towns of Townsend and Elkmont during the early twentieth century. The road connects with Fighting Creek Gap Road and continues to the Sugarlands Visitor Center. The sinuous roads follow two rivers that are separated by a divide near Elkmont at Fighting Creek Gap. East of Elkmont, Fighting Creek Gap Road follows Fighting Creek from its confluence with the West Prong of the Little Pigeon River at Sugarlands to its headwaters at Fighting

Creek Gap. West of Elkmont, Fighting Creek Gap Road and Little River Gorge Road follow Little River, which has its headwaters on Clingmans Dome, then flows north through Elkmont and then west toward Townsend.

In this part of Great Smoky Mountains National Park, strata of the Snowbird Group were thrust over younger Great Smoky Group rocks along the Greenbrier fault. The rock layers are deformed due to movement along the fault. The road crosses the Greenbrier fault in three places: east of Metcalf Bottoms, east of Little River Gorge, and west of Meigs Falls. Vegetation and soil cover the fault trace; however, exposures of the Metcalf Phyllite, part of the Snowbird Group, and the Thunderhead Sandstone, part of the Great Smoky Group, will alert you to the road's location relative to the fault. These units are well exposed in the riverbed and along the road. Waterfalls are common along the road and have tended to form where the Little River and tributary streams flow over the resistant Thunderhead Sandstone. Valleys and wider streambeds have been carved from the more easily eroded Metcalf Phyllite.

Metasandstones of the Roaring Fork Sandstone, part of the Snowbird Group, underlie the road between the Sugarlands Visitor Center and Laurel Falls. Maloney Point Overlook provides a view northeastward down the valley of Fighting Creek toward Sugarlands Valley and Gatlinburg. The Greenbrier fault is located near the base of Mt. LeConte (6,594 feet), visible on the eastern skyline. The Gatlinburg fault truncates the Greenbrier fault in the Fighting Creek drainage. At 2,000 to 2,500 feet in elevation, the central foothills have been eroded out of the Roaring Fork Sandstone, which dips steeply southeastward. Both Gatlinburg and Sugarlands Valley are built atop this sandstone.

The turnoff to Elkmont is just west of Laurel Falls. Once a rough-and-tumble lumber town, Elkmont eventually became a major hub for early Great Smoky Mountains tourism. The Little River Railroad provided mountain access to people from Knoxville, Maryville, and Chattanooga. Many trails in this part of the park are former railroad beds. Historic lumber and tourism buildings are preserved in Elkmont adjacent the park's largest campground. The Elkmont Sandstone, the oldest unit in the Great Smoky Group, was first described in this area.

West of Elkmont, the road follows the Little River. Look for light-colored, massive Thunderhead Sandstone exposed along the road and in the riverbed. Mountain rivers, such as Little River, are generally confined to steep, narrow, V-shaped valleys. Bedrock and large boulders typically line the river bottom as the river's energy cannot move them except at flood stage.

The road crosses the Greenbrier fault near Metcalf Bottoms. The area around the Metcalf Bottoms picnic area is underlain by the Metcalf Phyllite, which is more easily eroded than the Thunderhead Sandstone. Consequently, the valley is considerably wider in contrast to areas underlain by the resistant Thunderhead Sandstone.

In the 3 miles between the Metcalf Bottoms picnic area and Meigs Falls, Thunderhead Sandstone is exposed along the road as it again crosses the Greenbrier fault. This section of road twists and turns through the narrow and steeply walled Little River Gorge. Artificial embankments along this section of road

Laurel Falls drops 80 feet over the Thunderhead Sandstone, which is well exposed along the paved 1.25-mile-long Laurel Falls trail. —Michael Hicks photo

catch rockfall debris. Limestone fill helps fortify the riverbanks against erosion during periods of high water.

Between Metcalf Bottoms and the Townsend Wye, old river terraces, left behind as the Little River incised the sediments in response to regional uplift, are preserved at higher elevations. At the Sinks, an old stream terrace is preserved about 80 feet above the current river level. Ordinarily, the term *sinks* is used as a shortened version of *sinkhole*, which is a karst feature. At the Sinks, the term refers to the deep plunge pool that lies at the base of a significant drop in the river. This drop-off exists because the river is cutting off an old river meander neck that goes around the small rocky hill southeast of the bridge. The shorter path increases the river gradient. Thick beds of Thunderhead Sandstone are overturned here as a result of movement and subsequent deformation along the Greenbrier fault.

The turnout out for Meigs Falls is located on the south side of Little River Gorge Road a little over 1 mile west of the Sinks and about 5 miles east of the

The Elkmont Sandstone is a grayish-brown, fine-grained metasandstone with some beds of meta-siltstone. High iron content gives weathered surfaces of the Elkmont a rusty patina. The upper part of the Elkmont Sandstone grades into the overlying Thunderhead Sandstone.
—James St. John photo

At the Sinks, the Little River makes a dramatic turn under the bridge and churns over a blocky, 10-foot-high outcrop of Thunderhead Sandstone into impressive rapids and a roiling pool. The river's abandoned meander and old stream terrace are preserved at a higher elevation to the right of the photo. (35.669266N, 83.662345W) —Chuck Sutherland photo

Townsend Wye. The falls are located on Meigs Creek, a tributary to Little River, and descend about 30 feet over the Thunderhead Sandstone just above where the two streams meet. Meigs Falls is a horsetail-type waterfall, meaning the water descends nearly vertically but stays in contact with the bedrock surface.

Little River Gorge Road crosses the Greenbrier fault for the third time west of Meigs Falls. The Metcalf Phyllite is present all the way to the junction with Laurel Creek Road.

US 321

MARYVILLE—GATLINBURG—COSBY

63 miles

Most residents and visitors to Tennessee know US 321 as the road that connects points of interest on the Tennessee side of Great Smoky Mountains National Park. Eventually, parts of US 321 between Walland and Cosby will be included in the Foothills Parkway, and this segment of road will become part of the park.

Maryville lies at the eastern edge of the Valley and Ridge. Carbonates belonging to the Knox Group underlie the city. East of Maryville, US 321 approaches Chilhowee Gap, a water gap the Little River cut through Chilhowee Mountain. The Great Smoky fault, which forms the tectonic boundary between the Valley and Ridge and Blue Ridge physiographic provinces, is exposed at Chilhowee Gap in a roadcut below the retaining wall near the gap's northern end. The fault placed conglomerates and sandstones of the Cambrian-age Chilhowee Group on Ordovician-age shales and dips southeastward under Chilhowee Mountain. Chilhowee Group rocks, which make up Chilhowee Mountain, were pushed more than 200 miles to their present location along the Great Smoky fault. The Sevier Shale underlies the fault and is highly deformed. Look for exposures at the north end of the retaining wall.

Walland sits in Miller Cove, a 10-square-mile lowland, on the south side of Chilhowee Gap. US 321 follows the Little River, which begins high in the Great Smoky Mountains, between Walland and Townsend. Greenish-gray slate and siltstone of the Wilhite Formation, part of the Walden Creek Group, are exposed along the highway for about 5 miles. The rocks exhibit tight folding that likely occurred during the Taconic orogeny in Ordovician time.

The old lumber town of Townsend is built in Tuckaleechee Cove, a large tectonic window eroded through the Great Smoky thrust sheet. Wear Cove, east of Townsend, is another tectonic window. The Sevier Shale of the Chicka-mauga Group and younger carbonate rocks of the Knox Group are exposed beneath the fault in the windows and form the flat floors of the coves. Sinkholes and caves, such as Tuckaleechee Caverns southwest of Townsend, developed in the Jonesboro Limestone, part of the Knox Group. High ridges of Neo-proterozoic-age Ocoee Supergroup surround the oval-shaped coves. Wilhite Formation, part of the Walden Creek Group, crops out along the north side of the Tuckaleechee and Wear Coves, while rocks of the Snowbird Group and Cades Sandstone are found along the south side.

Great Smoky fault at Chilhowee Gap near Walland. The fault crosses diagonally from the geologist's feet up to the right, toward the retaining wall. (35.734150N, 83.819568W)
—Robert Hatcher photo

Tilted beds of the Roaring Fork Sandstone are exposed along the Little Pigeon River at Greenbrier. The unit is part of the Snowbird Group and contains metasandstone and metasiltstone. —Marcy Davis photo

US 321 turns northward as Wear Valley Road in Townsend on the northeastern side of Tuckaleechee Cove. Look for light-gray rocks belonging to the Jonesboro Limestone at road level about 0.75 mile north of the junction.

In Pigeon Forge, US 321 merges with US 441 for several miles through the chaos that is the gateway to Great Smoky Mountains National Park. Between Pigeon Forge and Gatlinburg US 321 follows the Little Pigeon River and transects a few miles of wilderness. The highway is part of a planned section of the Foothills Parkway. Snowbird Group strata are exposed along the road.

In the 20 miles between Gatlinburg and Cosby, US 321 follows the northern boundary of Great Smoky Mountains National Park through the northern foothills and several popular areas of the park. In Gatlinburg you can take Roaring Fork Road (cars only) to access the Roaring Fork Motor Nature Trail, a one-way, 6-mile scenic loop through historic homesteads and native hardwood forest. Several trails along this loop provide access to beautiful waterfalls, such as Rainbow Falls, which plunges 80 feet over Roaring Fork Sandstone, part of the Snowbird Group. The Roaring Fork Sandstone underlies the Sugarlands Visitor Center and parts of Gatlinburg and Greenbrier.

Cosby was ideally situated for making moonshine due to heavy forestation, dense laurel thickets, clear streams and springs, and remote, rugged terrain. In the mountain hollows and caves surrounding Cosby, descendants of the German, French, and Scotch-Irish immigrants who had settled the area in the 1700s and early 1800s made illicit corn whiskey in copper pot and silver cloud stills. During and following Prohibition, Cosby residents signaled the arrival of federal agents with dynamite blasts. The Great Smoky Mountains Visitor Center in Cosby has a Moonshine Museum, where you can learn more about the area's history.

US 441 (NEWFOUND GAP ROAD)
Sugarlands Visitor Center—
Oconaluftee Visitor Center
30 miles

Newfound Gap Road, a 30-mile stretch of highway through the center of Great Smoky Mountains National Park, connects the Sugarlands Visitor Center south of Gatlinburg with the Oconaluftee Visitor Center in Cherokee, North Carolina. On the Tennessee side, the highway follows the West Prong of the Little Pigeon River to its headwaters on the southeast side of Mt. LeConte. On the North Carolina side, the highway follows the Oconaluftee Valley. The many overlooks and trailheads accessible from Newfound Gap Road provide ample opportunity to explore the geology of the Great Smoky Mountains.

Newfound Gap Road passes over Neoproterozoic-age rocks of the Ocoee Supergroup. Higher knobs and ridges are held up by more resistant quartz-rich rocks, such as metasandstone and quartzite, whereas valleys are floored by shale and metasiltstone that tend to erode. The Thunderhead Sandstone, part of the Great Smoky Group, is well exposed on the Tennessee side of the park, particularly where it forms resistant cliffs 50 to 100 feet high on the western limb of the Alum Cave synclinorium. Near Newfound Gap, at the center of the synclinorium, the thinly bedded Anakeesta Formation forms rugged and rocky ridges.

In Tennessee, Newfound Gap Road begins at the Sugarlands Visitor Center, located about 2 miles south of Gatlinburg in the central foothills. Limited exposures of the Roaring Fork Sandstone, part of the Snowbird Group, and the Elkmont Sandstone, the oldest unit in the Great Smoky Group, are visible in roadcuts east of the visitor center. The contact between the two units is the Greenbrier fault, along which the Elkmont Sandstone was thrust over the Roaring Fork Sandstone. The Greenbrier fault is not visible at the surface here, its trace represents both the geologic and topographic transition between the foothills and highlands sections of the Great Smoky Mountains. Between the Greenbrier fault and Mingus Mill, near the Oconaluftee Visitor Center, US 411/Newfound Gap Road lies entirely on the Greenbrier thrust sheet and traverses the Alum Cave synclinorium.

For a good orientation to the western Great Smoky Mountains, pull over at the larger of the two turnouts at Carlos Campbell Overlook, about 2 miles southeast of the Sugarlands Visitor Center. The Roaring Fork Sandstone and Pigeon Siltstone, both part of the Snowbird Group, are present in Sugarlands Valley and the western foothills section of the Great Smoky Mountains near here. Sugarlands Valley, named for its sugar maple trees, is one of the original settlements in the area. The flat valley floor, rich soils, and location on the West Prong of the Little Pigeon River made it a good place to call home.

The overlook faces the drainage of Big Branch. Balsam Point, capped by the resistant Thunderhead Sandstone, is at the head of Big Branch at the western end of the Mt. LeConte ridge. Named for exposures on Thunderhead Mountain, located west of Clingmans Dome, the Thunderhead Sandstone forms resistant cliffs and steep, north-facing slopes. These thick beds of fine-grained conglomerate, metasandstone, and metasiltstone dip southeastward along the northwestern limb of the Alum Cave synclinorium.

The road steepens along the south side of the narrowing valley of the West Prong of the Little Pigeon River, south of Carlos Campbell Overlook. Between the overlook and the Loop, where the highway circles back over itself, massive and blocky brownish-gray metasandstone of the Thunderhead Sandstone crops out along the road. It's well exposed for a couple of miles.

The Chimney Tops are visible to the southeast from the Chimney Tops Overlook, which is about 1 mile east of the Chimneys Picnic Area. The scraggy nature of the rocks at the top of the chimneys is typical of the Anakeesta Formation when it's weathered. The thick-bedded Thunderhead Sandstone is exposed across the highway

At higher elevations you may notice dense concentrations of large, angular boulders, particularly at the bases of tall cliffs. The boulders were split from the cliffs by a physical weathering process called frost-wedging. During the daytime and in the warmer summer months, water seeps into cracks in the rock. As temperatures drop at night or during winter, the water freezes and expands, thereby acting as a wedge to widen the cracks. With enough freeze-thaw cycles,

The Thunderhead Sandstone caps Balsam Point, at the head of Big Branch, a tributary to the West Prong of the Little Pigeon River, which flows northward through the foreground. Large fan-shaped colluvium deposits extend into the valley from Balsam Point. These ancient debris flow deposits are now tree covered and being reworked by modern streams. (35.658209N, 83.519934W) —Chuck Sutherland photo

The view from the Chimney Tops Overlook. The Anakeesta Formation forms the backbone of the Chimney Tops, to the left. The higher ridge in the center and to the right is Sugarlands Mountain. A good look at the Anakeesta Formation, along with a fantastic view down the valley of the West Prong of the Little Pigeon River, are the rewards of the steep hike to the top of Chimney Tops. (35.638544N, 83.491901W) —Chuck Sutherland photo

the rock splits into large angular pieces that fall off the mountain and collect in large piles called talus, scree slopes, or colluvium. These accumulations are particularly visible at the base of cliffs made of Thunderhead Sandstone, areas that typically have little soil or vegetation. Frost-wedging is still happening today, but much of the scree seen throughout the park formed during the Pleistocene Epoch, when the climate was colder.

The contact between the Thunderhead Sandstone and the overlying Anakeesta Formation is located at the Loop but is not visible. It is difficult to see Anakeesta Formation rocks here because they are covered by vegetation, but note the change in topography. The resistant Thunderhead Sandstone forms prominent cliffs, whereas the Anakeesta Formation tends to form more rounded slopes.

East of the Loop the Alum Cave Trailhead is on the north side of the road. Alum Cave, located on the southern ridge of Mt. LeConte about 2.5 miles up the trail from the parking area, is not really a cave so much as an overhang that's nearly 100 feet high and 30 feet deep. It formed in the Anakeesta Formation, which contains large amounts of the mineral pyrite, an iron sulfide. When pyrite contacts moisture, a weak sulfuric acid may form that leaches elements out of other minerals in the rock. As the solution passes over the surface, the fluid evaporates to form a saltlike mineral crust, which is what the cave is named for. During the mid-1800s, three men from Oconaluftee, North Carolina, bought the land here and formed the Epsom Salts Manufacturing Company to mine the residue. They processed saltpeter (potassium nitrate) for the Confederacy's gunpowder reserve during the Civil War. Alum, a group of sulfate minerals used in a variety of products, was also mined here.

Alum Cave, a large overhang in the Anakeesta Formation, is named for the mineral crusts that form on its walls, ceiling, and floor. (35.638792N, 83.446007W) —Chuck Sutherland photo

The road follows Walker Camp Prong, a tributary to the West Prong of the Little Pigeon River, along the southern side of Anakeesta Ridge between the Alum Cave trailhead and Newfound Gap. The steeply eastward-dipping Anakeesta Formation is exposed along the road. The rock weathers into thin, platy layers that are prone to landslides where slopes are steeper than 40 degrees. In years of unusually heavy rain and snowfall, sections of Newfound Gap Road commonly wash out or are buried under landslide debris. Gray, V-shaped landslide scars are visible all over the Great Smoky Mountains, particularly where the Anakeesta Formation is at the surface.

Morton Overlook provides a spectacular view down the valley of the West Prong of the Little Pigeon River and through the highlands and foothills of the Great Smoky Mountains. Look for Chimney Tops on the left side of the valley. Landslide scars may be visible along the ridges.

The Tennessee–North Carolina state line crosses the Newfound Gap parking area, which is built atop the appropriately named State Line Ridge. On a clear day, the panorama from the eastern side of the lot is breathtaking: you can look across Oconaluftee Valley toward the Plott Balsam Range southeast of Cherokee, in North Carolina. Bryson City is due south, and Clingmans Dome is to the southwest.

Along the northwest side of the Newfound Gap parking area you can examine the Anakeesta Formation more closely. These thinly bedded and platy rocks were metamorphosed from shale to phyllite. In some places the rock has a metallic sheen, and layers may have a wavy look. This is the result of the clay minerals being altered to mica minerals. The formation's reddish color is the result of minerals high in iron, particularly pyrite, being oxidized. When pyrite weathers and oxidizes, a weak acidic solution of sulfuric acid and iron sulfate is produced. The acid facilitates the weathering of the other minerals in the rock and entrains iron, magnesium, aluminum, manganese, copper, and zinc in the fluid. During periods of heavy rain, a high concentration of these elements in solution can significantly alter water chemistry and sterilize stream headwaters. This solution can reach an acidic pH level of 2.0. This is why many areas with Anakeesta Formation lack vegetation, and the vegetation that does survive is limited to spruce-fir forests that can survive in acidic soils.

South of Newfound Gap the road follows Thomas Ridge, a long ridge that extends across the eastern limb of the Alum Cave synclinorium nearly to Bryson City, North Carolina. The Copperhill and Anakeesta Formations are exposed in places along the highway. Many turnouts along the ridge provide spectacular views of the southern Great Smoky Mountains. At Webb Overlook, you can look northwest to see Clingmans Dome on the skyline.

The road turns sharply into the Oconaluftee Valley near the Thomas Ridge Trailhead. The linear valley follows the trace of the Oconaluftee fault, which runs under the road and extends northwestward through Indian Gap at Clingmans Dome Road and on to the northwest side of the park where it joins the Gatlinburg fault system. The Oconaluftee fault is a steeply dipping right-lateral

Thinly bedded phyllite of the Anakeesta Formation dips into the northwest side of the Newfound Gap parking area. Fresh surfaces are dark due to the rock's high organic content, while weathered surfaces are rust colored, the result of the oxidation of iron sulfide minerals such as pyrite. Mica minerals give the rock a metallic sheen. (35.610758N, 83.426042W) —James St. John photo

strike-slip fault that displaced strata up to several miles. Local rocks are highly fractured and sheared as a result of fault movement.

The road crosses the Greenbrier fault between Tow String and Mingus Creek, but the fault is not visible because vegetation and river alluvium cover it. Here, the fault separates strata of the Ocoee Supergroup and older crystalline rocks of the Grenville basement complex. These dark-gray gneisses, which contain eye-shaped lenses of white quartz and feldspar, are exposed on the west side of the highway south of Mingus Mill.

Rocks of the crystalline basement complex are exposed south of Mingus Mill and the Oconaluftee Visitor Center. Formed during the Grenville orogeny, these gneisses are more than 1 billion years old! —James St. John photo

ROAD GUIDES IN EAST TENNESSEE

I-24
MONTEAGLE—CHATTANOOGA
45 miles

The town of Monteagle sits atop Monteagle Mountain, a 2.5-mile-wide spur of the Cumberland Plateau. The interstate follows deeply incised drainages on the west and east sides of the mountain. The highway's treacherous grades inspired Johnny Cash's trucker theme song "Monteagle Mountain," about a runaway truck, and Jerry Reed's "The Legend," with lyrics about a truck driver who survived the drive despite a heavy rainstorm and air brake failure. See the guide for I-24: Nashville—Murfreesboro—Monteagle in the Middle Tennessee chapter for a discussion of the climb up Monteagle Mountain from the west.

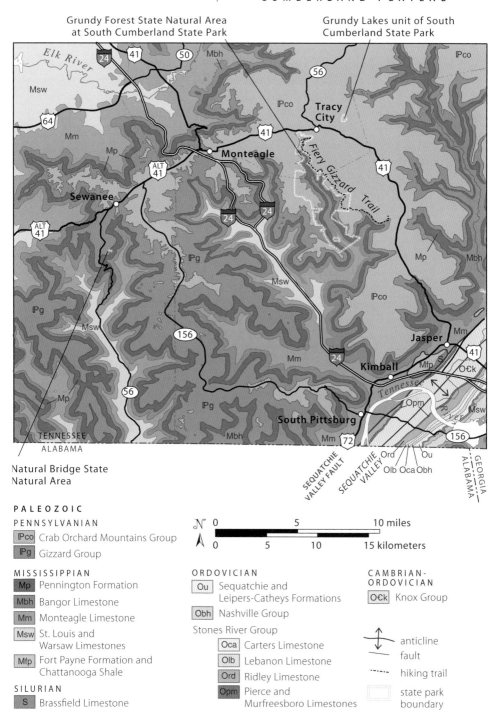

Grundy Forest State Natural Area
at South Cumberland State Park

Grundy Lakes unit of South
Cumberland State Park

Natural Bridge State
Natural Area

PALEOZOIC

PENNSYLVANIAN

| IPco | Crab Orchard Mountains Group |
| IPg | Gizzard Group |

MISSISSIPPIAN

Mp	Pennington Formation
Mbh	Bangor Limestone
Mm	Monteagle Limestone
Msw	St. Louis and Warsaw Limestones
Mfp	Fort Payne Formation and Chattanooga Shale

SILURIAN

| S | Brassfield Limestone |

ORDOVICIAN

| Ou | Sequatchie and Leipers-Catheys Formations |
| Obh | Nashville Group |

Stones River Group

Oca	Carters Limestone
Olb	Lebanon Limestone
Ord	Ridley Limestone
Opm	Pierce and Murfreesboro Limestones

CAMBRIAN-ORDOVICIAN

| OЄk | Knox Group |

↕ anticline
⊥ fault
- - - hiking trail
☐ state park boundary

0   5   10 miles
0   5   10   15 kilometers

Geology along I-24 between Monteagle and Kimball. See maps on pages 108 and 114 for section between Kimball and Chattanooga.

The top of Monteagle Mountain and surrounding areas are composed of nearly flat-lying, mostly nonmarine sediments of the Gizzard and Crab Orchard Mountains Groups. These strata were deposited in a variety of deltaic and river environments that became extensive across Tennessee as the Appalachian Mountains were rising in the east in Pennsylvanian time. The Sewanee Conglomerate, the oldest formation in the Crab Orchard Mountains Group, underlies the highway at Monteagle, where it's up to 130 feet thick and forms light-colored cliffs along the western plateau margin. The Sewanee Conglomerate was deposited as part of a southwest-flowing river system more than 1,000 miles long that extended from Canada to Arkansas. The conglomerate contains a high percentage of well-rounded, white quartz pebbles. Sands of the Sewanee Conglomerate are also silica rich, suggesting this sediment traveled a long distance before finally coming to rest. Clay and silt were washed away, and less resistant sediment, such as grains of feldspar or carbonate, did not survive the trip. The sands were mined near Sewanee and sent to the Chattanooga Glass Company for the manufacture of beer, soda, and medicine bottles and flasks during the 1930s.

Trees are a bit spindly around Monteagle due to the light-colored, sandy soils that are derived from the Sewanee Conglomerate. Relatively devoid of nutrients, these soils are not good for plants, but they do facilitate the development of good seasonal aquifers. These sandy soils, as well as those derived from the underlying Warren Point Sandstone, were important local water sources

Look for exposures of Sewanee Conglomerate at the front entrance to the University of the South in Sewanee and east of Monteagle. The light-colored rocks are cross-bedded in many areas. (35.207996N, 85.902039W) —Marcy Davis photo

until the 1950s. Native Americans, Civil War troops, and the founders of the University of the South were drawn to the area, in part, because of its good water supply.

In 1840, coal was discovered near Tracy City, about 5 miles east of Monteagle, on US 41. Much of the coal came from the Sewanee coal seam, an up-to-4-foot-thick layer in the Whitwell Shale, part of the Crab Orchard Mountains Group. The coal was used as fuel for iron production in nearby Chattanooga. You can visit the old coke ovens at the Grundy Lakes unit of South Cumberland State Park northeast of Tracy City. Also check out the coal miner statue on Main Street in Tracy City. The Miner's Museum and Heritage Center is located on TN 108 in Palmer, about 20 miles northeast of Tracy City.

For an interesting look at the structural geology of the area, take a hike on the Fiery Gizzard Trail out of Tracy City in the Grundy Forest State Natural Area. Cumberland Plateau strata are mostly flat; however, folded and faulted horizons in Gizzard Group strata are visible along the trail. This deformation includes shearing within coal horizons as well as folding and thrust faulting that affects up to 100 feet of section in some areas. Sycamore Falls cascades over two detachment thrust faults, both of which are in the Bon Air coal seams of the Raccoon Mountain Formation. These faults are splays of the Sequatchie Valley thrust fault, which is located about 7 miles to the southeast and is part of the Cumberland fault, the primary detachment thrust fault along which rocks of the southern Cumberland Plateau were transported northwestward.

Thick beds of Warren Point Sandstone form the bluffs of the southern Cumberland Plateau. These fine-to-medium-grained, cross-bedded sandstones were deposited by a southwest-flowing braided river that began in and flowed parallel to the rising Appalachian Mountains during Pennsylvanian time. On fresh surfaces, the sandstone is light gray, but it weathers to yellowish brown. Color variations are the result of oxidation of the iron oxide minerals hematite and limonite. Many buildings on and around the University of the South in Sewanee are made from locally quarried Warren Point Sandstone. The rock is also beautifully exposed at the nearby Natural Bridge State Natural Area.

Near exit 135, the westbound and eastbound lanes of I-24 split for about 5 miles to pass around an eroded knob of Monteagle Mountain. Eastbound lanes follow the valley of Battle Creek, and westbound lanes follow the valley of Cave Cove Branch, both tributaries of the Tennessee River. There is more than 1,000 feet of elevation change between Monteagle Mountain and the valley bottom. The interstate cuts through Pennsylvanian-age, plateau-capping strata and the Mississippian-age carbonates that the valleys have been eroded into. Roadcuts are quite spectacular along this section of highway in both directions.

Buff-colored, cross-bedded sandstones of the Sewanee Conglomerate are visible at the top of the hill from the eastbound lanes. The contact with the underlying Warren Point Sandstone is visible near mile 137. Beneath the Warren Point Sandstone are the olive-gray siltstones, sandstones, and shales of the Raccoon Mountain Formation, which contains nonmarine fossils and coal seams that have been mined all over the southern Cumberland Plateau. In this area, marine fossils, such as trilobites, brachiopods, gastropods, and crinoids,

Located in Sewanee, the University of the South's All Saints' Chapel was built in the early 1900s from locally quarried Pennsylvanian-age Warren Point Sandstone. The chapel floors are made of Tennessee "marble," a limestone that was quarried near Knoxville. A stained-glass image of Sir Charles Lyell, a Scottish geologist best known for his mid-1830s Principles of Geology, *is located at the rear of the chapel. (35.204034N, 85.920972W)* —The University of the South photo

The Warren Point Sandstone and Raccoon Mountain Formation, both part of the Pennsylvanian-age Gizzard Group, are exposed along the eastbound lanes of I-24 east of Monteagle. The Warren Point Sandstone (tan layer) is the main bluff-former of the southern Cumberland Plateau. The contact between the two units is at the level of the second bench. A thin layer of concrete, called gunite, is sprayed on roadcuts to help mitigate the erosion of shales within the Raccoon Mountain Formation. (35.206906N, 85.817886W) —Marcy Davis photo

can be found in calcareous sandstone layers likely deposited in a tidal flat with small streams and backswamps.

The Mississippian-age Pennington Formation is present on both sides of the eastbound lane between mile 138 and the first runaway truck ramp. Look for the unit's characteristic maroon and green shales. The Mississippian-age Bangor Limestone is exposed east of the first runaway truck ramp. The lighter-colored, thick-bedded Monteagle Limestone crops out near the base of the mountain.

Westbound travelers will see nearly all of the region's units of Late Mississippian age and Early Pennsylvanian age. At the base of Monteagle Mountain is an abandoned quarry in the Mississippian-age St. Louis Limestone. The Monteagle Limestone is exposed along the highway for about 2 miles to the west. Karst solution cavities filled with rock fragments, called collapse breccias, are evidence that the Monteagle Limestone was exposed to surface weathering during Mississippian time. The Monteagle Limestone and overlying Bangor Limestone are difficult to distinguish from one another. The Bangor Limestone is slightly darker in color. Both are massive, thick-bedded units that were deposited at the edge of a shallow carbonate platform that extended through parts of Georgia, Alabama, and Tennessee during most of the Mississippian Period. In this area, sandstone of the Hartselle Formation separates the units at milepost 139; however, the Hartselle Formation can be tough to spot as it is not very thick, and exposures may be obscured by vegetation.

The Pennington Formation overlies the Bangor Limestone and is exposed along a large westward bend in the westbound lane. Limestones and dolomites are interbedded with the Pennington's characteristic maroon and green calcareous shales and thin sandstone beds. Dark-gray and black shales contain

Fossilized helixes, built by Archimedes bryozoans, are found in the Mississippian-age Bangor Limestone. Archimedes formed the internal support structure for a lacy, spiral extension that wrapped around the helical structure; the extension, which is rarely found attached, is made up of small calcium carbonate windows that provided a home for the many tiny animals that made up the colony. The animal's genus name is a reference to a type of water pump, the invention of which is attributed to the Greek mathematician Archimedes. —Chuck Sutherland photo

siderite, an iron carbonate mineral. Pennington Formation sediments show the transition from the deeper water limestones of the earlier Mississippian-age seas to those of a nearshore tidal and intertidal environments. Offshore sandbars are also preserved in the Pennington Formation. Its shales have been sprayed with gunite to slow erosion. Overlying the Pennington Formation are Pennsylvanian-age sandstones and coal-bearing shales of the Raccoon Mountain Formation. The thick-bedded Warren Point Sandstone is exposed near

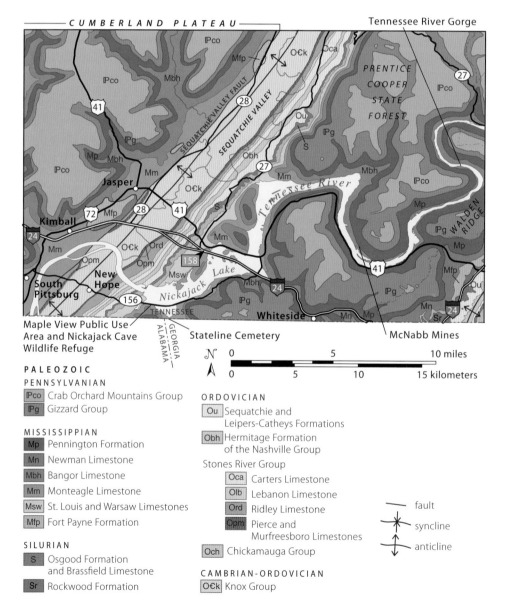

Geology along I-24 between Kimball and the Georgia state line. See map on page 114 for the Chattanooga area.

the top of Monteagle Mountain. Look for the large-scale crossbeds and thick channel fills that are characteristic of the unit.

At the base of the grade, the combined east and westbound lanes of I-24 follow Battle Creek, where crops are grown on the creek's floodplain alluvium between exit 143 (Martin Springs Road) and Kimball. Hundreds of caves have developed along the creek in the flat-lying Warsaw, St. Louis, and Monteagle Limestones that underlie the valley and are exposed along the highway to beyond exit 143 to Kimball.

South of Kimball on US 72 is the town of South Pittsburg, home of the Lodge Manufacturing Company, which was founded in 1896. Lodge used local iron and coal in the manufacture of cast-iron cookware. Although local materials are no longer used, the Lodge family still runs the company and will happily share their four generations of history with visitors to their South Pittsburg store. Tours of the foundry are available a couple of times a year. Visit the South Pittsburg Heritage Museum on Cedar Avenue for an interesting look at the history of iron making and other local industries.

I-24 crosses the Sequatchie Valley between Kimball and Nickajack Lake. The more than 100-mile-long valley is an eroded anticline that formed in the hanging wall of the Sequatchie Valley thrust fault, which runs along the west side of the valley close and parallel to TN 28. Along the southeast-dipping

The thick-bedded Monteagle Limestone dips gently eastward on the east limb of the Sequatchie Valley anticline at exit 158. Deposited in a setting very similar to today's Bahamas, the unit is highly fossiliferous. (35.031217N, 85.577336W) —Marcy Davis photo

thrust fault, Ordovician-age carbonates of the Knox, Stones River, and Nashville Groups were thrust over Mississippian-age strata. Between the Sequatchie River and exit 158, the interstate crosses east-dipping Ordovician and Mississippian-age units on the eastern limb of the Sequatchie Valley anticline. The hills near the Sequatchie River are part of a low ridge made of the chert-rich Mascot Dolomite, part of the Knox Group.

For an interesting peek into the area's coal mining history, visit the ruins of McNabb Mines in the southern section of the Prentice Cooper State Forest. Take exit 158 and head north 5 miles on US 27, then turn right on Mullins Cove Road, which follows the north bank of the Tennessee River through the gorge. The stone walls of a number of buildings associated with the mine and the community of Shakerag are preserved here and are accessible by foot not far from the road.

The interstate crosses a couple of small islands in the middle of Nickajack Lake that are made of Monteagle Limestone covered by Quaternary-age alluvium. Light-colored cliffs of the Bangor Limestone surround the lake. Walden Ridge lies east of Nickajack Lake.

The Nickajack Dam, located a couple of miles south of I-24, impounds the Tennessee River to create Nickajack Lake. Built in 1968, the dam replaced the leaky Haletown Dam, the remains of which are north of the interstate. The new dam partially flooded Nickajack Cave, which houses a large colony of endangered gray bats in the remaining 25 feet of headspace. During the Civil War, saltpeter (potassium nitrate) was mined from the walls and floor of the cave to make gunpowder. The mineral had leached from crystallized bat guano. A cave-viewing platform is accessible from a boardwalk at the Maple View Public Use Area, located off TN 156 a few miles east of South Pittsburg.

Tennessee, Alabama, and Georgia meet at the southern end of Nickajack Lake. This area, known in speleological circles as TAG, is a cave-rich region where many modern caving practices were developed, particularly vertical caving. Recreational cavers can explore more than 14,000 caves in TAG, many of which developed in Mississippian-age limestone. A monument is located at the intersection of the three states on the south shore of Nickajack Lake, west of the Stateline Cemetery on Huckabee Lane.

East of Nickajack Lake, I-24 winds through Walden Ridge parallel to Running Water Creek. Heavy vegetation obscures outcrops along much of this stretch of highway. Walden Ridge, the local name given to the southeastern part of the Cumberland Plateau in Tennessee, is a gentle, or open, syncline. Bangor Limestone is present at road level and in the creek drainage. Lower slopes are shales of the Pennington Formation, which is exposed along the road near the small community of Whiteside. Sandstones of the Warren Point Sandstone form the buff-colored cliffs that cap Walden Ridge. Scars from mountaintop coal mining were once visible north of the highway on Raccoon Mountain, but the land has been mostly reforested.

The interstate dips southward into Georgia near mile 167 for about 4 miles before returning to Tennessee west of Chattanooga. In northern Georgia, I-24 crosses the eastern margin of Walden Ridge, passing through Mississippian- and

Ordovician-age strata along the boundary between the Cumberland Plateau and the Valley and Ridge physiographic provinces.

The interstate follows the western edge of Lookout Valley north of the Tennessee-Georgia state line. The valley formed where the Lookout Valley anticline was eroded. The folded layers of the anticline once joined Walden Ridge and Lookout Mountain across the valley. Although the resistant Warren Point Sandstone and Sewanee Conglomerate cap both Walden Ridge and Lookout Mountain, they have been eroded from the middle of the Lookout Valley anticline, where Ordovician- and Mississippian-age strata are now exposed. A large quarry has been developed in Mississippian-age limestone north of the Tennessee Welcome Center.

Iron was once one of Tennessee's most economically important minerals. The iron industry began in Middle and East Tennessee during the mid-1700s. Near Chattanooga, iron was mined commercially from the Silurian-age Rockwood Formation, a 300-foot-thick sequence of green and reddish-brown marine sandstone, calcareous shale, and limestone. Limy mud, shell material, and sand-sized, hailstone-like grains called oolites accumulated in the tidal zone of a shallow shelf. As these sediments were deposited, iron that was dissolved

Red iron ore was mined in the Chattanooga area from the Silurian-age Rockwood Formation, a fossiliferous marine unit that is exposed in the Lookout Valley anticline. Look for exposures of the formation behind the hotel parking lots on the east side of the highway in Tiftonia (exit 174). There are also exposures along the interstate north of the Tennessee Welcome Center. (approximately 35.025610N, 85.362915W) —Chuck Sutherland photo

in ocean waters precipitated out of solution as hematite. Over time erosion and weathering have leached out the calcium carbonate from this formation so that the relative content of iron has actually increased. Hematite occurs as oolites and as casts of fossils. Ore was mined from lens-shaped beds of fossil lag, where coarser material accumulated and smaller material was removed by strong shelf currents.

Rockwood Formation ores were commonly called red ore due to their color, which came from hematite, an iron oxide mineral. Red ores were generally bigger producers of iron than the limonite brown ores found elsewhere in Tennessee. Red ore was mined from pits, trenches, and strip mines along the foot of the Cumberland Plateau's eastern escarpment between Alabama and Virginia. Cumberland Gap, Caryville, Oliver Springs, Elverton, Rockwood, and Chattanooga were all iron boomtowns during the mid-1800s. Iron was also mined from the Rockwood Formation on Stringers Ridge and at White Oak Mountain northeast of downtown Chattanooga. These red hematite deposits have been economically depleted and are no longer mined.

North of exit 174, the interstate crosses Lookout Valley. At milepost 176, the interstate is sandwiched between Lookout Mountain and Moccasin Bend, a large meander in the Tennessee River. The shallow Lookout Mountain syncline is visible in the roadcut in the Monteagle Limestone at the north end of Lookout Mountain.

Caves, including the famous Ruby Falls Cave, developed in the Mississippian-age limestones of Lookout Mountain. Ruby Falls Cave is a show cave with public tours; it's open most days. If you have the time and interest, head down the Scenic Highway from Ruby Falls to the Eagle's Nest quarry, where you can get a good look at the Bangor Limestone. Sandstone steps lead up to the old quarry.

Lookout Mountain Caverns is located below Ruby Falls at the base of Lookout Mountain. Confederate troops mined the caverns for saltpeter and both Confederate and Union troops used the location as a hospital, probably during and after the Battle of Lookout Mountain in 1863. A wall in the caverns reportedly bears Andrew Jackson's signature. Unfortunately, the caverns have been inaccessible since 2006 due to closure of the lower part of the old Ruby Falls elevator shaft.

The Moccasin Bend National Archaeological District, an area that has had 12,000 years of continuous human habitation, is across the Tennessee River at Moccasin Bend. There are currently two public hiking trails with plans for more to be built in the near future. The Bangor Limestone underlies low areas of the district, whereas the Fort Payne Formation forms Stringers Ridge along the east side of the bend.

Westbound travelers will be able to see the water gap between Raccoon and Signal Mountains. The Tennessee River flows through the gap in a dramatic valley known locally as the Tennessee River Gorge, or Tennessee's Grand Canyon. TN 27 offers a scenic drive through the gorge to Prentice Cooper State Forest. Several Chattanooga boat tours also take tourists into the gorge.

A light show highlights Ruby Falls as it plunges 145 feet into a pool and then flows through Lookout Mountain to join the Tennessee River. Ruby Falls Cave and other Lookout Mountain caves are products of the faulting, folding, and dissolution of Mississippian-age limestone. Note the crossbedding in the wall behind the falls. (35.019030N, 85.339235W)
—Chuck Sutherland photo

CHATTANOOGA GEOLOGY

Chattanooga lies at the transition between the Valley and Ridge and Cumberland Plateau physiographic provinces. Lookout Mountain, an eroded remnant of the Cumberland Plateau, towers more than 1,000 feet above Chattanooga and, along with the Tennessee River, is the city's focal point. Lookout Mountain, Raccoon Mountain, and Walden Ridge have the gentle structural warping typical of the Cumberland Plateau: they are broad, open synclines with upturned layers along

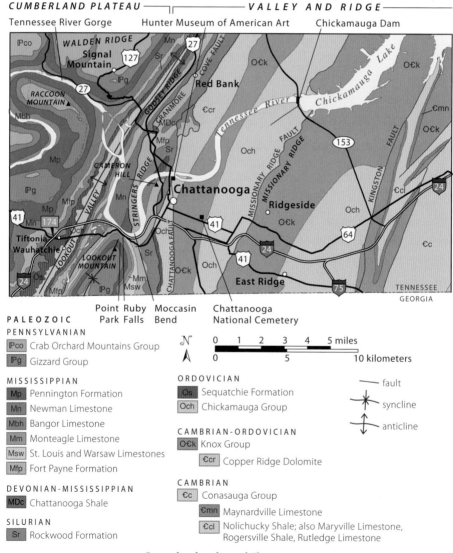

CUMBERLAND PLATEAU —— | | —— *VALLEY AND RIDGE* ——
Tennessee River Gorge   Hunter Museum of American Art   Chickamauga Dam

Point Ruby Moccasin   Chattanooga
Park Falls Bend   National Cemetery

PALEOZOIC

PENNSYLVANIAN
- |Pco| Crab Orchard Mountains Group
- |Pg| Gizzard Group

MISSISSIPPIAN
- |Mp| Pennington Formation
- |Mn| Newman Limestone
- |Mbh| Bangor Limestone
- |Mm| Monteagle Limestone
- |Msw| St. Louis and Warsaw Limestones
- |Mfp| Fort Payne Formation

DEVONIAN-MISSISSIPPIAN
- |MDc| Chattanooga Shale

SILURIAN
- |Sr| Rockwood Formation

ORDOVICIAN
- |Os| Sequatchie Formation
- |Och| Chickamauga Group

CAMBRIAN-ORDOVICIAN
- |OЄk| Knox Group
- |Єcr| Copper Ridge Dolomite

CAMBRIAN
- |Єc| Conasauga Group
- |Єmn| Maynardville Limestone
- |Єcl| Nolichucky Shale; also Maryville Limestone, Rogersville Shale, Rutledge Limestone

N

0   1   2   3   4   5 miles

0   5   10 kilometers

— fault

✳ syncline

⤬ anticline

Generalized geology of Chattanooga.

the margins. Mississippian to Pennsylvanian-age sedimentary rocks underlie Lookout Mountain, which extends southward into northern Georgia. Sandstones of the Gizzard and Crab Orchard Mountains Groups form the mountain's resistant cliffs. Many of Chattanooga's popular destinations are on Lookout Mountain including Rock City Gardens (in Georgia), the Lookout Mountain Incline Railway, Ruby Falls, Natural Bridge, Cravens House, and Point Park.

Point Park, at the northern end of Lookout Mountain, is part of Chickamauga and Chattanooga National Military Park. Chattanooga was an important position locale during the Civil War due to its location on the Tennessee River and its rail lines; the city's railroads connected all major areas of the Confederacy. Point Park's paved trails provide access to historic tablets, monuments, Confederate artillery positions, and the Ochs Memorial Observatory, and several of the

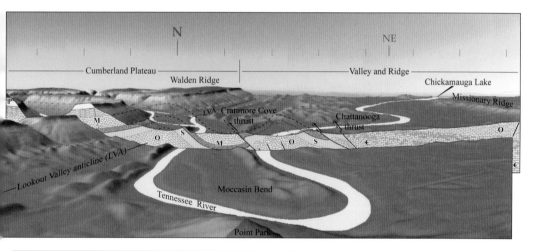

Point Park on Lookout Mountain is a good place to become familiar with Chattanooga's geology. In a classic example of topographic inversion, the Tennessee River has differentially eroded faulted and folded Paleozoic-age strata so that anticlines form the valleys. Pennsylvanian-age sandstone forms a protective cap over older, more soluble units so that Lookout Mountain, a syncline, remains topographically high. (35.012673N, 85.343760W) —Jonathan Mies, illustration and photo

more than 30 miles of maintained, unpaved trails on Lookout Mountain are accessible from the park. As you walk the trails, look for large-scale crossbeds in the 300-foot-tall cliffs of Warren Point Sandstone. This rock of the Gizzard Group was deposited in braided rivers that flowed parallel to the southern Appalachian Mountains during Pennsylvanian time.

In 1839, early settlers established Chattanooga as a trading post on the large meander in the Tennessee River called Moccasin Bend. Although a picturesque location, the city had a serious flooding problem. During high water, drainage was very slow through the narrow, steep-walled Tennessee River gorge that lies west of the city. Downtown flooding was so frequent that in the late 1800s Chattanoogans added enough fill dirt to a 40-block area to cover buildings to their second stories. Many businesses still operate from Underground Chattanooga, the buried first floors of Chattanooga's oldest buildings. Flooding still occurs but is mitigated by the Chickamauga Dam, which was constructed in the late 1930s upstream of the city.

The Old Stone Church on Georgia Avenue was built in 1882 of limestone of the Ordovician-age Pond Spring Formation, part of the Stones River Group. Stone blocks were quarried near the Chattanooga Golf and Country Club in North Chattanooga and were ferried across the river for use in many of downtown Chattanooga's original building foundations. (35.047799N, 85.307019W)
—Chuck Sutherland photo

Many of Chattanooga's older downtown buildings were constructed of stone from local quarries. During the late 1800s, the Stone Fort quarry, then located between Ninth, Eleventh, Market, and Newby Streets, sold Ordovician-age limestone. You can see the light-gray, dense, fossiliferous limestone at the entrance to the Confederate Cemetery, in the walls around the University of Tennessee at Chattanooga, in the Hamilton County Courthouse, and in the tower of St. Paul's Episcopal Church. You can read more about the rocks used in Chattanooga's older buildings in *Building Stones of Downtown Chattanooga*, written in 1979 by the late Dr. Robert "Rock" Wilson, a professor of geology at the University of Tennessee at Chattanooga.

Folded and faulted sedimentary strata, primarily of the Cambrian-to-Ordovician-age Conasauga, Knox, and Chickamauga Groups, underlie most of downtown and east Chattanooga. Long, linear valleys and ridges, typical of the Valley and Ridge physiographic province, trend northeast-southwest through the city. Valleys typically have been eroded into carbonate strata, whereas larger ridges, such as Missionary Ridge, are typically composed of erosion-resistant, silica-rich carbonates found in the hanging walls of major thrust faults. At Missionary Ridge, the cherty, resistant Copper Ridge Dolomite, the oldest unit of the Knox Group, was thrust over younger Chickamauga Group strata along the Missionary Ridge fault.

The light-gray, Ordovician-age Mascot Dolomite, part of the Knox Group, is exposed at Chattanooga National Cemetery on Bailey Avenue. These beds commonly have a crisscross pattern on weathered surfaces that is referred to as a "butcher block" texture. (35.035784N, 85.291694W)
—Chuck Sutherland photo

The Cambrian-age Copper Ridge Dolomite forms the cliffs that underlie the Hunter Museum of American Art along the Tennessee River in downtown Chattanooga. An abundance of chert makes the Copper Ridge Dolomite highly resistant to weathering and erosion. (35.055869N, 85.306439W) —Tim Griffith, Hunter Museum of American Art photo

This low-angle thrust fault follows the west side of the ridge northward to the community of Lakesite. Bauxite, the aluminum ore mineral, was mined in the early 1900s from the Copper Ridge Dolomite on the eastern slope of Missionary Ridge.

Iron was one of Chattanooga's first industries and was key to the city's development. Iron was a commercially developed resource prior to the Civil War, but Chattanooga became an iron center following the war. Ore came from local deposits of the Silurian-age Rockwood Formation. Local Cumberland Plateau coal reserves provided the fuel necessary for stoking Chattanooga's iron smelters and furnaces. Chattanooga's iron industry prospered until competition from Birmingham, Alabama, caused it to collapse in the early 1900s. Evidence of the iron foundries, forges, and blast furnaces remain in and around the city.

To get a taste of the old industrial Chattanooga, you might visit the Bluff Furnace site, which was owned by the East Tennessee Iron Manufacturing Company in the 1850s and closed at the start of the Civil War. An art installation depicts the furnace's history at the facility's original location on the Tennessee River's south bank. Access to the installation is from the Tennessee River Walk, between the Walnut Street Bridge and the Hunter Museum of American Art.

I-26
KINGSPORT—JOHNSON CITY—NORTH CAROLINA STATE LINE
53 miles

I-26 begins about 1 mile south of the Tennessee-Virginia state line at the junction of US 23 and US 11W on the north side of Kingsport. Sedimentary rocks belonging to the Cambrian- and Ordovician-age Conasauga and Knox Groups underlie the area between the state line and Kingsport. Kingsport sits at the confluence of the North and South Forks of the Holston River, and the downtown area is built both on Quaternary-age river terrace deposits and the Middle Ordovician Sevier Shale, part of the Chickamauga Group. The city has been an important shipping hub since the early 1800s when goods were sent downriver

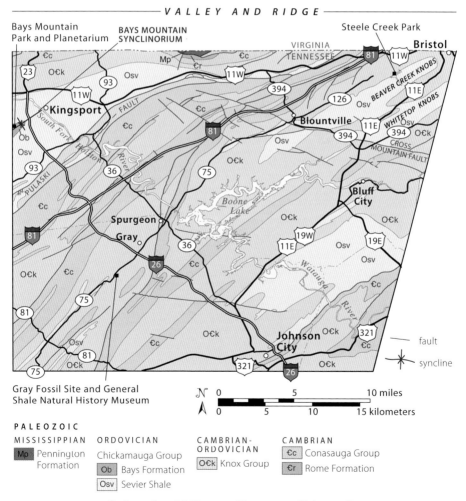

Geology along I-26 between Kingsport and Johnson City.

to Knoxville and the Tennessee River. The city was originally called King's Port after one of two (or both) Mr. Kings. William King shipped salt from a boatyard adjacent to his home on the Holston River. Colonel James King ran Tennessee's first iron furnace near Bristol and shipped goods downstream from the area.

South of the river, the interstate crosses the north end of Bays Mountain, one of a group of linear ridges that extends more than 100 miles southward from Kingsport to near Morristown. This group of folded ridges is known as the Bays Mountain synclinorium.

Folded beds of massive calcareous shale from the upper Sevier Shale are well exposed along the interstate at the toe of Bays Mountain. The lower part of the Sevier Shale is exposed from the south side of Bays Mountain to exit 4. Outcroppings are thinly bedded, dark-gray-to-black calcareous shales that weather to yellow and greenish-brown. Bays Mountain and other high ridges of the synclinorium are capped by maroon siltstone and yellowish sandstone of the younger Bays Formation, which is present in most of Bays Mountain Park. The youngest rock unit exposed in the synclinorium is the Martinsburg Shale, which occurs in a few locations at the park, including at Cherry Knobs.

The interstate cuts across the low rolling hills of the northern Valley and Ridge physiographic province between the I-81 junction and Johnson City. Repeated sections of folded and faulted Cambrian- and Ordovician-age carbonates, shale, and sandstone underlie the highway. Weathering is deep and there aren't many outcrops, with the exception of a few small roadcuts. Keep an eye out for resistant beds poking out of pastureland. A good example is south of the highway south of mile 11 where northwest-dipping Knox Group carbonates are exposed in a field.

Broad folds in massive, gray calcareous shales of the Sevier Shale are exposed in roadcuts along I-26 and to the northern end of Bays Mountain. This type of folding is characteristic of the Bays Mountain synclinorium, in which smaller folds are superimposed on a larger synclinal structure. (36.528578N, 82.580003W) —Marcy Davis photo

The herbivorous, piglike tapir is the mascot of the Miocene-age Gray Fossil Site. These animals used their long snouts to pick leaves and grasses and sometimes as a snorkel. More tapir fossils have been found at the Gray Fossil Site than at any other location in the world. Four species of tapirs exist today in Central and South America and Southeast Asia, but they are becoming increasingly endangered because of habitat destruction and poaching. Adult and juvenile tapirs are pictured in this artist's rendition of the Gray Fossil Site. A badger is at the top left and the other small animals are peccaries. —East Tennessee State University image; mural art by Karen Carr

You can take exit 13 to visit the Gray Fossil Site and museum, located about 2 miles south of the interstate in Gray. This rich deposit of Miocene-age fossils was found in 2000 when the Tennessee Department of Transportation was widening TN 75. The public can view the fossil dig and lab work in progress. Deposits of this age are rare in Tennessee and in eastern North America, especially where fossils of vertebrate animals are preserved, so the Gray Fossil Site is a true gem.

Tennessee's climate was warmer and wetter during Miocene time than it is today. Widespread grasslands and forests covered East Tennessee, and many species of grazing and browsing animals lived here. The Gray Fossil Site was an isolated pond that formed from a spring-fed sinkhole in dolomite of the upper part of the Knox Group. These rocks are exposed along the interstate near exit 13. The sinkhole is ellipsoidal—more than 600 feet long and 300 feet across—and is filled with thinly layered, fine black, gray, white, and tan sand and clay, and the boundary of the deposit is sharp and distinct along the sinkhole's steep sides. These sediments are anomalous for the area, which is commonly covered by reddish soils that developed on the surrounding carbonates. The sediment fill dips up to 45 degrees toward the center of the oval, probably due to the collapse of limestone below the sinkhole.

Animals gathered to drink and eat at the sinkhole. If they waded into the spring too far, they became trapped due to the sinkhole's steep sides and nearly 100-foot depth. The Gray Fossil Site contains well-preserved 4.5-to-7-million-year-old vertebrate remains, including tapirs, alligators, rhinoceroses, red-faced pandas, saber-toothed cats, turtles, fishes, mastodons, frogs, snakes, camels, sloths, and, peccaries. Wood, leaves, berries, seeds, and pollen of oak, alder, hickory, and pine trees are also preserved, along with freshwater aquatic invertebrate animals, such as ostracods, snails, and small clams.

Johnson City

Osv

O€k

€c

€c

321

81

Jonesborough

321

O€k

67

Osv

CHEROKEE
MOUNTAIN

BUFFALO MOUNTAIN FAULT

26

€h

O€k

PINNACLE
MOUNTAIN

€u

BUFFALO MOUNTAIN

€h

IRON MOUNTAIN FAULT

€r

Osv

Unicoi

107

River

€c

p€c
€s

Nolichucky

€h

€e

€u

€h

€s

€s

€u

€h

107

€e

€s

€e

107

Erwin

€u

GREAT SMOKY FAULT

€e

€u

€e

€h

p€s

395

€e

UNAKA MOUNTAINS

p€c

€h

€u

€u

p€ss

€h

43

€s

€u

€u

Rocky Fork
State Park

p€s

€u

p€ss

€u

p€s

p€ss

p€s

p€c

19W

352

p€c

Flag
Pond

p€b

TENNESSEE

NORTH CAROLINA

26

p€c

p€bg

Sams Gap

fault

state park
boundary

CAMBRIAN
€c Conasauga Group
€r Rome Formation
€s Shady Dolomite

Chilhowee Group
€e Erwin Formation
€h Hampton Formation
€u Unicoi Formation

PROTEROZOIC
Ocoee Supergroup
p€ss Sandsuck Formation of
the Walden Creek Group
p€s Snowbird Group

p€b Beech Granite
p€c Cranberry Gneiss/Max Patch Granite
p€bg biotite and granitic gneiss

PALEOZOIC
ORDOVICIAN
Osv Sevier Shale of the
Chickamauga Group

CAMBRIAN-ORDOVICIAN
O€k Knox Group

BLUE RIDGE

N

0   5   10 miles

0   5   10   15 kilometers

Geology along I-26 between Johnson City and the North Carolina state line.

Johnson City lies at the eastern edge of the Valley and Ridge physiographic province on Ordovician-age Knox Group rocks. Higher knobs are capped by the Sevier Shale. Cherokee and Buffalo Mountains form the prominent ridges south of Johnson City. Clastic sedimentary rocks of the Cambrian-age Chilhowee Group and the Shady Dolomite were thrust over younger Knox Group rocks along the Buffalo Mountain fault and folded into a syncline. These rocks make up the Buffalo Valley thrust sheet, which also contains the northernmost occurrence of Ocoee Supergroup rocks in Tennessee.

Between Johnson City and Erwin, the interstate follows the narrow valley of Buffalo and North Indian Creeks. Thick-bedded, blue-gray Knox Group carbonates are present to the town of Unicoi and are quarried on the west side of the highway. Look for exposures near milepost 28.

Exit 32 provides access to the Cherokee National Forest, which includes land between the Virginia and Georgia state lines. The national forest is bisected by Great Smoky Mountains National Park, and Tennessee's portion of the national forest includes much of the state's high and rugged topography and some of its oldest rocks. Look for the Buffalo Mountain/Pinnacle Mountain Fire Tower on the ridge west of exit 32. The tower is publicly accessible by road and trail and provides beautiful views of Unicoi, Washington, and Sullivan Counties.

Strata of the Cambrian-age Conasauga Group underlie the valley sediments between Unicoi and Erwin. Chilhowee Group strata make up the surrounding mountains and are exposed along the road near Erwin. Early settlers extracted small amounts of iron from these sedimentary rocks to make tools.

The Cambrian-age Rome Formation is present in the valley south of Erwin at exit 40. The older pink and gray Shady Dolomite is exposed in the roadcut at milepost 41 and is present in the valley to Temple Hill Road and exit 43. These units overlie Chilhowee Group strata.

The valley narrows south of Erwin and the road parallels the Nolichucky River for a couple of miles. Rich Mountain rises west of the highway, while the Unaka Mountains form the highlands south and east of the interstate along the state border. The Chilhowee Group makes up higher areas adjacent to the highway, while Proterozoic-age rocks form the surrounding highlands beyond.

Interstate 26 crosses highly deformed Neoproterozoic-age rocks between Temple Hill Road and the state line, a distance of about 15 miles. Black slates of the Walden Creek Group unconformably overlie the green and pink, more than 1.2-billion-year-old Cranberry Gneiss (also called the Max Patch Granite in this area) and are exposed on the west side of the road south of exit 43. Cranberry Gneiss is exposed along the interstate intermittently for a few miles beyond Temple Hill Road.

In this area, the Cranberry Gneiss was chemically altered to a semiprecious stone called unakite that is prized by collectors and lapidaries. The Cranberry Gneiss is typically coarse-grained and light gray or pink; however, the introduction of hydrothermal fluids during mountain building caused minerals to recrystallize as larger, darker-colored, pink feldspar and green epidote. There are good exposures of unakite near the rest area and welcome center at milepost 46, and along the road to Flag Pond. Those who climb the short path to

Unakite is a popular semiprecious stone used in lapidary and small carvings. Named for the Unaka Mountains, unakite consists of similar-sized crystals of pink feldspar, green epidote, black hornblende, and quartz. The cut and polished stone is about 2.5 inches long. —Deanna Lack photo

the scenic overlook, located about 1 mile south of the Tennessee Visitor Center (and accessible to northbound travelers only), will be richly rewarded with panoramic views of the Bald and Unaka Mountains to the south and east and Rich and Buffalo Mountains to the north and west.

Spectacular roadcuts between Flag Pond and Sams Gap expose some of the oldest rocks—more than 1 billion years old—in Tennessee. Most are granites and gneisses but are considered mylonites because they were highly deformed by movement along numerous Paleozoic-age faults. Mylonite is a rock fabric that develops in crystalline rocks that were intensely sheared by faulting at depths deep enough and temperatures high enough for the rock to behave plastically. Mineral grains become smaller and are flattened as the rock stretches, giving the rock a layered appearance.

A mylonite zone is exposed just southeast of exit 50 for Flag Pond on the east side of the interstate. Look for the thrust fault behind the chain-link fencing. The fault is easy to see because the rocks along it were ground up and have weathered as a result, and the oxidation of iron minerals gives them a rusty patina. The mylonites closest to the fault have undergone the most shearing, so the small, stretched mineral grains appear layered. The farther the mineral grains are from the fault, the larger and less stretched they are. In some areas, the intensity of shearing was so great that the coarse-grained granitic basement rocks now resemble phyllite, a metamorphic rock that has a characteristic wavy appearance.

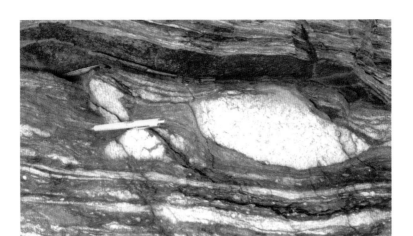

Mylonite exposed approximately 1 mile north of Sams Gap contains sheared boudins of granitoid rock. Boudins *form where layers of more competent rock were broken apart and then incorporated into surrounding material as the rock was stretched by tectonic forces. The darker rocks were probably dikes or layers that were surrounded by mylonitic granitic gneiss.* —Arthur J. Merschat, US Geological Survey photo

Layered biotite gneiss is well exposed near mile 53. Dark intrusions of the 735-million-year-old Bakersville Gabbro are also present here and in roadcuts over the next few miles. In some areas, dikes and sills may be a few inches to a couple of feet wide. In other areas, the gabbro appears as large, coarse-grained bodies that make up entire roadcuts. They are also highly sheared.

Local basement rocks were incorporated into the viewing platform wall at the Sams Gap scenic overlook (accessible to southbound travelers only). Highly deformed Mesoproterozoic-age metaplutonic and metavolcanic rocks in an I-26 roadcut are visible from the platform.

I-40
NORTH CAROLINA STATE LINE—DANDRIDGE (I-81)
32 miles

Between the North Carolina state line and Wilton Springs, I-40 parallels the Pigeon River through the steep and narrow Pigeon River gorge, which cuts through the Blue Ridge physiographic province. The river is popular with adventurous whitewater rafters who navigate class III and IV rapids out of Hartford. The surrounding mountains are rugged and wild, made of tilted and deformed metasedimentary rocks of the Ocoee Supergroup of Neoproterozoic

Geology along I-40 between the North Carolina state line and I-81 at Dandridge.

age. These strata are well exposed through the gorge. Great Smoky Mountains National Park is south of the interstate, and Cherokee National Forest is to the north. The Appalachian Trail crosses under the interstate at exit 451.

This section of highway is frequently closed due to landslides, especially following large storms when slopes become water saturated. The landslide problem is exacerbated by highway engineering; the interstate undercuts thinly bedded and highly fractured strata of the Ocoee Supergroup that dip into the

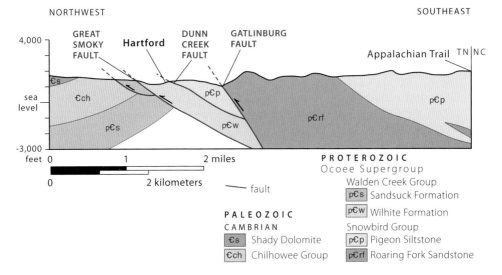

NORTHWEST

SOUTHEAST

4,000

GREAT
SMOKY   Hartford
FAULT

DUNN   GATLINBURG
CREEK   FAULT
FAULT

Appalachian Trail TN|NC

€s

sea
level

€ch

pЄp

pЄp

pЄrf

pЄs

pЄw

-3,000
feet   0   1   2 miles

0   2 kilometers

—— fault

PROTEROZOIC
Ocoee Supergroup

PALEOZOIC
CAMBRIAN

| €s | Shady Dolomite |
| €ch | Chilhowee Group |

Walden Creek Group

| pЄs | Sandsuck Formation |
| pЄw | Wilhite Formation |

Snowbird Group

| pЄp | Pigeon Siltstone |
| pЄrf | Roaring Fork Sandstone |

Generalized geologic cross section along I-40 between the North Carolina state line and Dandridge. —Modified from Hadley et al., 1974

roadway, making slopes very unstable. A number of engineering methods, including fencing, catchments, and large bolts, are employed to stop and contain rockfalls and slides. Look for landslide scars on the surrounding hills.

Gray metasiltstone of the Pigeon Siltstone is exposed between the state line and Waterville. The Roaring Fork Sandstone is well exposed south of Hartford. Both units are part of the Snowbird Group.

The Dunn Creek fault, one of the main thrust faults in the foothills of the Great Smoky Mountains, underlies the linear valley in which Hartford sits. The southeast-dipping, greenish-gray Pigeon Siltstone, exposed near exit 447 for Hartford, was thrust northward along the Dunn Creek fault over blue-gray slate of the Wilhite Formation, part of the Walden Creek Group. The Dunn Creek fault was active during the Taconic orogeny.

The interstate crosses strata of the Cambrian-age Chilhowee Group north of Hartford. Look for exposures on Stone Mountain along the north side of the highway. Sandstone and quartzite of the Unicoi Formation, with red and green interbeds of sandstone and siltstone, are well exposed at milepost 446.

Look for exposures of the Cambrian-age Shady Dolomite on both sides of the highway near exit 443. The ridge west of the highway, called Green Mountain, is an extension of Stone Mountain. These two landforms form a synclinal mountain bounded on both sides by the shallowly dipping Great Smoky fault, an important thrust fault that forms the geologic boundary between the Blue Ridge and Valley and Ridge physiographic provinces. I-40 crosses the fault north of Green Mountain.

The long ridge west of the highway near exit 440 is English Mountain, made up of Chilhowee Group rocks that were folded into a syncline and are bounded by the Great Smoky fault. Rocks in the valley between Green Mountain and English Mountain, which contains the interstate as well as the city of Newport, were folded into a broad anticline. In this valley, Chilhowee Group strata that were once continuous between Green and English Mountains have been eroded down through the Great Smoky fault so that Knox Group rocks below the fault plane are exposed in the valley.

Newport is located near the confluence of the Pigeon and French Broad Rivers that together form Douglas Lake about 2 miles north of the city. On the south side of the lake near milepost 426, eastbound travelers will begin to see the foothills of the Great Smoky Mountains, including Green Mountain west of the highway, and Stone Mountain east of the highway. I-40 crosses Douglas Lake south of the I-81 junction. The Middle Ordovician Sevier Shale, part of the Chickamauga Group, is exposed around the lake. Fresh surfaces of the unit are grayish, whereas weathered surfaces are a yellowish brown.

Douglas Lake lies in a seismically active area known as the East Tennessee Seismic Zone, a 200-mile-long-by-30-mile-wide belt that extends between northeastern Alabama and northwestern Georgia and southwestern Kentucky. Small earthquakes occur every few days in the seismic zone, but no severe damage has been caused as a result of them, and an earthquake larger than magnitude 4.8 has never been recorded.

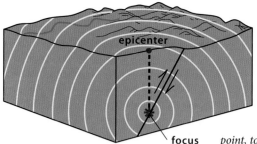

Earthquakes are generated when movement occurs along a fault. We feel earthquakes when seismic waves radiate in all directions from the focus, the fault rupture point, to the Earth's surface. Earthquake size is described by magnitude, a relative scale on which an earthquake of a given magnitude is ten times larger than that of the next lower magnitude. Earthquakes may occur on any fault type; however, not all faults generate earthquakes. The epicenter of an earthquake is the point on the Earth's surface directly above the origin, or focus, of an earthquake.

Earthquakes occur at depths of 3 to 16 miles in the seismic zone, well below the depth of Paleozoic-age faults that reach only about 1.5 to 3 miles of depth. The earthquakes occur within Mesoproterozoic-age basement rocks beneath the Valley and Ridge physiographic province, and there's some activity below the western edge of the Tennessee Blue Ridge physiographic province. Geologists think the earthquakes are distributed along a reactivated major strike-slip fault zone that was created during formation of the supercontinent Rodinia.

The fault zone separates silica-rich igneous rocks of the Laurentian craton to the northwest from Grenville-age basement rocks to the southeast.

Geologists recently found evidence of several large earthquakes preserved in Quaternary-age river terrace alluvium along the shoreline of Douglas Lake near Dandridge. Northeast-trending normal, thrust, and strike-slip faults cut through alluvium and the underlying Sevier Shale. These faults offset sediments up to 3 feet and, along with liquefaction features such as sand blows and clay-filled fractures, indicate that at least three large earthquakes, one of which was larger than magnitude 6.0, occurred in the East Tennessee Seismic Zone between 25,000 and 15,000 years ago during the Pleistocene Epoch. These findings show that some of Tennessee's faults are active, and that there's a potential for large future earthquakes in the seismic zone.

I-40
DANDRIDGE—KNOXVILLE
32 miles

East Tennessee's most productive zinc-mining area, called the Mascot–Jefferson City zinc district, lies several miles north of Dandridge along US 11E, which roughly parallels I-40. It is one of three zinc districts in East Tennessee, the others being the Copper Ridge district, in Grainger County, and the Powell River valley, north of Knoxville. Between 1958 and 1990 Tennessee was the largest producer of zinc ore in the United States, with most of the zinc coming from the Mascot–Jefferson City district. Zinc ore was originally mined from small open pits at the surface, but large underground mines became more common as surface ores were depleted and new milling and recovery methods were instituted.

Sphalerite, a brownish zinc sulfide mineral, is the primary zinc ore. It fills open spaces within the Mascot Dolomite and Kingsport Formation, both part of the upper Knox Group. After it was deposited, the Knox Group was exposed for more than 10 million years. Caves and sinkholes developed in the Mascot Dolomite and Kingsport Formation, and their collapse created zones of rubble. Later, hot fluids associated with mountain building during the Paleozoic Era circulated through the carbonate rubble and precipitated sphalerite in the spaces between the detritus. These areas of broken, or brecciated, rock may be thousands of feet long, hundreds of feet wide, and up to 450 feet thick. Zinc ore bodies are irregularly shaped and delineated by abrupt boundaries with relatively solid limestone. Within the Kingsport Formation, sphalerite sometimes replaced limestone beds that were connected to a mineralized breccia body.

These types of mineral deposits, in which mineralization occurred as mineral-rich hydrothermal brines passed through fractured and altered carbonate rocks, are called Mississippi Valley–type deposits. These deposits are found all over the world but are named for locations in the Mississippi River basin where they were first recognized and described. Other minerals, such as galena, barite, fluorite, and calcite, are also typical in these types of deposits but are less common than sphalerite.

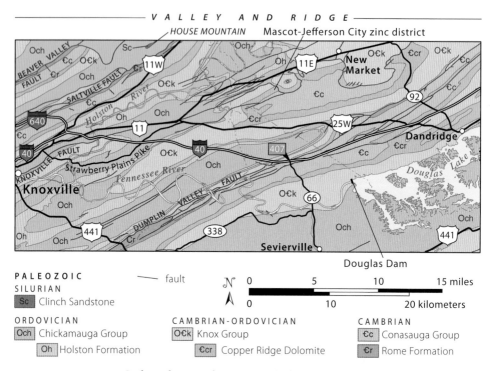

VALLEY AND RIDGE

HOUSE MOUNTAIN   Mascot-Jefferson City zinc district

Geology along I-40 between Dandridge and Knoxville.

PALEOZOIC   —— fault

SILURIAN
| Sc | Clinch Sandstone

ORDOVICIAN
| Och | Chickamauga Group
| Oh | Holston Formation

CAMBRIAN-ORDOVICIAN
| OƐk | Knox Group
| Ɛcr | Copper Ridge Dolomite

CAMBRIAN
| Ɛc | Conasauga Group
| Ɛr | Rome Formation

0   5   10   15 miles
0   10   20 kilometers

Tilted shale and limestone of the Conasauga Group are exposed along the eastbound on- and off-ramps at exit 412 for Deep Springs Road/Douglas Dam. Near exit 407 the interstate crosses the 100-mile-long Dumplin Valley fault zone, which consists of at least two major thrust faults. Light-colored Knox Group carbonates and reddish Ottosee Shale, part of the Chickamauga Group, are present from west of the fault zone to Midway Road at exit 402. The older, gray Lenoir Limestone is exposed where the power lines cross the interstate just west of the exit. Eastbound travelers will notice English Mountain and the foot-hills of the Blue Ridge coming into view along the eastern horizon.

The large CEMEX Portland cement plant can be seen to the north where I-40 crosses the Holston River. Limestone of the Holston Formation of Middle Ordovician age is quarried adjacent to the plant and heated with clays to make Portland cement that is shipped throughout East Tennessee. Portland cement is a constituent of concrete, mortar, and other construction products.

The pink and gray Holston Formation, part of the Chickamauga Group, crops out in a 120-mile-long belt that is quarried near Knoxville as a building stone. Its coarse-grained appearance has earned it the name Tennessee Marble, even though it is limestone and not marble. I-40 crosses the formation between the I-640 junction and Hall of Fame Drive (exit 389).

Zinc mineralization in the Mascot–Jefferson City zinc district is concentrated within zones of brecciated, or broken, rock in the Kingsport Formation and Mascot Dolomite.
—Chuck Sutherland photo

At the I-40/I-640 junction, look for Sharp Ridge north of the highway. The Rome Formation was pushed up and over the Knox Group along the Saltville fault, one of the largest thrust faults in the Valley and Ridge, to form Sharp Ridge. I-640 wraps around the north side of the ridge. Cambrian- and Ordovician-age strata are present in the valley between Sharp Ridge and I-40.

At exit 387A, south of the interstate are two white towers that house the Tennessee Valley Authority (TVA) headquarters. In 1933 President Franklin Delano Roosevelt established the TVA as part of the New Deal. Lawmakers conceived of the TVA as a federally owned power company that would help modernize rural areas along the Tennessee River, a region hit especially hard by the Great Depression. Indeed, the agency created jobs related to conservation, social programs, and dam construction. Other perks included improved flood control, hydroelectric power, navigation, and irrigation, which spurred new agricultural practices and the manufacturing of materials like fertilizer. Unfortunately, the TVA was not universally loved in this region because many people were forced from their homes to allow for reservoir flooding. Today the TVA is the nation's largest public power company and has authority over most of Tennessee and parts of Alabama, Mississippi, Kentucky, Georgia, North Carolina, and Virginia. It supplies power via hydroelectric facilities, fossil fuel plants, natural gas plants, wind and solar farms, and nuclear power plants.

KNOXVILLE GEOLOGY

The Tennessee River flows through downtown Knoxville, which sits on folded and faulted Cambrian- and Ordovician-age strata. The Great Smoky Mountains are visible in the background. —Casey Fox photo

For more than two centuries, Knoxville's location on the Tennessee River has ensured its position as a hub of mid-South manufacturing and trade, particularly in agricultural products and geologic resources, such as coal, zinc, copper, brick, and quarried stone. For a good overview of Tennessee's geologic history, as well as many impressive Tennessee fossil and mineral specimens, visit the McClung Museum of Natural History and Culture on the University of Tennessee campus.

Folded and faulted Cambrian- and Ordovician-age strata, primarily of the Conasauga, Knox, and Chickamauga Groups, underlie the city in narrow, linear, northeast-trending belts. The local topography is hilly, especially in North Knoxville, where Sharp Ridge rises 200 to 300 feet above the valley floor, and in South Knoxville, where the Middle Ordovician Holston Formation, part of the Chickamauga Group, forms low ridges.

The Knox Group, a regional unit of Cambrian to Ordovician age that extends beneath the surface in other areas of Tennessee and across the east-central United States, was first described by James Safford in 1869. He mapped the group along Second Creek in what is now downtown Knoxville. The Knox Group

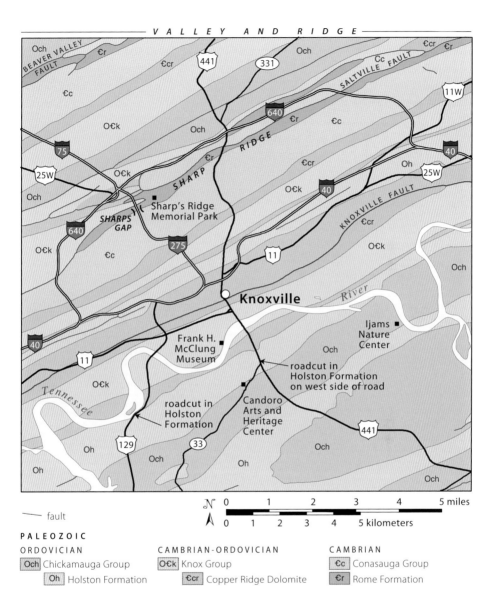

Generalized geologic map of Knoxville.

— fault

PALEOZOIC

ORDOVICIAN
- Och Chickamauga Group
- Oh Holston Formation

CAMBRIAN-ORDOVICIAN
- OCk Knox Group
- Ccr Copper Ridge Dolomite

CAMBRIAN
- Cc Conasauga Group
- Cr Rome Formation

includes several formations that are made primarily of limestone, dolomite, and chert that together may be more than 3,000 feet thick in Tennessee. Knox Group strata form important East Tennessee aquifers and are host rocks for oil, natural gas, and minerals. In places, Knox Group strata were thrust over shales of the younger Chickamauga Group along the Knoxville fault, the trace of which parallels the railroad tracks through downtown.

The Saltville fault, one of the largest thrust faults in the Appalachian fold-and-thrust belt, spans from Georgia to Virginia. In some areas of Tennessee, the lower Cambrian-age Rome Formation was thrust over Mississippian-age units along this thrust fault. At Sharp Ridge, however, the Rome Formation was thrust over the Mascot Dolomite, the upper unit in the Knox Group. If you visit Sharp's Ridge Memorial Park, located on top of Sharp Ridge, you can get an idea of the scale of the Saltville fault, as well as a great view of downtown Knoxville and the eastern Valley and Ridge and western Blue Ridge physiographic provinces.

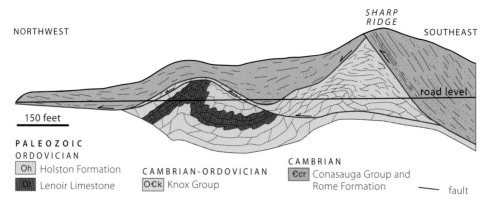

The Saltville fault is exposed on the eastern frontage road (Bruhin Road) at Sharp Gap, where I-275 cuts through Sharp Ridge. The fault is a complex structure here that along which strata were folded and faulted. Variegated shales, sandstones, and thin carbonate beds of the Cambrian-age Rome Formation were thrust over Ordovician-age carbonates. —From Hatcher et al., 2004

Tennessee Marble has been quarried in East Tennessee since 1838 when the first quarry opened in Hawkins County, near Rogersville. Hawkins County marble was chosen to represent the State of Tennessee at the Washington National Monument. The dark-pink stone, inscribed with a quotation from President Andrew Jackson, "Our Federal Union, it must be preserved," was sent to Washington in 1850. It attracted the attention of Thomas U. Walter, an architect building the new wings of the United States Capitol. Walter ordered variegated Tennessee Marble from Hawkins County for three interior staircases and the Senate Retiring Room at the Capitol. In the early 1850s, architect William Strickland ordered similar marble from a quarry in Knox County for the grand staircase and the house and senate chambers at the Tennessee State Capitol. After the Civil War, due to its larger marble beds and superior railroad connections, the area around Knoxville developed into the center of East Tennessee's marble industry, which furnished dimension stone and interior flooring for public buildings across the United States and in Canada, including the Grand Central Terminal floor in New York City; the National Air and Space Museum in Washington, DC; the main stairway inside the San Francisco City Hall; and the Illinois Centennial Monument in Chicago.

Tennessee Marble is not a true marble (metamorphosed limestone), but rather a very pure, dense, coarse crystalline limestone that resembles marble when cut and polished. The rock is quarried from the Holston Formation, part of the Chicka-mauga Group of Middle Ordovician age. The Holston Formation is composed of an accumulation of coarse fragments of fossil shells, especially bryozoans and crinoids. These animals thrived in reefs along the western edge of the Appalachian Basin. The reefs created shoals that could survive the high-energy environment of the carbonate bank on which they grew. During large storms, strong waves and currents broke pieces off the reefs that combined with shell fragments along the reef flanks. The coarse fossil material recrystallized with compaction and burial, giving the rock a crystalline look similar to true marble. In addition to well-preserved fossils, sedimentary structures are common in Tennessee Marble. The stone comes in many colors that are related to the amount of iron oxide minerals present in the rock; pink has traditionally been the most popular color. Look for maroon-colored exposures of the Holston Formation on US 441 between Lippencott Street and Woodlawn Pike, and on US 129 between the University of Tennessee Medical Center and Woodson Drive.

Tennessee pink marble faces many of Knoxville's buildings, including the Knoxville Museum of Art, Ramsey House, and US Post Office on Main Street (pictured here). Up close, fossils, such as crinoids, bryozoans, and cephalopods, are visible, as are interesting features such as stylolites (at the top of the lettering). Stylolites look like jagged fractures but are actually surfaces that form parallel to the bedding in homogeneous, porous, and soluble sedimentary rocks, such as limestone, as a result of differential sediment compaction and solution along bedding planes. These surfaces are visible because of the concentration of insoluble constituents along them, such as clay, mica, iron, and manganese minerals, and some organic materials. (35.961104N, 83.919107W) —Chuck Sutherland photo

During the late 1800s a dozen quarrying companies operated in and near Knoxville, earning Knoxville the nickname Marble City. The name now refers to the neighborhood along Sutherland Avenue where quarry workers lived and quarry company processing sites operated. The stone was incorporated into the interiors and exteriors of many buildings in Knoxville's Old City and downtown. The Tennessee Marble Company remains the only company that operates on a relatively large scale, with a few quarries near Friendsville southwest of Knoxville. The buildings and grounds of the Candoro Arts and Heritage Center were home to the Candoro Marble Company, which was the largest supplier of Tennessee pink marble during the early 1900s. For more information about East Tennessee's marble industry, visit easttnhistory.org/RockofAges. The site features a list of buildings in which Tennessee Marble was incorporated, a map of sites in Knoxville, and several short videos on the formation of the Holston Formation, local quarrying operations, and the industry's legacy.

The Mead and Ross marble quarries are now part of Ijams Nature Center, located in South Knoxville. These quarries, which furnished marble for the Morgan Library in New York City and the National Gallery of Art in Washington, DC, are listed in the National Register of Historic Places. Pictured here are quarried blocks of the Holston Formation at the Keyhole, a man-made passage, built in the 1920s, that allowed workers to pass from one side of the Ross Marble Quarry to the other. Visitors to Ijams can explore the old quarry sites and railroad line along a number of well-maintained trails. (35.948292N, 83.871898W)
—Chuck Sutherland photo

I-40
KNOXVILLE—ROCKWOOD
48 miles

Between Knoxville and Rockwood, I-40 crosses northeast-southwest-trending valleys and ridges that give the Valley and Ridge physiographic province its name. Seven major Valley and Ridge thrust faults are present along this stretch of highway where they come to the surface along ramps. These faults merge below the surface with a detachment fault in the Rome Formation. The highest ridges form the western edge of each thrust sheet brought to the surface along a thrust fault. Typically the ridges are formed from the Rome Formation. The Rome Formation and overlying strata dip toward the southeast, such that repeated sections of southeast-dipping Cambrian-to-Ordovician-age strata—the Rome Formation and Conasauga, Knox, and Chickamauga Groups—underlie the highway.

The interstate crosses the Saltville fault, one of the major thrust faults in the Valley and Ridge, near exit 378A for Cedar Bluff Road. The Saltville fault spans

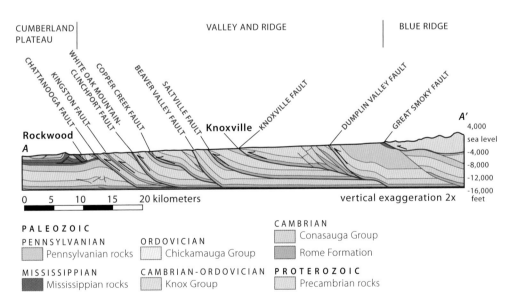

I-40 crosses several major Valley and Ridge detachment thrust faults that dip southeastward, become horizontal at depth, and intersect a master detachment fault in the Cambrian-age Rome Formation. The Rome Formation and Conasauga, Knox, and Chickamauga Groups are repeated across imbricate thrust sheets. The Rome Formation produces narrow ridges that weather with a characteristic knobby shape. —Modified from Hatcher et al., 2007

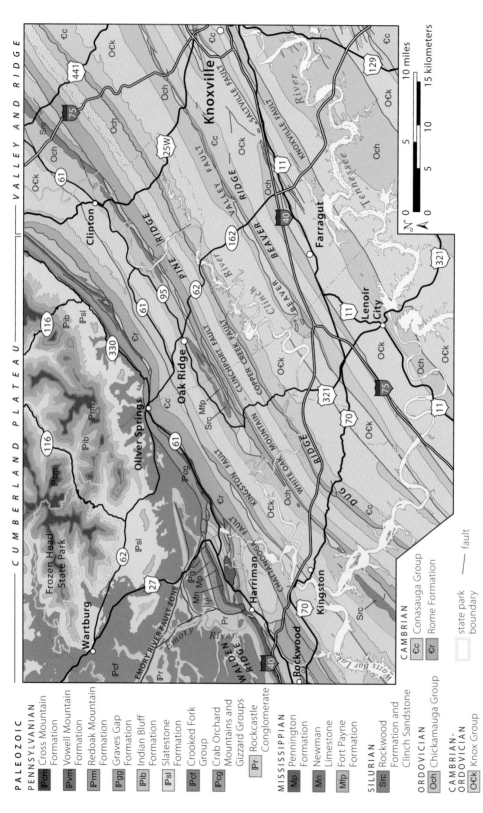

Geology along I-40 between Knoxville and Rockwood.

PALEOZOIC

PENNSYLVANIAN

- ℙcm Cross Mountain Formation
- ℙvm Vowell Mountain Formation
- ℙrm Redoak Mountain Formation
- ℙgg Graves Gap Formation
- ℙib Indian Bluff Formation
- ℙsl Slatestone Formation
- ℙcf Crooked Fork Group
- ℙcg Crab Orchard Mountains and Gizzard Groups
- ℙr Rockcastle Conglomerate

MISSISSIPPIAN

- Mp Pennington Formation
- Mn Newman Limestone
- Mfp Fort Payne Formation

SILURIAN

- Src Rockwood Formation and Clinch Sandstone

ORDOVICIAN

- Och Chickamauga Group

CAMBRIAN-ORDOVICIAN

- O€k Knox Group

CAMBRIAN

- €c Conasauga Group
- €r Rome Formation

☐ state park boundary

— fault

10 miles
15 kilometers

from Georgia to Virginia. Cambrian- and Ordovician-age strata were thrust over strata as young as Mississippian age along the Saltville fault. Here, the Rome Formation was thrust over the younger Chickamauga Group.

At exit 376 you can head northeast on TN 162 to Oak Ridge, home of the Oak Ridge National Laboratory. In 1942, 59,000 acres in Oak Ridge served as one of three sites in the United States devoted to developing the atomic bomb as part of the Manhattan Project. The American Museum of Science and Energy and the Manhattan Project National Historical Park in Oak Ridge offer lots of information about the history of this fascinating place.

West of the I-75 interchange at exit 368, I-40 passes through Hope Gap, a pass in Beaver Ridge. Here, the Rome Formation was thrust over Knox Group strata along the Beaver Valley fault. Beaver Valley has been eroded in the Knox Group west of the Beaver Ridge.

At Dug Ridge, near mile 358, the Rome Formation is again thrust over younger Chickamauga Group strata along the Copper Creek fault. Cambrian- and Ordovician-age carbonates form the low hills west of Dug Ridge.

The Rome Formation is again thrust over younger Chickamauga Group strata along the White Oak Mountain–Clinchport fault at Pine Ridge, between exit 356 and 355. Look for steeply east-dipping, thinly bedded shales of the Conasauga Group at road level west of the westbound on-ramp at exit 356. These shales overlie the Rome Formation.

At Kingston, the shales of the Conasauga Group were thrust over Knox Group carbonates along the Kingston fault. The carbonates are exposed along the margins of the Clinch River and Watts Bar Lake.

North of the highway where it crosses the Clinch River, you'll notice the towers of the Kingston Fossil Plant, a coal-fired steam plant that sits at the confluence of the Emory and Clinch Rivers. The Kingston Fossil Plant was the site of the 2008 coal-ash spill, the largest spill of its kind in US history. The ash is residual material scrubbed from a power plant chimney as a by-product of coal combustion. Dry ash is sold to the concrete industry as a substitute for cement in making concrete. Unsold material is combined with water to form a slurry that can be piped into surface ponds. Due to a failure in the retaining wall that held the slurry, gray sludge flooded the surrounding community to a depth of 6 feet and flowed into the Clinch River, which joins the Tennessee River about 1 mile south of the interstate. The total cost for cleanup and restoration amounted to more than $1 billion.

The Rome Formation was thrust over Conasauga Group along the Chattanooga fault and creates the knobby hills north of the Kingston Fossil Plant. The interstate crosses the ridge west of the Clinch River. The high peaks along the northern skyline belong to the Cumberland Mountains, an undeformed section of the northern Cumberland Plateau. North of Harriman, the Emory River fault forms the northern terminus of the Cumberland thrust sheet. Between the Clinch River and the Cumberland Plateau's eastern escarpment, the structural geology becomes more complex because several Valley and Ridge faults come together against the edge of the plateau.

Near mile 349, westbound travelers will see the resistant buff-colored sandstone cliffs that cap the Cumberland Plateau. They're especially visible in fall and winter, when there's less vegetation. These are conglomeratic sandstones of the Warren Point Sandstone, part of the Pennsylvanian-age Gizzard Group. Silurian- and Mississippian-age units form the base of the mountain.

I-40

Rockwood—Crossville—Cookeville
61 miles

Rockwood began as a company town. During the late 1800s, the Roane Iron Company mined coal from the Sewanee Seam in the Whitwell Shale and iron from the Silurian-age Rockwood Formation, which is exposed along the base of Rockwood Mountain. Coal fed the Rockwood blast furnace that produced coke and pig iron, which were shipped via the Tennessee River to Knoxville and to Chattanooga for use in railroad construction. Homes and other buildings built by the Roane Iron Company still stand in the Kingston Avenue Historic District near downtown Rockwood, east of TN 27.

The interstate crosses Walden Ridge, the Cumberland Plateau's eastern escarpment, west of the city. This stretch of highway was one of the most difficult sections of I-40 to construct. Strata are upturned along the escarpment, dipping 30 to 60 degrees northwestward, and covered with a thick blanket of colluvium. Consequently, the escarpment near Rockwood is highly prone to landslides. Conditions were made worse where road construction undercut slopes, Construction of this section of the interstate was delayed and extended for several years while slopes were stabilized with sandstone and limestone buttresses and appropriate drainage mitigation. Road construction began in 1967 and was originally scheduled to be completed within a few years, but was not finished until 1976.

Mississippian-age limestone overlies the Rockwood Formation and the Chattanooga Shale at the base of the Cumberland Plateau escarpment. Weathered exposures of the younger Pennington Formation—multicolored shale, siltstone, and shale-rich limestone beds—can be seen periodically in the escarpment's middle elevations. Strata dip northwestward along Walden Ridge and flatten out into a broad syncline westward to the Crab Orchard Mountains. Pennsylvanian-age sandstones form impressive cliffs near the top of Rockwood Mountain. Westbound travelers may spot coal seams. Eastbound travelers may catch some stunning eastward views that, on a clear day, can extend across the rolling hills of the Valley and Ridge physiographic province to Tennessee's Blue Ridge. Look for the Great Smoky Mountains about 40 miles to the southeast. You can see the same view from the Mt. Roosevelt Overlook, accessible via Mt. Roosevelt State Forest Road off US 70 from Rockwood, which lies at the base of the mountain.

I-40 crosses the broad flat-bottomed syncline that is Walden Ridge for the next 20 miles. The Sewanee Conglomerate, the only unit of the Crab Orchard

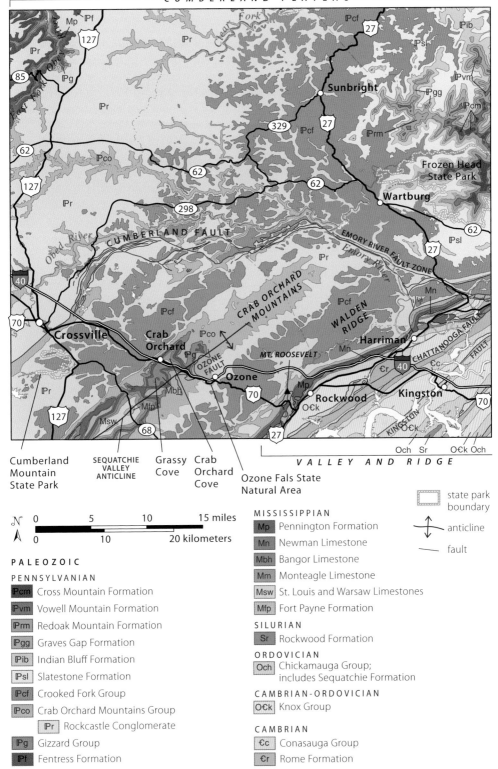

Geology along I-40 between Rockwood and Crossville.

Cumberland Mountain State Park

SEQUATCHIE VALLEY ANTICLINE

Grassy Cove

Crab Orchard Cove

Ozone Fals State Natural Area

VALLEY AND RIDGE

state park boundary

anticline

fault

N

0   5   10   15 miles

0   10   20 kilometers

PALEOZOIC

PENNSYLVANIAN

ℙcm Cross Mountain Formation

ℙvm Vowell Mountain Formation

ℙrm Redoak Mountain Formation

ℙgg Graves Gap Formation

ℙib Indian Bluff Formation

ℙsl Slatestone Formation

ℙcf Crooked Fork Group

ℙco Crab Orchard Mountains Group

ℙr Rockcastle Conglomerate

ℙg Gizzard Group

ℙf Fentress Formation

MISSISSIPPIAN

Mp Pennington Formation

Mn Newman Limestone

Mbh Bangor Limestone

Mm Monteagle Limestone

Msw St. Louis and Warsaw Limestones

Mfp Fort Payne Formation

SILURIAN

Sr Rockwood Formation

ORDOVICIAN

Och Chickamauga Group; includes Sequatchie Formation

CAMBRIAN-ORDOVICIAN

OЄk Knox Group

CAMBRIAN

Єc Conasauga Group

Єr Rome Formation

Mountains Group preserved on this part of the plateau, underlies the highway at exit 340. The Crab Orchard Mountains, the northern extension of the Sequatchie Valley anticline, become visible from westbound lanes near here. Unlike the Sequatchie Valley to the south, the Crab Orchard Mountains have not yet been breached by erosion, except in the southern part of the range at Grassy Cove and Crab Orchard Cove. One day in the distant future, the Crab Orchard Mountains will no longer exist, and Sequatchie Valley will extend another 25 miles northward, having been eroded by the headwaters of the Sequatchie River and smaller tributaries.

The Rockcastle Conglomerate, the youngest unit in the Crab Orchard Mountains Group, is exposed along the interstate near Ozone. It is a yellowish-brown sandstone that contains crossbeds and coal in some areas, as well as beds or rounded quartz pebbles.

The Ozone thrust fault comes to the surface west of Ozone. Similar to the Cumberland thrust fault, the fault follows a thin coal bed in the Pennsylvanian-age Whitwell Shale from Rockwood to the eastern limb of the Sequatchie Valley anticline at Ozone. The Ozone fault, which is not visible from the interstate, is structurally related to western Valley and Ridge faults and may represent the westward extension of the Chattanooga fault in the Cumberland Plateau.

The Rockcastle Conglomerate is well exposed at Ozone Falls State Natural Area in Ozone. Ozone Falls is accessible to the public via US 70 from Crab Orchard. The top of the falls is a short 300 feet from the parking area, and a 0.75-mile-long trail leads to an impressive view of the plunge pool, 110-foot falls, and surrounding amphitheater. (35.880223N, 84.810284W) —Chuck Sutherland photo

I-40 crosses the Crab Orchard Mountains west of Ozone. Thick beds of the Rockcastle and Sewanee Conglomerates are well exposed near milepost 333. At Crab Orchard Gap the road is underlain by the Mississippian-age Pennington Formation. Warren Point Sandstone is exposed at higher elevations.

Mississippian-age Monteagle Limestone is quarried north of the highway in Crab Orchard. Rock is extracted through an underground room-and-pillar process in which pillars of rock are left in place to support the mine roof. High-calcium limestone beds are selectively mined for stone or aggregate. The stone is ground to meet customer specifications, for use in carpet backing, fillers in plastics and paper, tile and glass manufacture, among other uses, and shipped by rail to users.

Crab Orchard, the self-proclaimed Stone Capital of Tennessee, is famous for colorful building stone called the Crab Orchard Sandstone. Deposited in a tidal flat and delta system, it is part of the Pennsylvanian-age Crossville Sandstone of the Crooked Fork Group. The Crab Orchard Sandstone is a fine-grained, dense, homogeneous, and durable rock with a silica content of more than 90 percent. A consistent bedding thickness of up to 4 feet makes the rock relatively easy to quarry; workers can strip mine slabs of it. You can have a look at the Crab Orchard Sandstone at the stone yards along US 70 and Main Street.

The Crab Orchard Sandstone's popularity stems from its consistent bedding and distinctive streaks of brown and orange called Liesegang *bands, which are iron oxides that precipitated from groundwater long after the sediments were buried. Although Liesegang bands may form in any kind of sedimentary rock, they are typically most dramatic in quartz sandstones. Many structures in and near Crab Orchard are faced with the stone. The red ruler is about 8 inches long.* —Rich Kyle photo

Although the stone has been locally quarried and used as a building stone since the nineteenth century, it really gained popularity during the 1920s. It has been used for many buildings, fireplaces, and even sidewalks in Crab Orchard and Crossville. The cemetery at the west end of town contains Crab Orchard Sandstone headstones that are more than two hundred years old. The sandstone has an impressive résumé; it was integrated into Graceland in Memphis, the Country Music Hall of Fame in Nashville, and the Internal Revenue Service Headquarters in Washington, DC. The lodge, cabins, bridges, and dam at Cumberland Mountain State Park, south of Crossville on US 127, are also built of local Crab Orchard Sandstone.

West of Crab Orchard, the road climbs through Mississippian- and Pennsylvanian-age units as it crosses the western limb of the Sequatchie Valley anticline. Travelers in eastbound lanes will get their first glimpse of the Crab Orchard Mountains near Crossville.

Near Crossville, the interstate crosses a complex system of faults, an extension of the Emory River fault zone that connects to the Cumberland thrust fault. Small thrust faults are connected by cross faults that strike perpendicularly to the regional strike of bedding and other structures. The Emory River fault zone forms the northern boundary of the Cumberland thrust sheet.

Crossville is located in the middle of the Cumberland Plateau at the headwaters of the scenic Obed River. The town was founded at the junction of two important roads: the Great Stage Road, which connected Nashville and Knoxville, and the Kentucky Stock Road, which connected Chattanooga and Middle Tennessee with Kentucky. Many buildings in Crossville are built of Crossville Sandstone of the Crooked Fork Group. One of the town's architectural highlights is the Palace Theater on Main Street, an art deco auditorium that has been a popular music venue and community center since 1938. The front of the building is faced with the Crossville Sandstone.

Between Crossville and Monterey, I-40 crosses the flat Cumberland Plateau, with few roadcuts. Look for brown, cross-bedded sandstones of the Rockcastle Conglomerate near the Putnam-Cumberland County line.

In Monterey the Standing Stone Monument at the city park, near the library on East Commercial Avenue, contains a piece of cultural and geologic history. The chunk of Pennsylvanian-age rock at the top of the monument is what remains of a 16-foot-tall, dog-shaped rock that stood about 1 mile west of town. The original monolith marked a trail, first used by Native Americans that ran between Rockwood and Monterey. The rock was destroyed during the construction of the Nashville & Knoxville Railroad.

Coal and other units of the Gizzard Group, deposited along a shifting, dynamic shoreline, are exposed along the road west of Monterey. The contact between Gizzard Group strata and the overlying Sewanee Conglomerate, part of the Crab Orchard Mountains Group, is well exposed between mileposts 299 and 298. For more information about coal mining in the area, as well as about railroads and local history, visit the Bon Air Mountain Historical Society Museum in Sparta, south of Monterey.

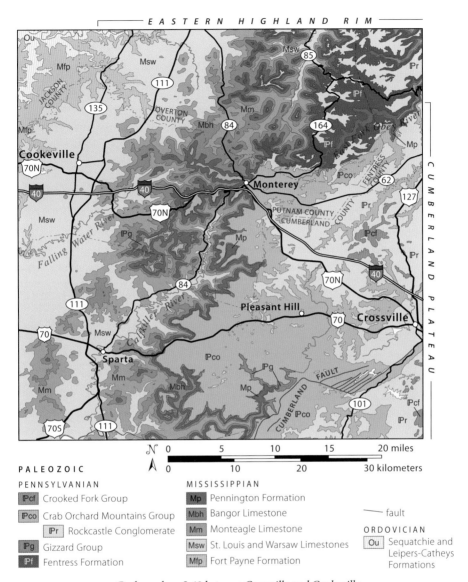

Geology along I-40 between Crossville and Cookeville.

PALEOZOIC

PENNSYLVANIAN

Pcf	Crooked Fork Group
Pco	Crab Orchard Mountains Group
Pr	Rockcastle Conglomerate
Pg	Gizzard Group
Pf	Fentress Formation

MISSISSIPPIAN

Mp	Pennington Formation
Mbh	Bangor Limestone
Mm	Monteagle Limestone
Msw	St. Louis and Warsaw Limestones
Mfp	Fort Payne Formation

fault

ORDOVICIAN

Ou	Sequatchie and Leipers-Catheys Formations

Between miles 297 and 292 the interstate follows the transition between the Cumberland Plateau and the eastern Highland Rim of Middle Tennessee. The road drops down through most of the Mississippian-age section over the next 5 miles, crossing into older rocks the farther west it goes. Colorful green and red shales and siltstones, and thin, gray carbonate beds of the Pennington Formation are exposed near milepost 296. Dark-gray Bangor Limestone is well exposed at milepost 295. The Hartselle Formation separates the Bangor Limestone from the underlying Monteagle Limestone.

Orangish-gray, cross-bedded Sewanee Conglomerate (right) fills ancient river channels that were scoured into underlying grayish-brown lagoon and tidal flat sediments. This paleochannel is exposed on I-40 west of Monterey between mileposts 299 and 298. (36.137661N, 85.310951W)
—Chuck Sutherland photo

The Hartselle is a relatively thin sandstone unit that lies between two fairly thick limestone units. It was deposited during a brief lowering and rising of the sea following the deposition of the Monteagle. The Hartselle Formation thins southward and thickens northward. Although the unit is tough to spot along the interstate, the rust-colored sandstone forms resistant benches along the western escarpment. Thick-bedded, light-gray beds of the Monteagle Limestone crop out near mile 294. Look for deeply weathered, medium-bedded St. Louis and Warsaw Limestones to near mile 292, about 2 miles east of Cookeville.

I-75
Chattanooga (East Ridge)—Farragut
91 miles

West of exit 3A, I-75 crosses the Kingston fault, one of the major thrust faults in Tennessee's Valley and Ridge. Knox Group strata, which were thrust over Chickamauga Group strata along the fault, form a low ridge along the fault where I-75 crosses it. The Kingston fault extends from northeastern Alabama through Tennessee to the Powell Valley, northwest of Knoxville, where it dies out in the Powell Valley anticline.

Rocks of the Conasauga and Knox Groups underlie the road between Shallowford Road (exit 5) and Ooltewah. The topography is hillier where Knox Group carbonates are present.

Blue Hole Spring is about 12 miles southeast of Ooltewah at Red Clay State Historic Park, accessed from exit 9. The spring is also called Council Spring because it sustained the government of the Cherokee Nation during council meetings prior to their removal from the area in 1832. The spring is about 15 feet deep and produces 0.5 million gallons a day.

The area east of Ooltewah is known as the Tennessee Overhill, referring to Cherokee settlements that were located in the western foothills of the southern Blue Ridge, "over hill" from settlements located in the valley.

Near exit 9 northbound travelers will see White Oak Mountain, a long, linear ridge on the eastern horizon. Here the mountain comprises White Oak Ridge on the northwest side and Lauderback Ridge on the southeast side. I-75 crosses

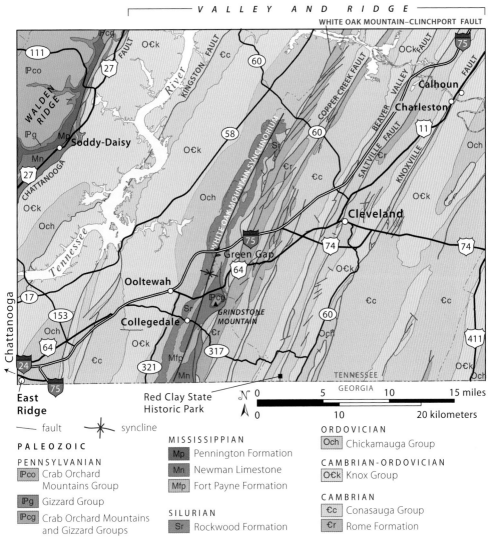

Geology along I-75 between East Ridge and Calhoun. See map on page 149 for section between Calhoun and Farragut.

the mountain at Green Gap, about 4 miles north of Ooltewah. The mountain is part of the White Oak Mountain synclinorium, a group of folds that take the overall shape of a syncline. These folded strata are on the eastern side of the Kingston thrust sheet and are the result of thrust faulting along the adjacent White Oak Mountain–Clinchport fault, another major Valley and Ridge thrust fault that extends from northern Georgia to southwest Virginia. Ordovician-to-Pennsylvanian-age rocks are preserved in the White Oak Mountain synclinorium. Ordovician units form the western slopes of White Oak Ridge to the elevation of the southbound scenic overlook.

Grindstone Mountain, east of White Oak Mountain and south of US 64, is also part of the White Oak Mountain synclinorium. Its cap, at more than 1,400 feet of elevation, is Warren Point Sandstone of the Gizzard Group, a remnant of the Pennsylvanian-age strata that were once continuous across the Valley and Ridge.

Southeast-dipping sandstones and shales of the Rockwood Formation of early Silurian age are relatively well exposed between mileposts 15.5 and 16. These sandstones contain the mineral hematite that was mined from shallow pits along White Oak Mountain and the base of Walden Ridge (to the west) around the turn of the twentieth century. At mile 18, I-75 crosses the White Oak Mountain–Clinchport fault, where the Cambrian-age Rome Formation was thrust over Knox Group strata.

The Rockwood Formation is well exposed on both sides of the highway through Green Gap. These folded, faulted, and nearly vertical or overturned beds are on the southeast limb of the White Oak Mountain synclinorium, which was deformed by movement along the White Oak Mountain–Clinchport fault. (35.130995N, 85.003650W) —Marcy Davis photo

The highway crosses the Copper Creek fault at exit 20. This fault extends from Georgia to Virginia and is another major Valley and Ridge fault along which the Rome Formation was thrust over the Conasauga Group.

At exit 25, I-75 cuts through Candies Creek Ridge, which is made up of Copper Ridge Dolomite, part of the Knox Group. Rocks of the Conasauga Group were thrust over the Copper Ridge Dolomite here along the Beaver Valley fault, another major Valley and Ridge thrust fault that extends into northeastern Tennessee. The interstate parallels the Beaver Valley fault for the next 10 miles. Limestones and shales of the Conasauga Group underlie the road to the Hiwassee River and Calhoun at exit 36.

At Calhoun, the interstate crosses the Saltville fault, along which rocks of the Conasauga Group were placed on the Knox Group. The highway follows

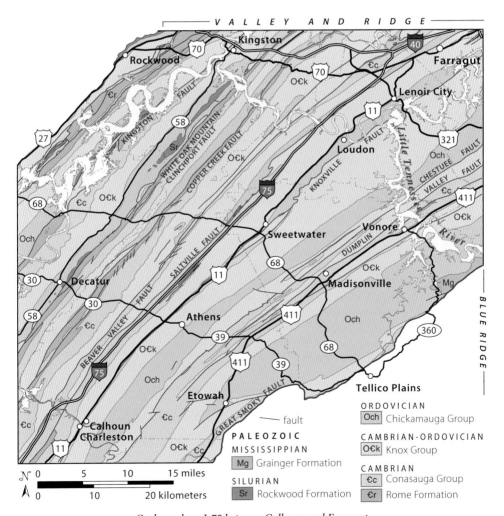

Geology along I-75 between Calhoun and Farragut.

Barite (white mass, center), smithsonite (tiny gray crystals throughout), and fluorite (purple) are three of the most common minerals found in the Sweetwater district. This sample is from the Ballard Mine in Monroe County, and the field of view is about 1.5 inches wide.
—Mike Streeter photo

the trace of the Saltville fault to Lenoir City. For the 30 miles between Calhoun and Sweetwater, the Conasauga Group underlies the highway while resistant carbonates of the Knox Group form the low hills on both sides of the road.

The area around Sweetwater contains Mississippi Valley–type mineral deposits that are similar to those found elsewhere in Tennessee. Barite was the only mineral economically extracted at Sweetwater, although fluorite and minor amounts of sphalerite and galena are present. In the United States, barite is mostly used in mud during drilling operations, but it's also widely used as a white pigment in liquids ingested for x-raying the digestive system, and in the manufacture of products such as rubber, paper, and cloth. The mineralization in the Sweetwater district, as well as Tennessee's other zinc districts, occurred during the Alleghanian orogeny. (See the TN 68: Ducktown—Sweetwater road guide for information about the Lost Sea south of Sweetwater.)

The Knox Group is present in the valley between exit 68 and the Little Tennessee River, where the highway again crosses the Saltville fault. Cambrian- and Ordovician-age shales and limestones underlie the road to the I-40 junction west of Farragut, where the Rome Formation was thrust over the Knox Group along the Beaver Valley fault.

I-75
KNOXVILLE—JELLICO (KENTUCKY STATE LINE)
58 miles

I-75 joins I-40 for about 20 miles from Farragut to West Knoxville. (See the I-40: Dandridge—Knoxville road guide for that section and the Knoxville area.) In West Knoxville, the joined I-640 and I-75 cross the Saltville fault at the Western Avenue exit. The Cambrian-age Rome Formation was thrust over

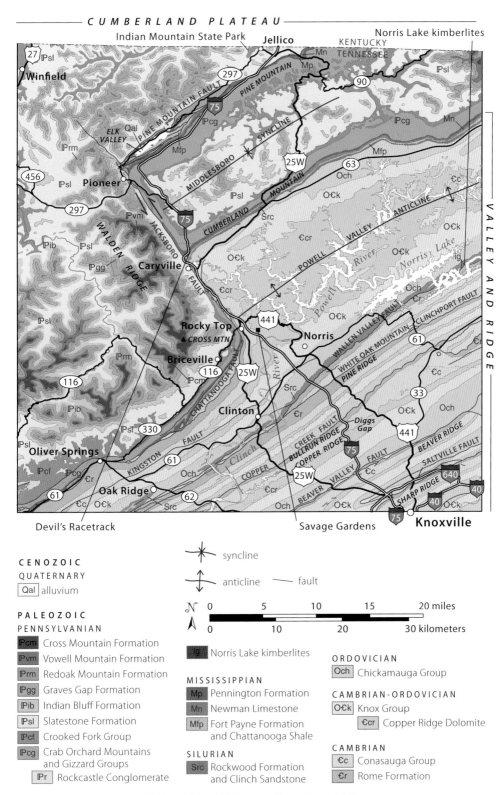

Indian Mountain State Park
Jellico
Norris Lake kimberlites
KENTUCKY
TENNESSEE

Winfield

27 | IPsl

IPsl

297

PINE MOUNTAIN FAULT
75

IPcg

PINE MOUNTAIN

Mn

Mp

90

IPsl

IPcg

Mn

Qal
ELK
VALLEY

PINE MOUNTAIN FAULT

IPrm

Mfp

MIDDLESBORO SYNCLINE

25W

Mfp

456

IPsl

Pioneer

297

IPsl

JACKSBORO FAULT

IPvm

CUMBERLAND MOUNTAIN

IPsl

Src

Och

63

O€k

VALLEY ANTICLINE

Norris Lake

O€k

€c

O€k

ig

WALDEN RIDGE

IPib

IPsl

IPgg

Caryville

€cr

O€k

POWELL

River

O€k

Och

IPsl

€cr

441

O€k

Rocky Top
▲ CROSS MTN

Norris

O€k

WALLEN VALLEY FAULT

CLINCHPORT FAULT

61

IPrm

CHATTANOOGA FAULT

Briceville

116

25W

Src

WHITE OAK MOUNTAIN
PINE RIDGE

€c

IPcm

116

33

IPib

IPsl

330

Clinton

€r

O€k

Och

CREEK FAULT

Diggs
Gap

441

BEAVER RIDGE

KINGSTON FAULT

IPsl

Oliver Springs

61

IPcf

IPcg

€r

Och

COPPER

COPPER RIDGE

BULLRUN RIDGE

75

BEAVER VALLEY FAULT

€c

SALTVILLE FAULT

640

62

Clinch

25W

Och

SHARP RIDGE

40

61

Oak Ridge

€c

O€k

Src

€cr

Och

O€k

40

O€k

75 Knoxville

Devil's Racetrack

Savage Gardens

VALLEY AND RIDGE

* syncline

anticline — fault

N 0   5   10   15   20 miles

A 0   10   20   30 kilometers

CENOZOIC

QUATERNARY

Qal alluvium

ig Norris Lake kimberlites

ORDOVICIAN

Och Chickamauga Group

PALEOZOIC

PENNSYLVANIAN

IPcm Cross Mountain Formation

IPvm Vowell Mountain Formation

IPrm Redoak Mountain Formation

IPgg Graves Gap Formation

IPib Indian Bluff Formation

IPsl Slatestone Formation

IPcf Crooked Fork Group

IPcg Crab Orchard Mountains
and Gizzard Groups

IPr Rockcastle Conglomerate

MISSISSIPPIAN

Mp Pennington Formation

Mn Newman Limestone

Mfp Fort Payne Formation
and Chattanooga Shale

SILURIAN

Src Rockwood Formation
and Clinch Sandstone

CAMBRIAN-ORDOVICIAN

O€k Knox Group

€cr Copper Ridge Dolomite

CAMBRIAN

€c Conasauga Group

€r Rome Formation

Geology along I-75 between Knoxville and Jellico.

the Ordovician-age Knox Group here to form Sharp Ridge. I-75/I-640 parallels the northern side of Sharp Ridge for about 1.5 miles to the junction with I-275.

North of Knoxville, I-75 cuts perpendicularly across folded and faulted Cambrian- and Silurian-age sedimentary strata. As is typical of the Valley and Ridge physiographic province, the Rome Formation was placed over younger strata of the Knox and Chickamauga Groups along several regional southeast-dipping thrust faults. Consequently, the stratigraphy is repeated several times between Knoxville and Caryville, but you'll only see rocks where the road cuts through ridges.

At exit 110 for Callahan Drive, the highway crosses Beaver Ridge. Here, the Rome Formation was thrust over red and green siltstones and fossiliferous limestones of the Moccasin Formation, part of the Chickamauga Group, along the Beaver Valley fault. These beds are exposed along East Beaver Creek Road, which parallels the east side of the interstate at milepost 111.

The Cambrian-to-Ordovician-age stratigraphic section is repeated north of Beaver Ridge. Look for the light-gray, medium-bedded Maynardville Limestone and the Nolichucky Shale, both part of the Conasauga Group, that form Copper Ridge at milepost 115.

The Rome Formation was thrust over the Middle Ordovician Moccasin Formation along the Copper Creek fault at Bullrun Ridge. Deformed beds of the Rome Formation are exposed along the east side of the road at milepost 16, and multicolored shales and limestones of the Moccasin Formation are exposed about 0.5 mile to the north. The Copper Creek fault extends from Georgia to Virginia and is a major Valley and Ridge fault.

The Copper Creek fault is exposed at Diggs Gap, where I-75 cuts through Bullrun Ridge about 20 miles north of Knoxville. Dark-colored shales and sandstones of the Rome Formation were thrust over lighter-colored shale and limestone of the Moccasin Formation. (36.098194N, 84.019938W)
—Rachel K. Wells photo

The light-gray, fine-grained Mascot Dolomite, part of the Knox Group, is exposed north of Raccoon Valley Road. The unit is quarried for aggregate just east of the interstate. Steeply dipping beds of the Rome Formation are exposed at Moore Gap at milepost 119 where the interstate crosses Pine Ridge. The deformation resulted as the Rome was pushed up along a fault associated with the White Oak Mountain–Clinchport fault system, and thrust above the younger Conasauga Group. The narrow Brushy Valley north of the fault has been eroded into the Conasauga Group.

Weathered beds of the Rome Formation are intermittently exposed on the east side of the road near milepost 20. The Rome Formation was thrust over the Silurian-age Rockwood Formation along the Wallen Valley fault, a splay of the White Oak Mountain–Clinchport fault. North of the Wallen Valley fault, I-75 crosses the Pine Mountain thrust sheet.

Between Norris and Caryville, the Knox Group underlies the interstate in the eroded core of the Powell Valley anticline. Southeast-dipping beds of the anticline's southern flank are exposed near the Clinch River. Northbound travelers will see Walden Ridge and Cumberland Mountain on the horizon near mile 124.

A small thrust fault displaced steeply dipping beds of the Rome Formation about 10 feet at Moore Gap. The fault (A) is marked by a change in the orientation of the bedding and a thin, yellowish shaley layer. Units B, C, and D were also displaced. The photo was taken north of the Moore's Gap United Methodist Church on Moores Gap Road. Ripple marks, rain drop impressions, salt hoppers, and mud cracks are also preserved in the rocks here. (36.136607N, 84.041427W) —Robert Hatcher photo

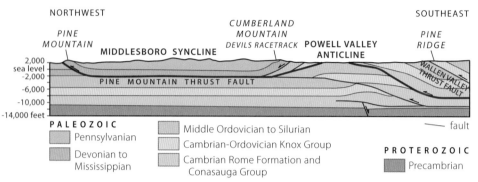

Movement of the Pine Mountain thrust sheet along the Pine Mountain fault created the Powell Valley anticline and Middlesboro syncline. The eroded core of the anticline, bounded by Pine Ridge and Cumberland Mountain, exposes Cambrian-to-Ordovician-age carbonates. The syncline, bounded by Cumberland and Pine Mountains, contains resistant Pennsylvanian-age clastic units and remains a topographically high and rugged area. —Modified from Mitra, 1988

Two kimberlites are exposed on the north shore of Norris Lake near Sharps Chapel in Union County. Kimberlites—named for Kimberley, South Africa, where they first were described—are relatively uncommon, vertically oriented igneous intrusions. Kimberlites seem to result from a type of volcanism wherein a buildup of volatile fluids and gas pressure blows a hole in the overlying rock, creating a pipe-shaped conduit through which igneous material may escape from magma reservoirs deep in the mantle. Kimberlites have a distinctive mineralogy and chemical signature. Diagnostic minerals include magnesium-rich olivine, diopside, ilmenite, and phlogopite, a type of mica. A red, magnesium-rich garnet, called pyrope, and magnetite, are both common. All of these minerals are present in the Norris Lake kimberlites. Kimberlites also often yield diamonds. In 1904 two diamonds were found in gravels downstream of the Norris Lake kimberlites. One weighed 3 carats, and the other 1.69 carats. Both were bought by a jeweler in Knoxville.

The molten material of kimberlites cools to form a fine-grained matrix of microcrystals that surrounds larger crystals and rock fragments. Most of the material is composed of rock fragments of mantle material and rocks torn from the walls of the conduit, carbonates in the case of the Norris Lake kimberlites. Individual crystals, called xenocrysts, may also be present. The Norris Lake kimberlites are the southernmost in a chain of kimberlites that spans the length of the Appalachian fold-and-thrust belt. These intrusions likely resulted from Appalachian mountain building processes during the end of the Paleozoic Era. The kimberlites were altered and sheared by movement along the Wallen Valley fault.

At milepost 127, travelers in the northbound lanes will notice Cross Mountain, the highest point (3,534 feet) in Tennessee west of the Blue Ridge. Coal was mined on and near Cross Mountain from the late 1800s to the early 1900s.

Magnetite, an iron oxide, is magnetic, as its name implies. Its crystal form is characteristic of the spinel family of minerals to which it belongs. In the Norris Lake kimberlites, magnetite crystals, such as the one pictured here, are up to 0.5 inch wide.
—Mike Streeter photo

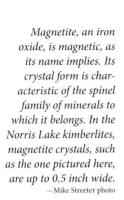

In 1911, a coal mine explosion occurred near the community of Briceville. Eighty-four miners died, twenty-two of whom are buried in the Cross Mountain Miners' Circle, a memorial located in the cemetery at the south end of Briceville. The central obelisk, which includes the names of the miners who died, and the headstones are made of Tennessee Marble quarried near Knoxville. The Coal Creek Miners Museum, located in Rocky Top, has interesting displays about local coal mining

North of the Clinch River, Copper Ridge Dolomite of the Knox Group and strata of the Cambrian-age Conasauga Group underlie the road. These units crop out south of exit 128 on the northeast side of the highway.

Between Rocky Top and Caryville, the interstate parallels the Cumberland Plateau's eastern escarpment. Undeformed Pennsylvanian-age strata forms the plateau's resistant cap here. At Rocky Top, the eastern escarpment takes a jog to the northwest along the Jacksboro fault, the trace of which is at the base of the escarpment. The Jacksboro fault extends northward about 10 miles to Caryville, where it passes through Bruce Gap; it continues northwest, extending several miles beyond the town of Pioneer. The Jacksboro fault is a type of strike-slip fault called a tear fault or cross fault. Tear faults strike perpendicular to the trend of major structural features and connect at least two larger faults that strike parallel to the regional trend. In this case, the Jacksboro fault is a nearly vertical fault that connects the Chattanooga fault with the Pine Mountain fault. About 11 miles of left-lateral strike-slip displacement and about 500 feet of vertical displacement have occurred on the Jacksboro fault. Slivers of deformed Cambrian-to-Mississippian-age units were sliced up along the fault trace and underlie the road between Rocky Top and Caryville. South of the Jacksboro fault, the Chattanooga fault ramps to the surface from the Rome Formation. Northeast of the Jacksboro fault, the Pine Mountain fault ramps from the Rome Formation to the Chattanooga Shale, and then to the surface north of Pine Mountain.

Savage Gardens, a privately owned natural rock garden that is open to visitors in the spring, is near Rocky Top (exit 128). Here, interesting shapes and pinnacles have been naturally sculpted in the Ordovician-age Copper Ridge Dolomite, part of the Knox Group. (36.215370N, 84.131200W) —Chuck Sutherland photo

Ordovician-age carbonates are exposed near milepost 133 on the east side of the interstate, while Pennsylvanian-age strata are present (but concealed) along the west side. This stratigraphic difference is due to displacement along the Jacksboro fault.

Caryville sits at the base of Cumberland Mountain, the southern end of which comes into view for northbound lanes near exit 134. This linear ridge trends northeastward 100 miles, passing through the town of Cumberland Gap and into Kentucky and Virginia. The Silurian-to-Pennsylvanian-age sedimentary layers dip steeply northwestward along the northern limb of the Powell Valley anticline.

North of Caryville, the Jacksboro fault runs through a narrow valley between the Middlesboro syncline and the undisturbed part of the Cumberland Plateau. The Mississippian-age Newman Limestone is exposed between mileposts 136 and 137. Beds of limestone dip to the northeast here along the northern limb of a small anticline that parallels the Jacksboro fault. The anticline was created as strata became crowded with movement along the Jacksboro fault. Beds of the anticline bend around the southwest end of the Middlesboro syncline to form Cumberland Mountain.

Vertical pinnacles of Pennsylvanian-age sandstones become visible along the edge of Cumberland Mountain for northbound lanes near milepost 136.

Travelers in southbound lanes will have a great view of the fins during the winter months near milepost 138. The nearly vertical rock fins, known as Devil's Racetrack, are a popular destination for rock climbers and hikers. It is accessible to the public via a 3-mile section of the Cumberland Trail that begins at the Cove Lake State Park parking area on Bruce Gap Road, off exit 134.

Nearly horizontal Pennsylvanian-age strata underlie the highway for the next several miles through the interior of the Middlesboro syncline. You can have a closer look at some of the strata behind the businesses on the northeast side of the highway at exit 141.

Vertical fins of Pennsylvanian-age conglomeratic sandstone are exposed at Devil's Racetrack. The fins are a product of differential weathering. The intervening shale strata were eroded from between the more resistant sandstone layers. These dipping rock layers are on the northwestern limb of the Powell Valley anticline. (36.321075N, 84.225711W) —Marcy Davis photo

The high peaks southwest of the highway are south of the Jacksboro fault and on the undisturbed part of the northern Cumberland Plateau. Pennsylvanian-age sedimentary rocks also cap this part of the plateau. Travelers in northbound lanes will notice Pine Mountain on the horizon, while southbound travelers will see Cumberland Mountain.

At milepost 146, I-75 makes a nearly 90-degree turn to follow the top of Pine Mountain along the leading edge of the Pine Mountain thrust sheet. From Pine Mountain there are occasional views southeastward across the Middlesboro syncline to Cumberland Mountain. The Pine Mountain fault surfaces in Elk Valley along the north side of Pine Mountain and extends another 100 miles into Kentucky and Virginia. In Elk Valley, rocks as old as the Silurian-age Rockwood Formation are exposed at the surface. Elk Valley and the northern, undisturbed part of the Cumberland Plateau become visible north of the Rarity Mountain Road exit.

Between Rarity Mountain Road and Jellico, the interstate crosses southeast-dipping Pennsylvanian-age sandstones, shales, and siltstones and colorful shales and limestones of the underlying Mississippian-age Pennington Formation along the north flank of Pine Mountain. Pennsylvanian-age strata on Pine Mountain are about 500 feet above their equivalents on the northern Cumberland Plateau due to thrust faulting along the Pine Mountain fault. The interstate crosses the Pine Mountain fault near milepost 159, where the Pennington Formation was thrust over Pennsylvanian-age strata.

Jellico, on flat-lying Pennsylvanian-age strata of the northern Cumberland Plateau, is nearly 1,000 feet lower in elevation than Pine Mountain. The city was a boomtown during the late 1800s and early 1900s when bituminous coal was discovered in the surrounding hills. Indian Mountain State Park was developed as part of a reclamation project in which abandoned strip mines were converted to recreational areas.

Pennsylvanian-age sandstones, siltstones, and shales of the Crab Orchard Mountains and Gizzard Groups are exposed on Pine Mountain. Layers dip southeastward toward the road along the northwest limb of the Middlesboro syncline. Large block slides sometimes undermine the road, so this stretch of interstate requires slope stabilization and erosion mitigation efforts. (36.436099N, 84.291541W) —Marcy Davis photo

I-81
I-40 Junction—Bristol
75 miles

I-81, which splits from I-40 east of Dandridge, follows northeast-striking valleys that characterize Tennessee's Valley and Ridge physiographic province. Low, linear ridges parallel the valleys and are visible intermittently on both sides of the highway. Every so often the road crosses a ridge and then follows an adjacent valley for many miles before doing it again. Folded and faulted Cambrian- and Ordovician-age sedimentary strata underlyie the highway to the Virginia state line.

There are few outcrops along this stretch of road, with the exception of small exposures of Knox Group carbonates between exits 8 and 12. These rocks were brought to the surface along a small local fault that the highway crosses at exit 8. The reddish soils derived from Knox carbonates contrast with the tan soils derived from surrounding Sevier Shale.

Quartz crystals, known as "Tennessee field diamonds," have been found in dolomite of the Knox Group south of I-81 at exit 8, within about 0.5 mile of the road. The site was excavated for fill dirt and is no longer exposed; however, with some effort and luck, you may find some "diamonds" in the residual, red soils weathered from the dolmite. The very clear quartz crystals are doubly terminated, meaning both ends are naturally pointed. Field diamonds are found in brecciated Knox Group dolomite and in faulted and folded Sevier Shale in the eastern Valley and Ridge. There are a number of sites for Tennessee field diamonds between Kingsport and Maryville. One of the best places to search

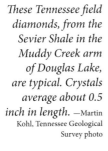

These Tennessee field diamonds, from the Sevier Shale in the Muddy Creek arm of Douglas Lake, are typical. Crystals average about 0.5 inch in length. —Martin Kohl, Tennessee Geological Survey photo

for them is along the shores of Douglas Lake, which is about halfway between the two cities near Dandridge. Much of the area is accessible, especially near the boat launch south of Douglas Dam.

Small zinc and barite deposits are found south of the interstate, near Greeneville. The deposits were first explored around 1900 but were not developed until the 1940s. Some barite was extracted from small mines, but no zinc or lead ore was produced. The area remained of interest for some time because the

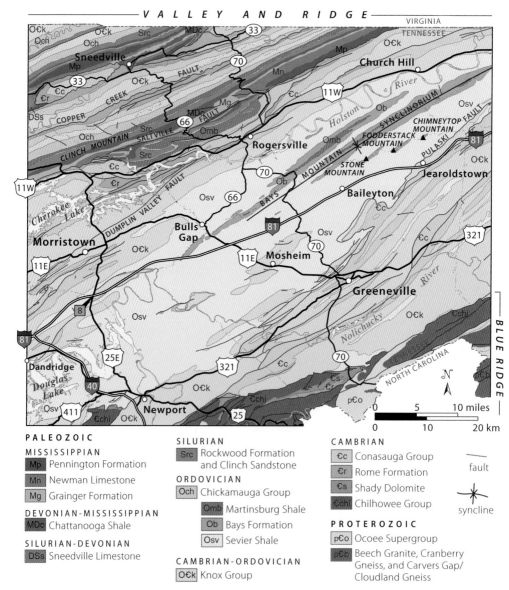

PALEOZOIC

MISSISSIPPIAN
Mp Pennington Formation
Mn Newman Limestone
Mg Grainger Formation

DEVONIAN-MISSISSIPPIAN
MDc Chattanooga Shale

SILURIAN-DEVONIAN
DSs Sneedville Limestone

SILURIAN
Src Rockwood Formation
     and Clinch Sandstone

ORDOVICIAN
Och Chickamauga Group
Omb Martinsburg Shale
Ob   Bays Formation
Osv Sevier Shale

CAMBRIAN-ORDOVICIAN
OЄk Knox Group

CAMBRIAN
Єc   Conasauga Group
Єr   Rome Formation
Єs   Shady Dolomite
Єchi Chilhowee Group

PROTEROZOIC
pЄo Ocoee Supergroup
pЄb Beech Granite, Cranberry
     Gneiss, and Carvers Gap/
     Cloudland Gneiss

— fault
✳ syncline

Geology along I-81 between I-40 and Jearoldstown. See map on page 119 for the east end of the route.

rocks hosting these minerals are the equivalent to those found in the Mascot–Jefferson City zinc district near Knoxville.

I-81 crosses a low ridge between mileposts 16 and 19. The ridge is one of several that together form the Bays Mountain synclinorium, a structural feature that includes a large-scale syncline on which several smaller folds are superimposed. The ridge is capped by the Ordovician-age Bays Formation. The older Sevier Shale forms the valley and synclinorium flanks between exit 23 and Jearoldstown. Ridges of the synclinorium parallel I-81 on the north side of the highway between exit 23 and the I-26 junction at exit 57, and Stone, Fodderstack, and Chimneytop (3,094 feet) Mountains are also part of the synclinorium.

The Knox Group is exposed along the road near the Jearoldstown exit and forms the low ridges south of the highway for the next few miles. Also near Jearoldstown, the interstate crosses the Pulaski fault and passes from the Saltville thrust sheet onto the Pulaski thrust sheet. The Pulaski fault extends 210 miles, from near Greeneville through Bristol and into Virginia. Although it is one of the major Valley and Ridge detachment thrust faults, the Pulaski fault differs from other major Valley and Ridge faults. It's rooted in Cambrian-age rocks of the Chilhowee Group rather than in the younger Rome Formation. The Cambrian-age Honaker Dolomite, part of the Conasauga Group, was thrust over Knox Group strata here along this fault.

Steeply southeast-dipping beds of the Conasauga and Knox Groups are exposed along the road intermittently. Dark-gray beds of the Cambrian-age Honaker Dolomite are exposed on the southbound side of the highway near exit 59, in the cliffs south of the Holston River bridge, at exit 69 where beds dip steeply northwestward, and in a large roadcut south of exit 74. The Honaker Dolomite contains stromatolites, as well as organic material that gives off a sulfurous odor when the rock is hit with a rock hammer. Higher areas are capped by the Sevier Shale.

Bristol straddles the Tennessee-Virginia state line. On the Tennessee side, Bristol has developed around two prominent ridges, Beaver Creek Knobs and Whitetop Knobs. Knox Group underlies lower elevations, including the downtown area, which lies at the north end of the southwestward-plunging Beaver Creek syncline. The syncline, cored by the Ordovician-age Sevier Shale, forms Beaver Creek Knobs, which is home to Steele Creek Park. Rooster Front Park, located at Steele Creek Park's south entrance on Vance Drive, is presumed to be the location of the first iron furnace in Tennessee. It was built in the late 1780s by Colonel James King (for whom the town of Kingsport may be named). Colonel King and several family members are buried at Ordway Cemetery, located about 1 mile southwest of Rooster Front (off Volunteer Parkway, US 11E). Their graves are covered with iron plates that were made at the ironworks. James King's grave is marked with a coffin-shaped iron slab.

Volunteer Parkway (US 11E) follows the valley of Beaver and Cedar Creeks. The valley is eroded into Knox Group strata that form the core of an anticline that separates the Beaver Creek syncline from another syncline that forms Whitetop Knobs, southeast of the highway. The Sevier Shale lies at the center of this syncline as well. The famous Bristol Motor Speedway is located at the southern end of Whitetop Knobs and is built on the Sevier Shale.

US 25E
MORRISTOWN—CUMBERLAND GAP
50 miles

US 25E, a national scenic byway known as East Tennessee Crossing, traverses the state between the North Carolina state line near Del Rio and the Kentucky state line at Cumberland Gap. North of I-81, the highway cuts across Tennessee's central Valley and Ridge physiographic province. Typical of the Valley and Ridge, southeast-dipping rock layers are repeated because a series of overlapping thrust sheets were stacked up on southeast-dipping thrust faults.

Between I-81 and Morristown, US 25E crosses Cambrian-to-Ordovician-age limestone and shale of the Conasauga, Knox, and Chickamauga Groups. Despite the hilly topography, rock exposures are limited. South of Morristown, Clinch Mountain comes into view for northbound travelers, while southbound travelers will see the high ranges of the western Blue Ridge.

North of Morristown, the highway crosses Cherokee Lake, a reservoir formed by the damming of the Holston River. The Copper Ridge Dolomite, part of the Knox Group, underlies the southern part of the lake. Southeast-dipping brown shales of the Conasauga Group are exposed in a few roadcuts where US25E crosses islands. These beds are also exposed around the lake's northern shoreline when water levels are low. At Peninsula Drive, the road crosses a narrow strip of Rome Formation that was thrust over rocks of the Conasauga Group, which underlie the highway to Bean Station.

Bean Station lies in the valley between Big and Poor Valley Ridges, both of which are held up by the Rome Formation. West of Bean Station, US 25E cuts across Clinch Mountain, a narrow, linear, 150-mile-long ridge that extends northeastward into Virginia and separates the Clinch and Holston River valleys.

Geologists know this area as the Thorn Hill geologic section, named for the community of Thorn Hill on the north side of Clinch Mountain. The Thorn Hill geologic section is one of the most complete and best-exposed Paleozoic-age stratigraphic sections in Tennessee's Valley and Ridge. The section begins north of the US 11W south exit and extends across Clinch Mountain to War Ridge north of Thorn Hill. Over a distance of about 9 miles with nearly 2,000 feet of total elevation change, the road passes through nearly 11,000 feet of stratigraphic section—a slice through the Copper Creek thrust sheet. Roadcuts provide exposures of everything from the Cambrian-age Rome Formation to the Mississippian-age Grainger Formation. These strata are bounded by the Saltville and Copper Creek faults, both major thrust faults in the Valley and Ridge physiographic province that originate in the Rome Formation. Academic and professional geologic field trip groups have frequented the Thorn Hill geologic section for decades. For those who want to dive more deeply into the geology, see *The Geological History of the Thorn Hill Paleozoic Section*, by K. R. Walker, and *Thorn Hill: A Classic Paleozoic Stratigraphic Section in Tennessee*, by D. W. Byerly and others.

The fissile maroon shales of the Rome Formation are exposed at the base of Poor Valley Ridge. The road narrows here and chain-link fencing is bolted to

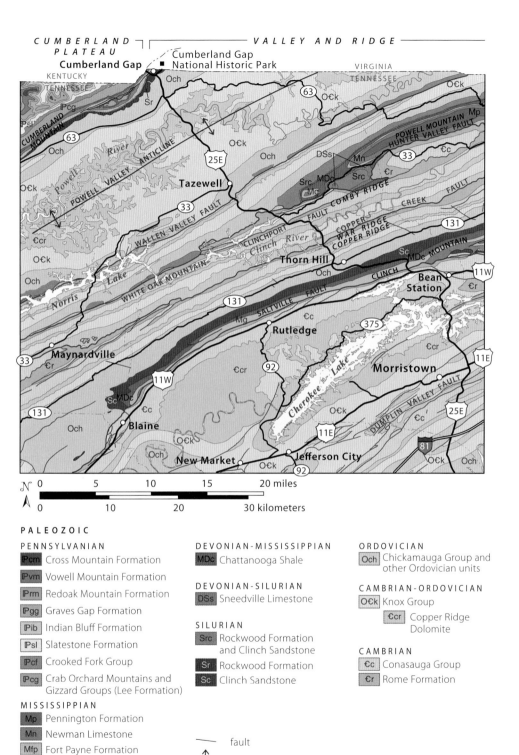

Geology along US 25E between Morristown and Cumberland Gap.

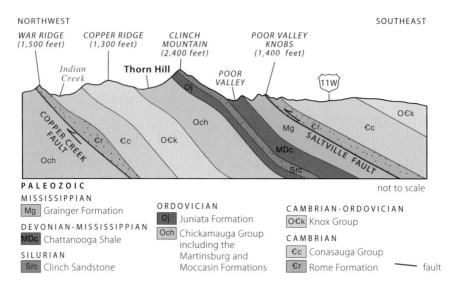

NORTHWEST   SOUTHEAST

WAR RIDGE (1,500 feet)   COPPER RIDGE (1,300 feet)   CLINCH MOUNTAIN (2,400 feet)   POOR VALLEY KNOBS (1,400 feet)

Generalized geologic cross section of the Thorn Hill geologic section between Bean Station and Thorn Hill. —Modified from Moore, 1994

PALEOZOIC

MISSISSIPPIAN
Mg Grainger Formation

DEVONIAN-MISSISSIPPIAN
MDc Chattanooga Shale

SILURIAN
Src Clinch Sandstone

ORDOVICIAN
Oj Juniata Formation
Och Chickamauga Group including the Martinsburg and Moccasin Formations

CAMBRIAN-ORDOVICIAN
O€k Knox Group

CAMBRIAN
€c Conasauga Group
€r Rome Formation — fault

the rock in an effort to mitigate rockfalls. The Saltville fault surfaces along the north side of Poor Valley Ridge, placing the Rome Formation on the Mississippian-age Grainger Formation, which the narrow valley between Poor Valley Ridge and Clinch Mountain has been eroded into. Because strata are tilted southeastward, rocks are older on the north side of Clinch Mountain than on the south side. Black shales of the Devonian-to-Mississippian-age Chattanooga Shale are exposed on the east side of road at the southern edge of Clinch Mountain.

Fields of blocky tan and brown boulders line the east side of the highway on the south side of Clinch Mountain. These rock piles are the result of creative road engineering. Rock layers dip 20 to 30 degrees southeastward here, so highway construction often undercut these layers, causing large sections of detached bedrock to slide downward along planar bedding surfaces. In an effort to mitigate the sliding, the Tennessee Department of Transportation employed a process called shoot-in-place buttressing. Rock was blasted from the Silurian-age Clinch Sandstone and then left in place as "natural" retaining structures to keep the rest of the hill from sliding.

The Clinch Sandstone, a clean, well-sorted, white quartz sandstone, is the prominent ridge-former in the area and is well exposed near the top of the Clinch Mountain. Sedimentary structures such as crossbeds, symmetrical ripple marks, and graded bedding indicate that the sandstone was deposited along a beach and shallow shelf. Sediments were transported westward from the mountains that formed during the Taconic orogeny. The Clinch Sandstone contains few body fossils, but it does contain some impressive trace fossils, including *Arthrophycus, Skolithos,* and *Planolites* from the activity of burrowing worms, and *Rusophycus,* the resting trace of a trilobite. A good exposure of *Rusophycus* lies behind the restaurant west of the lookout. The outcrop must be accessed by walking through the dining area, so please be considerate and ask permission first.

The contact between the Clinch Sandstone and the distinctive red beds of the underlying Juniata Formation is on the northwest side of William Bean

Many layers of the Clinch Sandstone are rich in trace fossils, particularly those of wormlike burrowers that churned up sediment as they tunneled through it. One of the most common is Arthrophycus, *which is typically found at the base of sandstone beds underlain by shale beds. This block of Clinch Sandstone, one of many that make up the wall at Veterans Overlook, on Clinch Mountain is about 18 inches wide.* —James St. John photo

Thick beds of the Silurian-age Clinch Sandstone are well exposed near the top of Clinch Mountain. (36.350572N, 83.393338W) —James St. John photo

Gap, across from the restaurant parking lot. Look for mud cracks on the tops of Juniata Formation shale beds. Mud cracks form in shallow tidal zones where clay flats are periodically wet then dry, a process that causes the clay to swell and then shrink and crack. The Juniata Formation weathers to dark-red soils that are visible at the top of the steep north side of Clinch Mountain.

Also on the steep north side of Clinch Mountain are soils derived from the red, green, and brown calcareous shales and limestones of the Martinsburg Shale and Moccasin Formation, both of the Chickamauga Group. Along with the Juniata Formation, these units were deposited in a broad tidal flat complex that covered much of the southern Appalachian region at the end of Ordovician time.

Tennessee Imperial Black Marble was quarried near Thorn Hill. It's not marble at all but the dark-gray and relatively homogeneous Maryville Limestone, part of the Cambrian-age Conasauga Group. The stone was cut and polished to specific sizes and shapes and sold as dimension stone.

Knox Group carbonates are exposed near the Kincaid Farms Drive/ Old Highway 25E turnoff north of the TN 131 junction. Shale and carbonates of the Knox Group are exposed across Copper Ridge, which the highway crosses northwest of Thorn Hill. Look for the dark-gray limestones of the Maryville Limestone north of Broken Valley Road.

North of Indian Creek, maroon shales of the Cambrian-age Rome Formation are exposed along the highway at War Ridge. The Copper Creek thrust

The Copper Creek fault is exposed on the north side of War Ridge on the east side of US 25E, north of Indian Creek Road and south of Dry Valley Road. Highly deformed Rome Formation was thrust over the Moccasin Formation along the fault, which runs diagonally across the photo from the upper left to lower right. (36.381959N, 83.447160W) —James St. John photo

fault comes to the surface and is visible in the roadcut on the north side of War Ridge. Here, the Copper Creek fault forms the lower boundary of the Thorn Hill geologic section. The Rome Formation was thrust over Chickamauga Group strata, which are well exposed along the highway to the Clinch River. Chain-link fencing holds back impressive Knox Group carbonates for about 1 mile along the river.

Cambrian-age shales and limestones are exposed along the road across Comby Ridge, where the Rome Formation was thrust over rocks of the Conasauga Group along the White Oak Mountain–Clinchport fault. Similar to the Saltville fault, the White Oak Mountain–Clinchport fault is a major structural feature of the southern Appalachian Mountains; it can be traced continuously for nearly 380 miles, from Georgia, through Tennessee and Virginia, and into West Virginia. The Clinchport thrust sheet overrode two adjacent thrust sheets to the west: the Hunter Valley and Wallen Valley thrust sheets. The Hunter Valley and Wallen Valley faults are splays of the White Oak Mountain–Clinchport fault. This fault system marks the southern edge of the Pine Mountain thrust sheet, the interior of which is folded into an anticline-syncline pair. See page 154 for a cross section of the structure.

North of Big Sycamore Creek, part of Norris Lake, the Rome Formation was thrust over the Chickamauga Group along the Hunter Valley thrust fault. Lower Silurian-age strata underlie Powell Mountain east of the highway.

About 2 miles south of Tazewell, strata of the Conasauga Group was placed on Chickamauga Group strata along the Wallen Valley fault. Powell Valley between Tazewell and Harrogate has developed in the Powell Valley anticline, a broad fold that formed on the Pine Mountain fault during the Alleghanian orogeny. The Pine Mountain fault is not exposed here but surfaces north of Pine Mountain. Knox Group strata are present across the valley, with the Copper Ridge Dolomite forming the core of the anticline. The limestone beds on the north side of the Powell River dip northwestward along the fold's northern limb.

Cumberland Mountain, made of Silurian-to-Pennsylvanian-age sedimentary rock, becomes visible from northbound lanes north of the Powell River. Its rock layers dip northwestward about 40 degrees in the northernmost part of the Powell Valley anticline.

At milepost 20, the highway crosses Poor Valley Ridge, the second ridge with this name along this route. The steeper, southeast-facing scarp is underlain by red beds of the Late Ordovician-age Sequatchie Formation, deposited at the same time as the Juniata Formation that's exposed at Clinch Mountain. Northwest-dipping Rockwood Formation, deposited in the Silurian Period at the same time as the Clinch Sandstone, is exposed in the Poor Valley Ridge gap.

The Cumberland Gap Tunnel was excavated through the northwest-dipping strata of Cumberland Mountain. Look for Mississippian-age limestones and shales near the opening. The tunnel connects Cumberland Gap, Tennessee, with Middlesboro, Kentucky, a city built inside an impact crater approximately 3 miles in diameter. For more information on the Middlesboro impact structure, see *Field Guide to the Middlesboro and Flynn Creek Impact Structures*, edited by Keith Milam and others.

CUMBERLAND GAP NATIONAL HISTORIC PARK

Pinnacle overlook provides a panoramic view of Cumberland Mountain, which stretches into the distance toward Caryville, Tennessee. The northern limb of the Powell Valley anticline (which is the southern limb of the Middlesboro syncline), forms Cumberland Mountain. Note that the Middlesboro syncline is a topographically high region while the Powell Valley anticline is topographically low. The stretched and fractured rock layers in the anticline facilitated weathering and erosion, whereas strata in the syncline were compressed and thickened and are more resistant to weathering as a result. Fern Lake (far right) is north of Cumberland Mountain, and TN 63 (at left) is to the south. Also at left you can see the double lanes of US 25E heading toward the tunnel through the mountain. The Valley and Ridge physiographic province is southeast (left) of Cumberland Mountain. (36.605242N, 83.667214W) —Marcy Davis photo

Cumberland Gap National Historic Park lies at the intersection of Tennessee, Virginia, and Kentucky. Cumberland Gap is a low spot about 1,000 feet deep in Cumberland Mountain, a 100-mile-long ridge that extends from Caryville, Tennessee, to Norton, Virginia. The gap is a notch formed by wind and water erosion. A tributary to the Tennessee River once flowed through the gap, but as Alleghanian faulting and folding raised and tilted Cumberland Mountain, stream piracy diverted streams to the north, and the one that flowed through the gap was eventually captured by a tributary of the Cumberland River. Erosion of the gap was likely facilitated by the Rocky Face fault, a left-lateral strike-slip fault, the trace of which passes through Cumberland Gap. Movement along the Rocky Face fault created a local zone of weakness that allowed for preferential weathering through the mountain.

Cumberland Gap was first used by Native Americans traveling between hunting grounds as they followed migrating animals. Euro-Americans began traveling through the gap during the eighteenth century. In 1775 frontiersman Daniel Boone led a group that improved the gap trail, which eventually became known as the Wilderness Road, the primary route for pioneers looking to settle in Kentucky, Tennessee, and the American West. Union and Confederate troops exchanged control of Cumberland Gap several times during the Civil War, but there were no major battles fought here. Earthworks and gun emplacements created by both armies are preserved in the park. Today, visitors to Cumberland Gap National Historic Park may enjoy the natural history offered by the many miles of trails. Part of the Tennessee portion of Cumberland Mountain is in the park, as is the historic settlement of Cumberland Gap, but most of the park infrastructure, including visitor centers, is in Virginia and Kentucky.

Pinnacle Overlook, at the top of Cumberland Mountain, offers an overview of local geology. The overlook is in Virginia, but the view is southward into Tennessee. To get there, take the first exit north of the tunnel and follow the signs. (Please note that Pinnacle View Road is narrow and winding and not appropriate for larger vehicles or trailers.) Most rocks exposed along the road belong to the Pennsylvanian-age Lee Formation. A short trail leads from the parking area to the overlook at Pinnacle Rock. Directly below the overlook are calcareous shales and sandstones of the Pennington Formation and dark-gray cliffs of the Mississippian-age Newman Limestone.

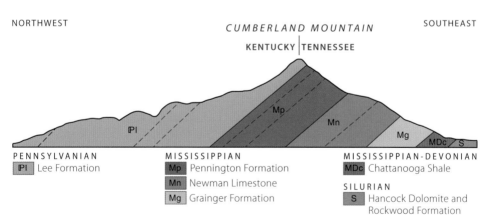

Generalized geologic cross section of Cumberland Mountain. —Modified from Dean, 1989

Northwest-dipping, Devonian-to-Pennsylvanian-age rocks make up Cumberland Mountain. Conglomeratic sandstones of the Lee Formation are exposed near the overlook. The coarse-grained sandstone is highly cross-bedded and contains ripple marks and fossilized flora typical of the Late Mississippian and Early Pennsylvanian Periods, such as *Calamites*, a genus of extinct, tree-sized plants related

to modern horsetails. In some areas it contains brackish-water and marine invertebrate animals that lived along a dynamic coastline.

The historic town of Cumberland Gap lies at the base of Pinnacle Rock. The
Newlee Iron Furnace, a cold-blast charcoal-fueled iron furnace, provided fuel for
smelting operations at the Newlee Iron Works. Low-grade iron ore came from the
Silurian-age Rockwood Formation that forms Poor Valley Ridge southeast of the
town of Cumberland Gap. The furnace's sandstone chimney remains are accessible via Pennlyn Avenue.

The park's other geologic highlights include White Rocks, spectacular cliffs
of light-colored Pennsylvanian-age sandstone and conglomerate that tower
more than 1,000 feet above Powell Valley. Sand Cave is not really a cave, but a
large rock shelter. Both White Rocks and Sand Cave are accessible via trails in
the eastern section of the park. There are ranger-led tours of Gap Cave, one of
several park caves developed in Mississippian-age limestones on the north side
of Cumberland Mountain.

US 64/US 74/TN 40
CLEVELAND—DUCKTOWN
40 miles

To drive to the Blue Ridge from Chattanooga, you can take US 64 from exit 11
at Ooltewah or take exit 20 at Cleveland farther east. The Beaver Valley, Saltville, and Knoxville faults pass through downtown Cleveland, along which the
Conasauga Group was thrust over the Knox Group. East of Cleveland, US 64
follows the Old Copper Road over folded and faulted rocks of Cambrian and
Ordovician age. Built in 1853, the Old Copper Road connected copper mines in
southeastern Tennessee's Copper Basin at Ducktown to the railroad in Cleveland. The road is now a scenic byway through the Cherokee National Forest.

Little and Sugarloaf Mountains stand at the mouth of the Ocoee River
Gorge. The Ocoee River begins in northern Georgia and flows through southeastern Tennessee, where it is impounded by three dams before flowing north
for several miles to its confluence with the Hiwassee River north of Ocoee. The
Ocoee River ranks as one of the top ten whitewater rivers in the country, so
outfitters and their clients are a common sight throughout the gorge. Little and
Sugarloaf Mountains are both made of Cambrian-age Chilhowee Group strata,
which were thrust over the Knox Group along the Great Smoky fault that runs
along the western base of the mountains.

Look for thick, light-colored, steeply southeast-dipping beds of sandstone
and shale, part of the Chilhowee Group, along the north side of the road at
Ocoee Dam Number 1—Parksville Dam. These rocks contain abundant fractures and small faults associated with movement on the Great Smoky fault.

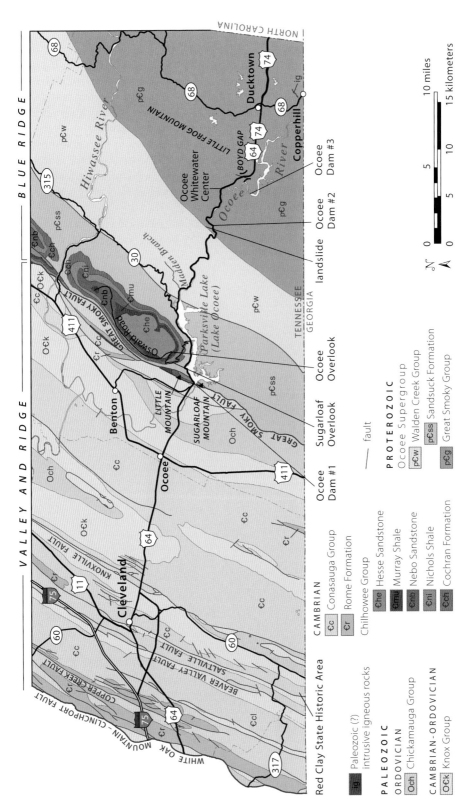

Geology along US 64 between Cleveland and Ducktown.

Red Clay State Historic Area

ig Paleozoic (?) intrusive igneous rocks

PALEOZOIC

ORDOVICIAN
Och Chickamauga Group

CAMBRIAN-ORDOVICIAN
O€k Knox Group

CAMBRIAN
€c Conasauga Group
€r Rome Formation

Chilhowee Group
€he Hesse Sandstone
€mu Murray Shale
€nb Nebo Sandstone
€ni Nichols Shale
€ch Cochran Formation

PROTEROZOIC

Ocoee Supergroup
p€w Walden Creek Group
p€ss Sandsuck Formation
p€g Great Smoky Group

— fault

In 1869 James Safford described the rocks of the Ocoee Supergroup from exposures in the Ocoee River Gorge. Between Ocoee Dam Number 1 and Boyd Gap, rocks belonging to the Neoproterozoic-age Walden Creek Group and the upper part of the Great Smoky Group are well exposed. Rocks are older, more deformed, and more intensely metamorphosed toward Ducktown.

Buff-colored soils derived from the Sandsuck Formation, the uppermost unit of the Walden Creek Group, surround the Lake Ocoee Inn and Marina. The Sandsuck Formation consists of shale and siltstone with minor amounts of conglomerate and limestone. The unit is exposed along the road to its junction with TN 30 at Greasy Creek.

On a nice day, a short side trip up Oswald Road is a worthwhile excursion. Two overlooks provide excellent views of Little and Sugarloaf Mountains and the contrasting landscapes of the Blue Ridge and the Valley and Ridge. The road also provides exposures of nearly all of the Chilhowee Group's rocks, including the Cochran Formation, the Nebo Sandstone, the Murray Shale, and the Hesse Sandstone. To take this excursion, turn left on Oswald Road, about 1.5 miles east of the marina, and head toward the Chilhowee Recreation Area.

Between TN 30 and the Ocoee Dam Number 2, fine-grained, greenish-gray and dark-gray slate and siltstone with beds of medium to coarse-grained

Skolithos, *trace fossils of vertical worm burrows, can be found in the light-colored quartzites of the Hesse Sandstone. This outcrop is directly across the road from the Ocoee Over-look. (35.113881N, 84.615388W)* —Jonathan Mies photo

sandstone more than 3 feet thick belonging to the Wilhite Formation of the Walden Creek Group are exposed along the road and in the riverbed. Rocks are highly deformed in this section of the Ocoee River Gorge. Small and large folds may vary in size by tens of feet, and some folds are overturned. Many folds lean toward the northwest, having been pushed this way by northwest-directed thrust faulting during mountain building in Paleozoic time. These rocks also exhibit slaty cleavage, a type of foliation that develops in fine-grained rocks that are metamorphosed at relatively low temperatures and pressures during deformation. The result is closely spaced planes of weakness that develop perpendicular to the direction of maximum stress.

Wilhite Formation beds up to 3 feet thick are deformed near Madden Branch, about 1 mile east of TN 30. (35.109263N, 84.558314W) —Jonathan Mies photo

These rocks also exhibit slaty cleavage (orange lines), a type of foliation common to fine-grained sedimentary rocks that have been metamorphosed. These are planes of weakness that give the rock a finely layered appearance that is usually at an angle to the original bedding (dashed black lines). —Jonathan Mies photo

East of Ocee Dam Number 2 the Ocoee River flows through a narrow, steep-walled gorge with many waterfalls along the edges. The contact between the Walden Creek and Great Smoky Groups is about 3 miles east of the dam. The contact is not visible, but the rocks have thinner bedding and are a deeper red color east of the contact. In general, rocks belonging to the Great Smoky Group are coarse-grained metasandstones and phyllites.

In 2009 a rockslide occurred just west of Ocoee Dam Number 2 during a period of severe rain and flooding. Large slabs of rock belonging to the Great Smoky Group slid toward the road and closed the highway for several months. The slide was captured on video, which is widely available online. The slide's scar remains visible on the gorge's northern wall, and bolts help stabilize the rock.

You can visit the Ocoee Whitewater Center to learn more about the white-water canoe, kayak, and slalom venue for the 1996 Olympics. A riverside trail highlights the geological engineering feats that went into creating the world-class whitewater race course. Visitors can also take a self-guided tour to learn more about the geology of the area. Look for highly deformed rocks belonging to the Boyd Gap Formation, part of the Great Smoky Group, on the north side of US 64 across from the Ocoee Whitewater Center parking lot.

East of the Ocoee Whitewater Center, the highway leaves the river and crosses the southern end of Little Frog Mountain at Boyd Gap. Highly deformed thick-bedded phyllite and metagraywacke of the Boyd Gap Formation are well

The bolted rock face is where the 2009 rockslide broke away from the hillside. (35.083268N, 84.492023W) —Chuck Sutherland photo

exposed along the road. The rocks of this formation here were more intensely metamorphosed than rocks exposed in the western part of the gorge.

East of Boyd Gap, US 64 crosses the Copper Basin of southeast Tennessee and northern Georgia, where extensive copper mining began in the mid-1800s. Between 1850 and the 1920s, copper and sulfuric acid (a by-product of copper smelting) were the primary products. The mining companies went to a milling program in the 1920s and were then able to also recover iron and zinc. The region's ore was also used to produce copper sulfate, fungicides, and organic chemicals. More money was made by the acid and chemical divisions of the mines than the metals divisions after the 1920s. By 1855, one thousand men were employed in the basin cutting trees, making charcoal, mining, operating smelters, and hauling copper, supplies, and other workers. Ducktown eventually became the largest metal mining district in the southeastern United States; it continued until the Tennessee Chemical Company closed in 1987.

Mines were dug to 2,400 feet below the surface. The copper, iron, sulfur, and zinc of Copper Basin were mined from the Copperhill Formation, part of the Great Smoky Group. The formation includes graywacke, a dark-colored, clay-rich sandstone that is deposited by turbidity currents, or underwater avalanches. These rocks were altered to slate and mica schist in many areas. Two large folds, the Burra anticline and Coletown syncline, contain the ore of the basin, which is either disseminated or in tabular-shaped masses.

In order to isolate copper from the rest of the minerals, it was smelted from sulfide minerals, including pyrite, chalcopyrite, and pyrrhotite, in an open-roasting process that required a lot of fuel. Not only did this process ensure that the surrounding land was completely deforested, smelting released great quantities of sulfur dioxide gas into the atmosphere. The resulting acid rain created

The Copperhill Formation contains the iron sulfide minerals pyrite, pyrrhotite, and chalcopyrite, which give the rock a champagne-colored sheen as well as a rusty patina where weathering has oxidized the surface. (35.035523N, 84.378408W)
—Marcy Davis photo

a local badlands by killing remaining vegetation and leaving the soil sterile and vulnerable to erosion. Tourists once visited the Copper Basin just to see the 50 square miles of denuded red soils that resembled a Martian landscape. Without vegetation, the contaminated topsoil washed into local creeks and rivers and severely impacted water quality. The methods used in the Copper Basin created one of the most severe environmental disasters in the southern United States and led to some notable environmental litigation, including the Supreme Court's first air pollution case, the State of Georgia versus the Tennessee Copper Company and the Ducktown Sulphur, Copper, and Iron Company, Ltd., in 1915.

One fix for mining companies was to capture the sulfur dioxide released during smelting, mix it with water, and sell the resulting sulfuric acid. Local companies had recognized the potential for making sulfuric acid as early as 1866, and the process had been under research prior to the Supreme Court case, but the technology wasn't perfected until the first decade of the twentieth century. Revegetation and remediation has been ongoing in the Copper Basin since the 1930s. The Ducktown Basin Museum, part of the Burra Burra Mine State Historic Site, located in the superintendent's office of the former Burra Burra Mine (212 Burra Burra Street off TN 68 in Ducktown), offers a great deal of information about the copper mining history of this region, including ongoing reclamation efforts.

The Martian-like Ducktown Desert resulted from deforestation, acid rain, and soil erosion associated with smelting during the late 1800s and early 1900s. This photo was taken during the 1940s when reforestation efforts were just beginning. —Ken Rush, Ducktown Basin Museum photo

US 127
CHATTANOOGA—DUNLAP—CROSSVILLE
78 miles

To begin this guide from northwest Chattanooga, take the exit for US 127 toward Signal Mountain off US 27. West of the interchange, US 127 crosses Godsey Ridge, where east-dipping layers of Silurian and Mississippian age form the eastern limb of the Lookout Valley anticline. The anticline axis is just east of Mountain Creek Road, where rocks of the Ordovician-age Chickamauga Group occupy the core of the fold.

The highway winds up the southeast flank of Walden Ridge. Near the base of the ridge, the road climbs steadily over Silurian-to-Mississippian-age limestone and shale. Rocks of the Mississippian-age Pennington Formation underlie the road at the hairpin turn near Balmoral Drive.

The road narrows and is perched on the mountainside north of Balmoral Drive at the Signal Mountain city limits. Impressive cliffs of the Pennsylvanian-age Warren Point Sandstone line the road and overlook the drainage south of the town of Signal Mountain. The Warren Point Sandstone is mainly

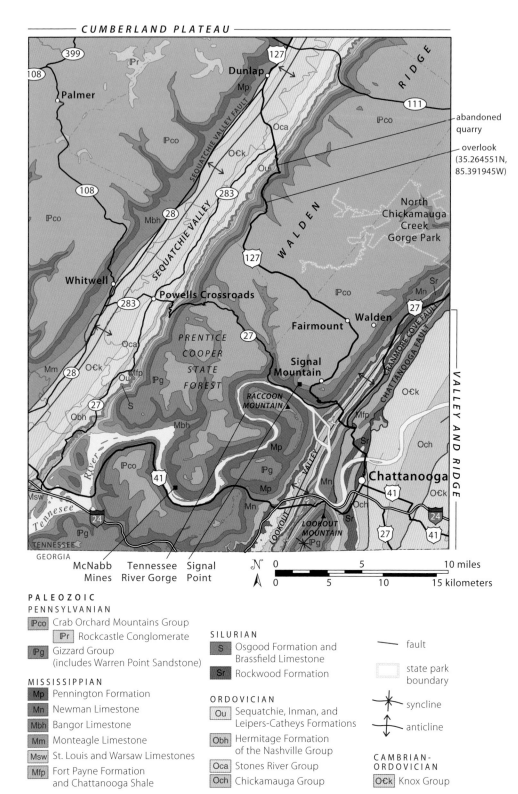

Geology along US 127 between Chattanooga and Dunlap.

PALEOZOIC

PENNSYLVANIAN

- IPco Crab Orchard Mountains Group
  - IPr Rockcastle Conglomerate
- IPg Gizzard Group
  (includes Warren Point Sandstone)

MISSISSIPPIAN

- Mp Pennington Formation
- Mn Newman Limestone
- Mbh Bangor Limestone
- Mm Monteagle Limestone
- Msw St. Louis and Warsaw Limestones
- Mfp Fort Payne Formation
  and Chattanooga Shale

SILURIAN

- S Osgood Formation and
  Brassfield Limestone
- Sr Rockwood Formation

ORDOVICIAN

- Ou Sequatchie, Inman, and
  Leipers-Catheys Formations
- Obh Hermitage Formation
  of the Nashville Group
- Oca Stones River Group
- Och Chickamauga Group

**CAMBRIAN-
ORDOVICIAN**

- OƐk Knox Group

- —— fault
- ▭ state park
  boundary
- ✳ syncline
- ↕ anticline

A roadcut in Godsey Ridge on the north side of US 127 north of New Baylor School Road includes a local favorite exposure of the Chattanooga Shale. The Chattanooga Shale (black layer) separates the Silurian-age Rockwood Formation (below) from greenish shale of the Mississippian-age Maury and Fort Payne Formations (above) along the eastern limb of the Lookout Valley anticline. (35.087012N, 85.327615W) —Jonathan Mies photo

a fine-grained quartz sandstone. It was deposited in a braided river system that flowed southwestward from and parallel to the southern Appalachian Mountains across a broad plain during Pennsylvanian time. The Warren Point Sandstone was deposited in the southern part of the river system at the same time the Fentress Formation of the northwest Cumberland Plateau was deposited farther upstream. Plant remains are preserved throughout the Warren Point Sandstone.

Strata along the eastern edge of Walden Ridge dip slightly northwestward along the western edge of the Lookout Valley anticline. While most rocks of Walden Ridge lay nearly flat, the upturned edges constitute an open syncline that trends northeast, parallel to neighboring anticlines.

Signal Point Park, off Signal Mountain Boulevard and part of Chickamauga and Chattanooga National Military Park, offers breathtaking views of the Tennessee River Gorge, Raccoon and Lookout Mountains, and Chattanooga. Signal Point gets its name from its long history as a communications hub. Native Americans sent smoke signals across the Tennessee Valley from Signal Point prior to European settlement. Pioneers followed suit. Using flags and torches, Union soldiers relayed information about Confederate troop movements, wagon resupply trains, and Tennessee River traffic from Signal Point to other signal

The Warren Point Sandstone, part of the Gizzard Group, is exposed along US 127 north of the "Welcome to Signal Mountain" sign. It was deposited in a sandy braided river system during Pennsylvanian time. Note the crossbeds in the middle layer. (35.117366N, 85.354098W)
—Chuck Sutherland photo

stations at Bridgeport, Stringers Ridge, Cameron Hill, and Lookout Mountain. From the park overlook you'll see just why this was an exceptionally strategic location during the siege of Chattanooga in the fall of 1863. On a clear day, the distant mountains of the Blue Ridge may be visible on the eastern horizon.

The Tennessee River cuts deeply through Walden Ridge west of Chattanooga, forming the Tennessee River Gorge. Why does the river flow across the folded, faulted, and uplifted strata of Walden Ridge rather than parallel to it? The Tennessee River is an old river that was superimposed on the younger Cumberland Plateau topography. The river existed prior to the uplift of Walden Ridge, so it kept its original course despite changes in topography.

The ancestral Tennessee River developed late in the Paleozoic Era. It had a meandering course across a coastal plain that extended westward from the Appalachian Mountains to the Mississippi Valley region. The gorge was likely created during a relatively recent phase of uplift that occurred in the southern Appalachian Mountains region about 7 million years ago. As the region rose, the river cut down through the rising Cumberland Plateau. Joints and faults in the area that is now Walden Ridge may have controlled the locations of the meanders. In Middle Tennessee, the Tennessee River migrated southward along the emerging Nashville Dome's southern flank. In West Tennessee, the Tennessee River now flows northward to meet the Ohio River in Kentucky, a course that likely reflects stream capture by an ancient Ohio River tributary.

Raccoon Mountain, another piece of Walden Ridge, is across the Tennessee River Gorge from Signal Point. The uppermost cliffs on Raccoon Mountain are

The spectacular view from Signal Point, looking southeast across the Tennessee River Gorge and Raccoon Mountain toward downtown Chattanooga and Lookout Mountain. Note the flat top and square shoulders of Raccoon Mountain. This shape is typical of Walden Ridge and the Cumberland Plateau due to the resistant and nearly flat-lying strata that caps the province. (35.119595N, 85.367050W) —Marcy Davis photo

stratigraphically equivalent to those at Signal Point. The Sewanee Conglomerate of the Crab Orchard Mountains Group caps the highest areas of Signal and Raccoon Mountains, while the Warren Point Sandstone of the Gizzard Group forms the resistant cliffs along the upper sides of the mountains. The underlying Raccoon Mountain and Pennington Formations form lower slopes. To have a closer look at the Warren Point Sandstone at Signal Point, walk down the first few hundred yards of the Cumberland Trail, which descends through the cliffs. Fresh surfaces of the sandstone are gray, but older surfaces weathers to yellow orange and yellow brown. It is fine-to-medium grained and often cross-bedded, and typically there's coal near the bottom of the unit.

Raccoon Mountain is also well-known locally for the Raccoon Mountain Pumped Storage Plant, operated by the Tennessee Valley Authority. At the facility, water is pumped from the Tennessee River to a reservoir at the top of Raccoon Mountain. Electricity is generated as water is released through a tunnel that advances generators within the mountain.

The Sewanee Conglomerate underlies downtown Signal Mountain and its western neighborhoods. There are stunning views of Chattanooga, and the Valley and Ridge and Blue Ridge physiographic provinces from East Brow Road and Palisades Drive, which run along the edge of Walden Ridge and are accessible

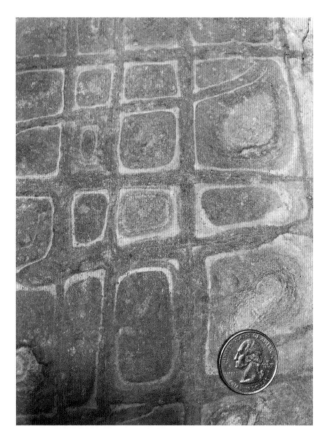

Boxwork is relatively common in Cumberland Plateau sandstone. Rectangular sandstone cavities are separated by relatively thin walls of calcite, silica, or oxide mineral cement. The cements are more resistant to weathering than the sandstone, so they remain conspicuous as the rock weathers.
—Jonathan Mies photo

from Miles Road on Signal Mountain. Warren Point Sandstone underlies this part of town and forms the cliffs along the eastern Walden Ridge escarpment.

North of Signal Mountain, the highway crosses Walden Ridge. There are few rock exposures for the next several miles, but light-colored sandy soils derived from the Sewanee Conglomerate line the road. Pennsylvanian-age shale, sandstone, and conglomerate of the Vandever Formation, also part of the Crab Orchard Mountains Group, underlie the highway at Fairmount and for several miles west. Near the Grand View subdivision, the road skirts the northern edge of Prentice Cooper State Forest.

At a pullout just north of Horseshoe and Patton Roads, take a moment to look across the Sequatchie Valley to the western Cumberland Plateau. The Sequatchie Valley has been eroded into the more than 100-mile-long, asymmetrical, faulted, northeast-plunging Sequatchie Valley anticline. Strata were once continuous across the valley, but the faulting and folding stretched, fractured, and weakened the rock layers, making them more susceptible to erosion. Between the Alabama state line and Melvine, a small town located at the northern end of the valley, all Pennsylvanian- and Mississippian-age strata have been eroded from the anticline. The low, linear hills in the center of the valley, at the core of the Sequatchie

Valley anticline, are chert-rich carbonates of the Knox Group. The spectacular cliffs along the sides of the valley are made of the Pennsylvanian-age Sewanee Conglomerate. The cliffs are 500 to 1,000 feet lower on the west side of the valley due to movement along the Sequatchie Valley thrust fault. The current valley had likely formed by the end of the Neogene Period.

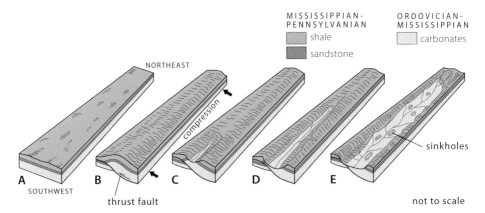

The Sequatchie Valley developed in several stages. (A) Flat-lying Ordovician-to-Pennsylvanian-age strata were (B) folded and faulted during the Alleghanian orogeny. (C) In Neogene time, erosion breached Pennsylvanian-age units. Mississippian-age units were exposed along the crest of the anticline, which was several thousand feet above the present valley floor. (D) Underlying Ordovician-to-Mississippian-age carbonates were extensively eroded. Karst systems developed and overlying strata collapsed. (E) Today, the Sequatchie Valley is slowly growing northward as surface streams and the underground solution of Mississippian-age limestones cause younger strata in Grassy and Crab Orchard Coves to erode and collapse. —Modified from Milici, 1967; Miller, 1974; Miller, 1990

North of the pullout, signs announce the steep, curvy descent into Sequatchie Valley on the west side of Walden Ridge. Gizzard Group sandstone is exposed along the road over the next couple of miles. Look for shiny black layers of coal. An abandoned quarry in Mississippian-age limestone is located about 3 miles north of the overlook on the east side of the road and is recognizable by two large rectangular openings in the rock.

At mile marker 11, northbound travelers enter the Sequatchie Valley and can see the southern Cumberland Plateau across the valley. East-dipping Ordovician-age strata of the Stones River Group lie hidden beneath the road to near the Sequatchie River, which marks the approximate center of the Sequatchie Valley. The low hills east of Dunlap are made of Knox Group strata that form the core of the anticline. At Dunlap, Stones River units again underlie the road but dip westward along the west limb of the Sequatchie Valley anticline. The Sequatchie Valley thrust fault parallels the highway north of the junction with TN 28 in Dunlap.

The small town of Dunlap is located along the west side of the Sequatchie Valley at the base of the Cumberland Plateau, locally referred to as Fredonia

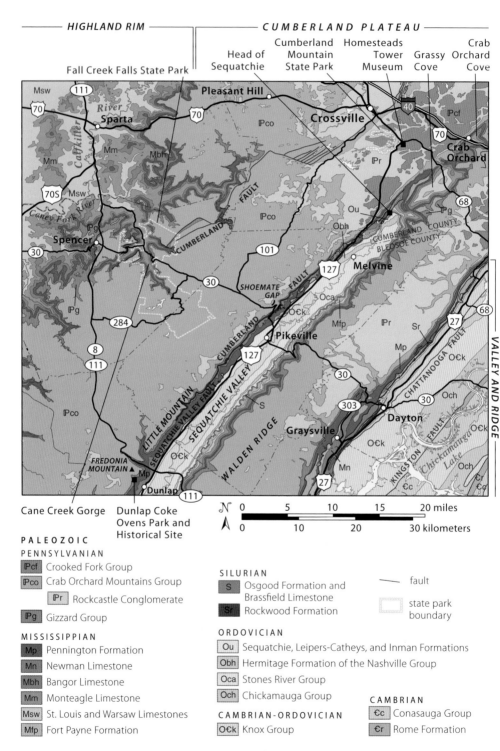

Geology along US 127 between Dunlap and Crossville. Sequatchie Valley anticline (not shown) runs the length of the Sequatchie Valley.

PALEOZOIC

PENNSYLVANIAN

Pcf	Crooked Fork Group
Pco	Crab Orchard Mountains Group
Pr	Rockcastle Conglomerate
Pg	Gizzard Group

MISSISSIPPIAN

Mp	Pennington Formation
Mn	Newman Limestone
Mbh	Bangor Limestone
Mm	Monteagle Limestone
Msw	St. Louis and Warsaw Limestones
Mfp	Fort Payne Formation

SILURIAN

S	Osgood Formation and Brassfield Limestone
Sr	Rockwood Formation

ORDOVICIAN

Ou	Sequatchie, Leipers-Catheys, and Inman Formations
Obh	Hermitage Formation of the Nashville Group
Oca	Stones River Group
Och	Chickamauga Group

CAMBRIAN-ORDOVICIAN

OЄk	Knox Group

CAMBRIAN

Єc	Conasauga Group
Єr	Rome Formation

— fault

☐ state park boundary

Mountain. Coal was mined from Fredonia Mountain from 1899 to 1927. Miners dug coal from the Sewanee coal seam in the Pennsylvanian-age Whitwell Shale of the Crab Orchard Mountains Group. The coal was sent down the mountain via an inclined railway and processed to coke at the base of the mountain in beehive ovens, named for their shape. Coke is a relatively clean fuel that burns more cleanly, longer, and at more consistent temperatures than coal. You can explore the remains of the 268 beehive coke ovens, mining equipment, and a museum built as a replica of the Douglas Coal and Coke Company store at Dunlap Coke Ovens Park and Historical Site, located about 1 mile west of downtown Dunlap on Mountain View Road.

For an interesting and not-too-out-of-the-way side trip, take TN 8 west toward Spencer for about 2.5 miles. Look for the outcrop of folded and faulted sandstones, siltstones, shales, and coals of the Gizzard and Crab Orchard Mountains Groups on the north side of the highway between mileposts 20 and 21. These structures are all related to the Cumberland fault, a detachment fault that underlies the Cumberland Plateau west and north of the Sequatchie Valley anticline. They developed as strata were pushed westward along the detachment during the Alleghanian orogeny. The TN 8 exposure, along with faulting and

Coal mined from Fredonia Mountain was sealed in these beehive ovens without oxygen and baked at temperatures as high as 3,600 degrees Fahrenheit for several days. Water, gas, and tar were burned off during this process. The remaining carbon, called coke, was shipped by rail to Chattanooga, where it was used to fuel iron foundries and blast furnaces. (35.380046N, 85.400680W) —Chuck Sutherland photo

folding along the Fiery Gizzard Trail (near Tracy City), faulting near Spencer, and minor faulting at Short Mountain (south of Gordonsville), is the farthest inland that Alleghanian-associated deformation reached in Tennessee.

The road parallels the main detachment fault, located within a coal-rich shale bed near the bottom of the Pennsylvanian-age section, which is at and below the level of TN 8, depending on where you are along the outcrop. There are many scales of folds visible, and thrust faults are common at the east end of the exposure. Look for small-scale folds and faults in coal beds, which are identifiable by recessions in the sandstone where they have been differentially eroded. Coal beds are internally folded, meaning the folds don't extend into the mechanically stronger sandstone layers.

The west end of the exposure is a good place to see normal faults, which are not typically seen in Tennessee. Thinly bedded sandstone was offset several feet by normal faults at the picnic area waterfall. A particularly interesting outcrop is just west of the picnic area, where a coal bed was thickened into several triangle-shaped wedges along normal faults. There are also northwest-dipping normal faults west of the picnic area, especially near and at mile marker 21.

The deformation zone associated with the Cumberland detachment fault includes folds, thrust faults, and normal faults, which are not typically seen in East Tennessee. Look for normal faults at the picnic area and downhill from mile marker 21 along TN 8, about 2.5 miles west of Dunlap. 35.423182, -85.424466) —Marcy Davis photo

US 127 follows the northwestern part of Sequatchie Valley north of Dunlap. The highway periodically crosses the Sequatchie Valley fault that roughly parallels the western edge of the valley. The fault is not exposed, so look for subtle changes in the soil color, which indicates the highway has crossed from one side of the fault to the other. Along most of the fault's length, rocks of the Knox or Stones River Groups of Ordovician age (mainly east of the highway) were thrust over flat-lying Mississippian-age limestones and shale (mainly along the west side of the highway), but there are few outcrops.

The valley's underlying structure becomes more apparent as you head north from Pikeville, if you trace the cliffs of Pennsylvanian-age sandstone and conglomerate across the Sequatchie Valley anticline in your mind's eye. The Sequatchie Valley anticline resulted from the type of thrust faulting that defines much of East Tennessee's geology. Ordovician-age strata were faulted and pushed nearly 2 miles westward along the southeast-dipping Sequatchie Valley thrust fault, and the overriding block was simultaneously folded into an anticline. Geologists call an anticline made in this way a drag fold. The anticline's southeastern limb dips gently, but the northwestern limb is steep and cut by the fault over the length of the valley. The anticline extends northeastward as the Crab Orchard Mountains and ends abruptly at the Emory River fault zone. Sequatchie Valley is the eroded core of the faulted Sequatchie Valley anticline.

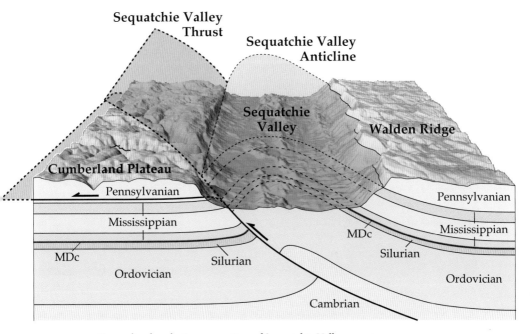

Generalized geologic cross section of Sequatchie Valley. —Jonathan Mies image

FALL CREEK FALLS STATE PARK

Fall Creek Falls State Park, Tennessee's second-largest and most visited state park, sits atop the Cumberland Plateau off TN 30 between Pikeville and Spencer. The park includes 26,000 acres of the Cane Creek watershed, with many steep and narrow gorges. Cane Creek drains the western Cumberland Plateau between its headwaters on Little Mountain, near Sequatchie Valley, to its confluence with the Caney Fork River on the eastern Highland Rim.

To access Fall Creek Falls State Park from Pikeville, take TN 30 west for 15 miles toward Spencer. Ordovician-age Stones River Group underlies the road for about 0.5 mile west of the turnoff. The Mississippian-age Pennington Formation forms the hills north of the highway and west of the turnoff for TN 402, at the base of the plateau. Sandstone, siltstone, shale, and coal belonging to the Pennsylvanian-age Gizzard Group crop out along the road as it climbs the hill. Near the top, thick-bedded sandstones of the Sewanee Conglomerate form cliffs. The unit, which is well exposed at Shoemate Gap, dips 45 degrees westward along the western limb of the Sequatchie Valley anticline. The steep dip flattens very quickly so that strata nearly lie flat on top of the Cumberland Plateau.

Fall Creek Falls, the centerpiece of Fall Creek Falls State Park, is the highest plunge-type waterfall east of the Rocky Mountains at 256 feet high. Fall Creek Falls (left) and Coon Creek Falls (right) cascade over Pennsylvanian-age Sewanee Conglomerate and Warren Point Sandstone. The amphitheater at the base of the falls occurs at the contact with shales of the underlying Raccoon Mountain Formation. (35.665830N, 85.355830W) —Chuck Sutherland photo

Pennsylvanian-age shale and sandstone of the Vandever Formation of the Crab Orchard Mountains Group underlie the highway between Shoemate Gap and Fall Creek Falls State Park. Rockcastle Conglomerate forms higher areas, while Newton Sandstone underlies major drainages. In many larger drainages, including at the bottom of Cane Creek Gorge west of the park, erosion has cut down to Mississippian-age limestone. Where this is the case, streams disappear into caves that developed in the soluble limestone along stream bottoms. Many of these streams reemerge along the western base of the plateau as springs.

Cane Creek Gorge, with its many tributaries, waterfalls, rapids, and grottoes, is the focus of the park. Cane Creek gradually incised the Cumberland Plateau, beginning about 200 million years ago, through headward erosion. The stream moved farther upstream over time as it naturally eroded in the direction opposite its flow. Headward erosion lengthens and widens a stream valley to include more drainage area, as the stream captures neighboring watersheds. Cane Creek erodes the shales and soluble carbonates that underlie the plateau's resistant caprock. This erosion undermines the caprock, which then breaks and falls off.

Fall Creek, a Cane Creek tributary, falls 256 feet over the resistant Sewanee Conglomerate and Warren Point Sandstone at Fall Creek Falls. Falling water excavates the amphitheater at the contact between the Warren Point Sandstone and the underlying shales of the Raccoon Mountain Formation. Rocks surrounding the falls are highly susceptible to physical weathering processes. Water vapor easily penetrates the porous rocks, and they then expand and contract with the temperature changes, particularly during winter freeze-thaw cycles. This expansion and contraction widens joints in the rocks over time, and eventually rocks break off. This physical process is also part of the stream's headward erosion. Look for the large blocks that litter the bottom of the gorge, evidence of headward erosion in progress; the amphitheater itself will migrate upstream over time. The Base of the Falls Trail provides a close look at the Sewanee Conglomerate and Warren Point Sandstone, as well as a view of the falls from the bottom. There is also an overlook of the falls not far from the parking area.

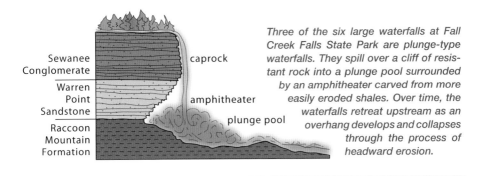

Three of the six large waterfalls at Fall Creek Falls State Park are plunge-type waterfalls. They spill over a cliff of resistant rock into a plunge pool surrounded by an amphitheater carved from more easily eroded shales. Over time, the waterfalls retreat upstream as an overhang develops and collapses through the process of headward erosion.

North of Pikeville, karst features, especially sinkholes and natural springs, form the headwaters of the Sequatchie River. In Grassy Cove, the next valley northward, water drains to a low point and disappears underground. It reemerges as the spring-fed headwaters of the Sequatchie River in Sequatchie Valley. Through headward erosion related to underground rivers and springs, as well as the Sequatchie River itself, Grassy Cove will someday become the northern end of Sequatchie Valley. The smaller valley of Crab Orchard Cove forming north of Grassy Cove will also be added to Sequatchie Valley in time.

The Rockcastle Conglomerate and the overlying Crossville Sandstone, part of the Crooked Fork Group, form the rolling hills to Crossville. Look for west-dipping Pennsylvanian age sandstone and conglomerate of the Gizzard, Crab Orchard Mountains, and Crooked Fork Groups north of Melvine. These units dip westward where US 127 cuts through the west limb of the Sequatchie Valley anticline and climbs onto the Cumberland Plateau near the Bledsoe-Cumberland county line. The ridge east of the highway is the northward extension of the Sequatchie Valley anticline.

Downtown Crossville sits on the Crossville Sandstone, quarried as a building stone called the Crab Orchard Sandstone. Many local buildings are built with

The Sequatchie River receives the underground drainage from Grassy Cove, which emerges as springs at the north end of Sequatchie Valley, at the Head of Sequatchie. Head of Sequatchie is part of Cumberland Trail State Park, accessible at Old TN 28 and Tranquility Lane north of Melvine, and open to the public one day a month. The park is also home to Devilstep Hollow Cave, which contains Native American rock art. (35.792851N, 85.007458W) —Chuck Sutherland photo

or faced with the stone. The Homesteads Tower Museum, located about 0.75 mile north of the entrance to Cumberland Mountain State Park, offers a closer look at the Crossville Sandstone. The tower was built between 1937 and 1938 to house the government administrative offices of the Cumberland Homesteads, a New Deal program that built a series of planned communities across the United States. The unique tower encloses a large water tank and viewing platform.

North of the museum, US 127 becomes Main Street in downtown Crossville. The highway crosses a northeast-trending thrust fault at East Adams Street, where the Sewanee Conglomerate on the southeast side was thrust over the Rockcastle Conglomerate. The fault can be traced both north and south to areas with concentrations of smaller-scale thrust faults that are parallel to the fault in Crossville. Similar to other thrust faults in the Valley and Ridge physiographic province, these faults developed in shale and coal beds. Typically, beds on the upthrown side of these thrust faults were intensely deformed, whereas beds below them were deformed very little. Most of these thrust faults show significantly more horizontal movement than vertical movement. Thrust faulted areas like that in Crossville join to form an interconnected pattern of faulting that extends eastward to Harriman along the northern edge of the Cumberland thrust sheet. Together, these faults represent the Cumberland fault, a detachment thrust fault.

US 321/US 19E
Johnson City—Roan Mountain
26 miles

US 321, accessible via I-26 exit 24, connects Johnson City with the Roan Mountain region of the Blue Ridge. Carbonates of the Knox Group underlie Johnson City and the highway for about 2.5 miles east of I-26. Older carbonates of the Honaker Dolomite, part of the Cambrian-age Conasauga Group, underlie Elizabethton. This area is prone to sinkholes; some reportedly have an area larger than 10 acres and depths of more than 80 feet. Downtown Elizabethton is built on the floodplain of the Watauga River, which meets the South Fork of the Holston River near Gray.

Where US 321 merges with TN 362 on the west side of Elizabethton, eastbound travelers will notice two ridges in the distance: Holston Mountain and a ridge of the Iron Mountains. These ridges form the limbs of the southwest-plunging Stony Creek syncline, which extends from southwest of Johnson City, Tennessee, to southwest Virginia. US 321 turns south where it merges with US 19E east of the Broad Street Bridge over the Doe River. US 19E follows the Doe River for about 19 miles, from Elizabethton to the town of Roan Mountain.

South of Valley Forge, the Doe River (and the highway) cuts through Jenkins Mountain, the southern part of Iron Mountain, and exposes the most complete section of the Cambrian-age Chilhowee Group in Tennessee. The contact between the brownish Shady Dolomite, and the underlying Erwin Formation, the youngest formation in the Chilhowee Group in northeastern Tennessee, is exposed at the west end of the roadcut. The Helenmode Member of the Erwin Formation, a calcareous shale and sandstone, lies directly under the contact. Beneath it are light-colored beds of the Hesse Sandstone Member of the Erwin Formation. Eastward along the roadcut the Erwin Formation becomes shale- and siltstone-rich. Look for the reddish-brown sandstones and dark shales of

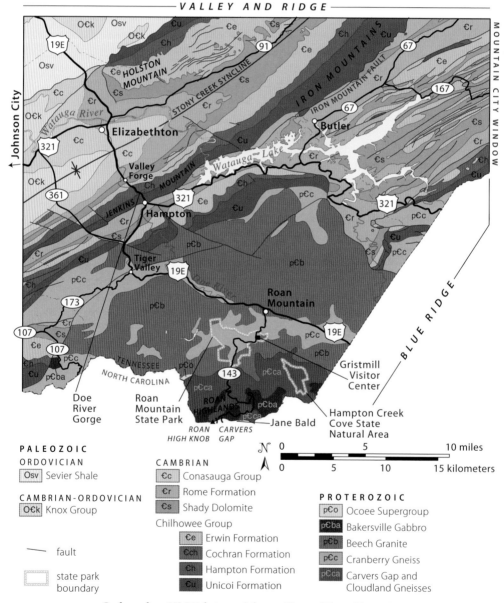

Geology along US 321 between Johnson City and Roan Mountain.

the Hampton Formation in the middle of Jenkins Mountain, where the road crosses a large bend in the river. The oldest formation in the Chilhowee Group, the Unicoi Formation, is made up of sandstones, conglomerates, siltstones, and shales that are exposed at the eastern end of the Doe River Gorge. Gray to black colored rocks are basalts that lie near the base of the Unicoi Formation. Chilhowee Group strata are 4,000 to 7,000 feet thick in northeast Tennessee.

The highway crosses the Iron Mountain fault at the eastern base of Jenkins Mountain. The fault is not exposed but forms an important boundary between the Shady Valley thrust sheet, of which the Stony Creek syncline is a part, and the Mountain City tectonic window, a complex structural feature that's present in the valley around Hampton and extends northeastward to Mountain City. In the Mountain City window, Chilhowee Group and Cambrian-age Shady Dolomite and Rome Formation are faulted in a series of imbricate thrust faults. The ridges southeast of Hampton are made up of Chilhowee Group sandstones that were brought to the surface along such faults at the center of the Mountain City window. Look for southwest-dipping sandstone of the Erwin Formation south of Hampton.

About 0.5 mile south of its junction with TN 361, US 19E crosses a fault. The approximately 750-million-year-old Beech Granite is exposed on the east side of the highway south of the fault. The coarse-grained rocks are grayish brown

At the west end of the Doe River Gorge, beds in the upper part of the Erwin Formation dip northwest along the eastern limb of the Stony Creek syncline. (36.300905N, 82.186302W)
—Marcy Davis photo

where highly weathered. On fresh surfaces they are light colored and often pinkish due to the presence of potassium feldspar. They also contain biotite and traces of the mineral fluorite. The Beech Granite intruded Rodinia's crust during the early stages of its rifting.

The 1.2-billion-year-old Cranberry Gneiss is exposed along the road in the small town of Tiger Valley. In this area, the light-gray, layered Cranberry Gneiss was intruded by black dikes of the approximately 750-million-year-old Bakersville Gabbro. These rocks are exposed intermittently for the next several miles to Roan Mountain, where the Beech Granite is present in and around town.

ROAN MOUNTAIN STATE PARK AND THE ROAN HIGHLANDS

Roan Mountain State Park encompasses more than 2,000 acres along the upper reaches of the Doe River valley. You can access the park, which is 2 miles south of the town of Roan Mountain, via TN 143. A dense spruce-fir forest covers most of the region except for the balds of the rugged Roan Highlands, where rhododendrons bloom in early summer.

Igneous and metamorphic rocks exposed at and near Roan Mountain State Park are some of the oldest rocks in Tennessee, having formed during Proterozoic time. During Paleozoic Era mountain building they were further deformed and metamorphosed. Magill Memorial Presbyterian Church, faced with local boulders, is a good place to see a variety of these old rock types. The Gristmill Visitor Center south of town has an informative geology display as well.

The Cranberry Gneiss, the oldest rock formation in Roan Mountain State Park, formed about 1.2 billion years ago during the Grenville orogeny. It is a coarse-grained metamorphic rock that contains pink feldspar and black mica minerals. In some areas the gneiss is migmatitic, which means it's composed of alternating layers of metamorphic and igneous material that give it a layered look called gneissic banding. The igneous material may have been injected into the metamorphic rock, or it may be the product of partial melting that occurred while the gneiss was being metamorphosed. Cranberry Gneiss is exposed north of the park along US 19E, along TN 143 between the town of Roan Mountain and the campground check-in station, and along park trails.

Iron ore was mined from the Cranberry Gneiss in and around the park from the late 1700s until the 1930s. Ore bodies were lens-shaped masses 100 to 300 hundred feet long and up to 50 feet thick. Magnetite and hematite, also called black and brown ore, were the primary ore minerals. The Cranberry Gneiss is exposed around the opening of the old Peg Leg Mine, accessed via the 0.4-mile-long Peg Leg Mine Trail at the Gristmill Visitor Center. The waterwheel at the visitor center was part of Peg Leg Mine. It powered a 500-pound hammer that crushed the ore before it was sent to a smelter on the Doe River and then shipped to Cranberry, North Carolina, for refining.

The Kings Mountain Men/Shelving Rock Encampment, on TN 143 about 1 mile south of Roan Mountain and a little more than 1 mile north of Smith Branch Road, is a good place to explore mylonite in the Cranberry Gneiss. Mylonite is a rock fabric comprising crushed and stretched minerals; it develops along faults. The amount of mineral deformation—that is, the change in their size and shape—depends on mineral type and proximity to the fault. The greatest deformation occurs close to the fault, where minerals are highly sheared. Mineral crystals are typically smaller and more foliated the closer they are to the fault zone. Mylonite zones are present in the Cranberry Gneiss in several areas of the Roan Mountain State Park. (36.183874N, 82.073895W) —Marcy Davis photo

The Beech Granite and the Bakersville Gabbro, igneous rocks found in Roan Mountain State Park, are younger than the Cranberry Gneiss. The Beech Granite was intruded into the Cranberry Gneiss, and then the Bakersville Gabbro was intruded into both rocks about 750 million years ago, as Rodinia broke apart and the Iapetus Ocean opened to the east. The iron ore mined from the Cranberry Gneiss was emplaced during this time by iron-rich magmas. Rodinia's crust was stretched and pulled apart in the Roan Mountain area, but it didn't completely break apart. Fractures and faults that resulted from the stretching created natural conduits for igneous material. The Beech Granite and Bakersville Gabbro both exhibit features of low-grade metamorphism that occurred during the Alleghanian orogeny, but this metamorphism did not overprint the older metamorphism preserved in the Cranberry Gneiss.

The Beech Granite looks pink with black speckles. Its primary mineral grains, including plagioclase and orthoclase feldspars, hornblende, and quartz, are fairly large and equally sized. It lacks the foliation present in the Cranberry Gneiss. Look for the Beech Granite along the Raven Rock Trail.

Bakersville Gabbro is darker in color than both the Cranberry Gneiss and the Beech Granite. The unit consists of dikes and sills that were intruded into the Cranberry Gneiss and other Mesoproterozoic-age units. The sills are between 1 inch and 60 feet thick. The rock looks dark gray to black due to pyroxene. Light-colored plagioclase feldspar looks like small grains of rice within the darker pyroxene matrix. The rock is not as fine-grained as basalt, nor is it as coarse-grained as a typical gabbro, although it is chemically equivalent to both rock types. Geologists refer to this rock type as diabase, despite the unit's formal name. Look for Bakersville Gabbro at the Twin Springs picnic area and in roadcuts on TN 143 near Carvers Gap at the North Carolina state line.

The Carvers Gap Gneiss, pictured here at Jane Bald in the Roan Highlands, is one of the oldest rocks in the Appalachians. It was originally a piece of non-Laurentian crust that was incorporated into the Grenville Mountains during the Grenville orogeny. —Jordan Mitchell photo

The Roan Highlands are part of Pisgah National Forest and are accessible via TN 143 at Carvers Gap (5,512 feet), located at the Tennessee–North Carolina state line about 8 miles south of Roan Mountain State Park. Several turnouts along the road provide excellent views westward across northeast Tennessee. Northeast from Carvers Gap, the Appalachian Trail snakes along the top of seven highland balds, including Round Bald, Jane Bald, Grassy Ridge Bald, Hump Mountain, and Little Hump Mountain—many with 360-degree views and excellent geologic exposures. Roan High Knob is the highest point along the ridge at an elevation of 6,285 feet. The trails are popular with day hikers, especially in mid-June when Catawba rhododendrons are in bloom across the highlands, and the annual Rhododendron Festival is being held at Roan Mountain State Park. Also, Gray's lily, a very rare species found only in the highlands of the Great Smoky Mountains and on Roan Mountain, blooms at about the same time as the rhododendron. They can be found along the west end of NC 1348.

The gneisses at Carvers Gap are the highest metamorphic grade of rock exposed in Tennessee. They were subjected to high temperatures (1,300 to 1,500 degrees Fahrenheit) and pressures corresponding to a depth of 15 to 20 miles in the Earth's crust before they were exposed here. The rocks appear layered due to gneissic banding. The darker minerals include garnet, orthopyroxene, and hornblende, and quartz and feldspar form the lighter bands.

These gneisses were once sedimentary rocks. They were deposited about 1.2 million years ago and were metamorphosed nearly 1 billion years ago. They are part of the Mars Hill terrane, a piece of exotic crust (not native to Laurentia) that was accreted to the Appalachians during the Grenville orogeny, the continental collision that created the supercontinent Rodinia. In fact, these rocks, and most of the southern Appalachian basement rocks, show chemical similarities to rocks found in ancient Amazonia, the craton of South America.

US 421
Bristol—Mountain City—
North Carolina State Line
44 miles

Southeast of Bristol, US 421 is a narrow, two-lane highway that crosses Paleozoic-age strata of the Valley and Ridge physiographic province. East of South Holston Lake, the highway crosses Cambrian- and Proterozoic-age strata of Tennessee's Blue Ridge.

Knox Group carbonates underlie the road for several miles south of Bristol. Beaver Creek Knobs and Whitetop Knobs, hilly areas southwest of downtown, are eroded synclines cored by the Ordovician-age Sevier Shale. Bristol Caverns, developed in Knox Group carbonates, is accessible via Bristol Caverns Highway (TN 435). It's about 2.5 miles east of the junction with US 421.

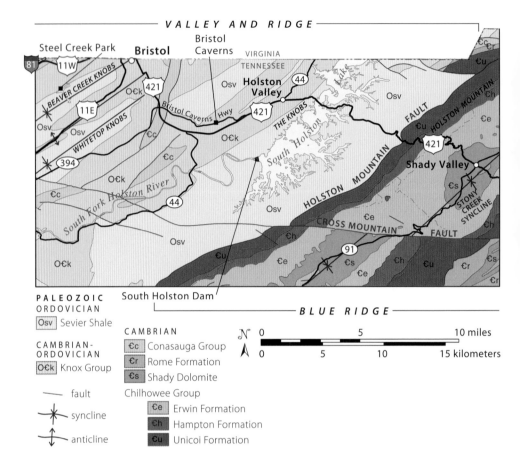

Geology along US 421 between Bristol and Shady Valley. See map on page 202 for eastern half of route.

South of the junction with Bristol Caverns Highway, the foothills and high ridges of the Blue Ridge come into view for eastbound travelers. Knox Group carbonates underlie the hilly pastureland to Holston Valley. Weathered red soils are derived from Knox Group carbonates that are exposed periodically for the next several miles.

Both Emmett Road (TN 2373) and Rooty Branch Road lead to the South Holston Dam, which impounds the South Fork of the Holston River that drains a large area of northeastern Tennessee. The dam, an earth-and-rock-fill structure, is 285 feet high and 1,600 feet long. A weir below the dam alters the river course in order to add oxygen to the water for the benefit of aquatic organisms.

Motorcycle enthusiasts call the section of US 421 between Holston Valley and Mountain City "the Snake" for the highway's nearly five hundred curves. The highway crosses the contact between the Knox Group and the Sevier Shale east of Holston Valley. The Sevier Shale forms the Knobs, the narrow, linear ridge east of Holston Valley. The unit is exposed around the margins of South

About 0.5 mile below the dam on South Holston Dam Road, look for conglomerates and sandstones of the Tellico Formation of the Chickamauga Group. The cobbles and pebbles within the conglomerates were eroded from the Taconic highlands and deposited in submarine fan channels on the east side of the foreland basin that had developed adjacent to the mountains. The pole is about 3.5 feet long. —John T. Haynes photo

Holston Lake and along the highway for the 5 miles between the Knobs and Holston Mountain fault.

US 421 crosses the Holston Mountain fault and passes onto the Shady Valley thrust sheet near milepost 33. The Shady Valley thrust sheet is considered transitional between the thrust sheets of the Valley and Ridge and those of the western Blue Ridge. Similar to Valley and Ridge thrust sheets, it contains rock units of Cambrian to Middle Ordovician age (the Shady Dolomite, the Rome Formation, and the Conasauga and Knox Groups). However, the thrust sheet also contains Mesoproterozoic-age basement rocks and the Cambrian-age Chilhowee Group that are common to Tennessee's western Blue Ridge.

Strata of the Shady Valley thrust sheet were folded into the Stony Creek syncline between Holston Mountain and the Iron Mountains. Cambrian-age Chilhowee Group, Shady Dolomite, and Rome Formation are exposed in the syncline. The fold is faulted on both sides and formed as the Shady Valley thrust sheet was shoved westward over the Pulaski thrust sheet. Strata of the Cambrian-age Unicoi Formation, the oldest unit in the Chilhowee Group, were thrust over the Sevier Shale along the Holston Mountain fault, which cuts through the western limb of the syncline. Southeast-dipping, thick-bedded sandstones of the Unicoi Formation are beautifully exposed for about 1 mile east of the fault.

Aerial view of the Stony Creek syncline looking northeastward across Holston Mountain (fore-ground) and the Iron Mountains (middle ground). Both are made of resistant rocks of the Chilhowee Group. The small town of Shady Valley lies in the center of the syncline, which is cored by the Shady Dolomite and Rome Formation. —James St. John photo

Look for the more thinly bedded sandstone, siltstone, and shale of the Hampton Formation, also part of the Chilhowee Group, near milepost 34. Weathered surfaces of the Hampton Formation may look reddish, but fresh surfaces are a dark greenish gray to black. There are limited exposures of the Erwin Formation, the youngest unit in the Chilhowee Group, near Low Gap and on the east side of Holston Mountain. The Erwin Formation consists mainly of medium to thick beds of shale, siltstone, sandstone, and quartzite. *Skolithos* fossils are common in its quartzites.

Shady Valley is known for its isolated wetlands, called fens or bogs, that are remnants of Pleistocene time, when colder-climate ecosystems extended farther south than they do today. The bogs form where water pools in the underlying Shady Dolomite, and plant matter, especially peat and moss, accumulates. The bogs have been shrinking over time as the climate warms, and they are filled with sediment derived from surrounding highlands. Cranberries, once farmed in the bogs, are no longer grown here, but they do grow wild in some areas of the valley. The town still celebrates the fruit with an annual cranberry festival held in October.

The axis of the Stony Creek syncline lies about 0.5 mile east of the US 421/TN 133 junction where the highway crosses a small patch of the Rome Formation

Backbone Rock is about 10 miles north of Shady Valley on TN 133. Here, the world's shortest tunnel was cut through a vertical fin of Erwin Formation quartzite in a spur of Holston Mountain. Bedding in the quartzite dips gently to the southeast. A small campground, picnic area, and trails allow for further exploration of Backbone Rock and the beautiful Beaverdam Creek. (36.593841N, 81.815019W) —Brian Greer photo

in the core of the syncline. On the eastern limb of the Stony Creek syncline, US 421 crosses a 1-mile stretch of the Shady Dolomite that ends at foot of the Iron Mountains.

US 421 climbs the Iron Mountains in the narrow valley of Green Mountain Branch. The Iron Mountains, the eastern limb of the Stony Creek syncline, are made of northwest-dipping rock layers of the Chilhowee Group, which are exposed along the winding road though the mountains.

The highway crosses a narrow strip of the Mesoproterozoic-age Cranberry Gneiss at the eastern base of the Iron Mountains. The road crosses the Iron Mountain fault at about milepost 11, where the topography flattens out on the west side of Mountain City. The Rome Formation was thrust on top of the Cranberry Gneiss along the fault.

At Mountain City, US 421 crosses the northern part of a complex 10-mile-wide geologic structure called the Mountain City window, which stretches more than 60 miles from near Konnarock, Virginia, to south of Erwin, Tennessee. A number of linear hills near Mountain City, called the Doe Ridges, are part of this larger structure. The Iron Mountain and Stone Mountain faults form the structure's boundaries. The window includes a series of relatively small, parallel, northeast-trending imbricate thrust faults that cut through the Rome

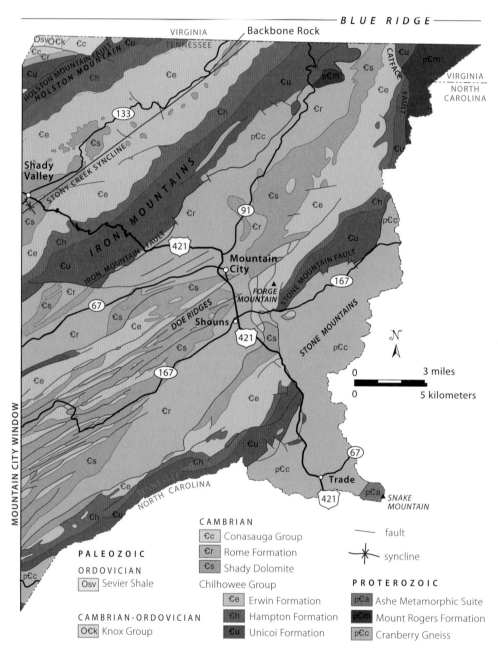

Geology along US 421 between Shady Valley and the North Carolina state line.

Formation, Shady Dolomite, and Erwin Formation. Geologists traced one of the faults along the base of the hill on the west side of the highway in Mountain City; white, *Skolithos*-bearing quartzite of the Erwin Formation was thrust over maroon shale of the Rome Formation on the fault.

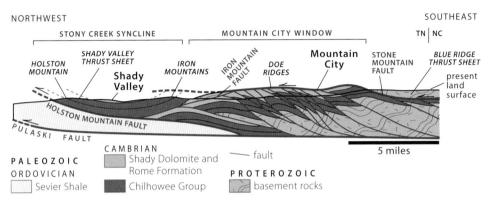

Generalized cross section through the northern part of the Mountain City window, crossing the Stony Creek syncline in the Shady Valley thrust sheet, the Doe Ridges, and the Blue Ridge thrust sheet (above the Stone Mountain fault). Closely spaced, southeast-dipping imbricate thrust sheets overlap between an upper and lower detachment fault. Movement along these faults caused the thrust sheets to fan outward and curve. The base of the Blue Ridge thrust sheet has been eroded through to produce the window, so only a tiny bit of that sheet remains here. —Modified from Diegel, 1986; Hatcher et al., 2007

During the early to mid-1900s manganese was mined throughout the Mountain City area. The manganese deposits were mainly in the Helenmode Member of the Erwin Formation at the contact with the overlying Shady Dolomite. Mineralization was also distributed throughout the overlying Shady Dolomite and Rome Formation, often concentrated in the rock immediately above thrust faults. There are several old mine pits hidden in the weeds along US 421.

The small community of Shouns is situated on southeastward-dipping, thinly bedded shale of the Rome Formation on the eastern side of the Mountain City window. At Old Prison Camp Road the Shady Dolomite was thrust over the Rome Formation. Shady Dolomite was quarried north of the highway here. The quarry exposed the Stone Mountain fault, which dips southeastward, and Mesoproterozoic-age Cranberry Gneiss. The Stone Mountain fault carried the crystalline rocks of the Blue Ridge thrust sheet northwestward over rocks of the Mountain City window. The dolomite is also quarried for aggregate about 0.25 mile south of Old Prison Camp Road.

US 421 follows the narrow valley of Roan Creek through the Stone Mountains south of Shouns. The valley follows the trace of the Stone Mountain fault, which separates Chilhowee Group units on the southwest side of the highway from Cranberry Gneiss on the northeast side. Look for exposures of Cranberry Gneiss from about 1 mile southeast of Midway to Trade at the state line.

Maroon and golden shale of the Rome Formation is exposed on the north side of the road about 0.5 mile south of the junction with TN 167 in Shouns. (36.439368N, 81.795781W) —Sarah Carmichael, Appalachian State University photo

Spectacular specimens of manganese oxide minerals weather out of the Rome Formation at Shouns. Many samples have a globular nature that is described as botryoidal, *a term derived from the Greek word for "grapes."* —Sarah Carmichael, Appalachian State University photo

The Tennessee–North Carolina state line southeast of Trade makes an odd angular jog to the east. Geologically it is noteworthy because the jog includes the only eastern Blue Ridge rocks in Tennessee: garnet amphibolite of the Ashe Metamorphic Suite. They form Snake Mountain, part of which is in Tennessee. Amphibolite is a black-and-white metamorphic rock that contains hornblende and plagioclase feldspar and lesser amounts of other minerals. The amphibolite at Snake Mountain is some of the Iapetus ocean floor that was accreted to Laurentia during the Taconic orogeny about 460 million years ago. The rocks were probably pushed northwest to their present location during the Alleghanian orogeny.

TN 52
LIVINGSTON—JAMESTOWN
29 miles

TN 52 crosses the eastern Highland Rim and the western escarpment of the northern Cumberland Plateau between Livingston and Jamestown. The landscape is hilly, with many streams and rivers. Karst features, especially sinkholes, are well developed in lower areas. The Mississippian-age Fort Payne Formation is present in more established drainages. Valleys in which a variety of row crops are grown, including the valley east of Livingston, are in the St. Louis and Warsaw Limestones. TN 52 winds between eroded outliers of the western Cumberland Plateau east of Livingston. Higher areas are capped by Pennsylvanian-age units, with lower slopes consisting of Mississippian-age units.

The low hills surrounding the valley east of Livingston are made of Monteagle Limestone and Bangor Limestone, which are exposed at the east end of the valley. Bangor Limestone underlies the highway in Oak Grove and is well exposed near milepost 16. The Pennington and Fentress Formations and the Rockcastle Conglomerate form Gullet Mountain south of the highway.

Limestones of the Monteagle Limestone are exposed as TN 52 descends into the valley of the West Fork of the Obey River, where the St. Louis and Warsaw Limestones again underlie the road at Alpine. The Rockcastle Conglomerate caps Alpine Mountain south of the highway. East of Alpine, the road follows the drainage of Nettlecarrier Creek, a tributary to the West Fork of the Obey River, which the road crosses in Cowan Hollow between mileposts 21 and 22. The Fort Payne Formation is well exposed in roadcuts west and east of the river.

A windy section of TN 52 crosses the northern end of King Mountain; look for exposures of blocky, gray Monteagle Limestone. Westbound travelers will enjoy the view across the Obey River valley.

The Fort Payne Formation is well exposed at and for about 1 mile east of Big Indian Creek. For the next 3 miles St. Louis and Warsaw Limestones underlie the highway, with a couple of small outcroppings. The Fort Payne Formation is again well exposed east of the bridge over the East Fork of the Obey River.

East of the East Fork bridge, TN 52 follows a tributary of the East Fork of the Obey River for a couple of miles before ascending the Cumberland Plateau's

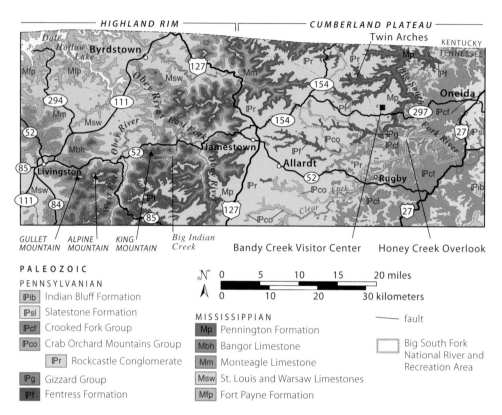

Geology along TN 52 between Livingston and Jamestown.

western escarpment. The Monteagle Limestone is exposed at the base of the plateau at an old quarry, and on both sides of the bridge over the river. Green and red sandstones, siltstones, and shales of the Pennington Formation are well exposed between mileposts 10 and 11.

Thinly bedded, organic-rich shales and sandstones of the Pennsylvanian-age Fentress Formation are present near the top of the plateau. For a closer look at this formation, stop at the first turnout with a picnic table on the westbound side of the road. The Fentress Formation is the northwestern equivalent of the Gizzard and Crab Orchard Mountains Groups, which are found on the southern Cumberland Plateau, but the Fentress contains more shale and coal. Trace fossils of horseshoe crabs and starfish are present in the top 65 feet of the formation. These animals lived in brackish waters in a tidally influenced zone along Tennessee's Pennsylvanian-age coast. The Fentress Formation is exposed mainly in larger drainages of the northwestern Cumberland Plateau and along its northwestern margin.

Jamestown has a rich history of family quarrying operations that span several generations. Tennessee Bluestone is the industry name given to a siltstone of the Fentress Formation that has a rich grayish-blue color. It is popular as a building stone and flagstone and is quarried at the surface throughout Fentress County. With a consistent thickness of 1 to 2 inches, it is relatively easy to extract slabs up to 10 feet long. Many historic buildings in and around downtown Jamestown are faced with or built from the Tennessee Bluestone, as well as the Rockcastle Conglomerate.

The Monteagle Limestone is exposed in an old quarry on TN 52 at Conaster Field Road. The Monteagle is typically quarried for construction aggregate material and for agricultural applications. (36.436939N, 84.979988W) —Chuck Sutherland photo

At the top of the hill on the west side of Jamestown, a rock shelter in the Fentress Formation provides a pleasant place to contemplate good crossbed exposures and have a picnic. The Rockcastle Conglomerate caps the plateau near here and underlies the road to Jamestown. (36.441046N, 84.957683W) —Chuck Sutherland photo

BIG SOUTH FORK NATIONAL RIVER AND RECREATION AREA

Big South Fork National River and Recreation Area encompasses 125,000 acres of the Cumberland Plateau in northern Tennessee and southern Kentucky. In Tennessee, the primary access points are via TN 154 and TN 297 from Jamestown and TN 297 from Oneida. TN 52 crosses the southernmost arm of the park near Rugby. The park's Bandy Creek Visitor Center lies just off TN 297 west of Leatherwood Ford.

The park is named for the north-flowing Big South Fork of the Cumberland River. The Big South Fork passes along the park's east side into southern Kentucky, where it joins the main Cumberland River. The river's gorge forms the heart of the park with its steep, rocky walls up to 600 feet high. Many sections of whitewater flow over and around large boulders that fall from the cliffs and into the river.

Mainly Pennsylvanian-age strata are exposed in the recreation area. The Rockcastle Conglomerate is typically found in middle elevations, while higher areas are capped with rocks of the Crooked Fork Group. Mississippian-age strata are present in larger drainages. The unconformity between Mississippian- and Pennsylvanian-age strata is well exposed near the Angel Falls Rapid Trailhead at Leatherwood Ford. Paleokarst and paleosols, or ancient soils, are well developed in limestones of the Pennington Formation, which were exposed above sea level

Large boulders of Pennsylvanian-age sandstone and conglomerate eroded from steep gorge walls accumulate in talus slopes along and in the river near the Honey Creek Overlook at Big South Fork National River and Recreation Area. Rocks of the Pennington Formation form the lower slopes, while the Fentress Formation forms the gorge walls. Rockcastle Conglomerate caps the plateau here, with strata of the Crooked Fork Group at higher elevations. —Michael Hicks photo

Tafoni, a honeycomb texture common in coarse-grained sedimentary rocks, is on display in the Pennsylvanian-age Rockcastle Conglomerate at Twin Arches. Tafoni form through the differential weathering of sand grains and cement and are common in many areas of the park. (36.543812N, 84.737796W) —Chuck Sutherland photo

for millions of years. Pennsylvanian-age river sediments were deposited on the erosional surface.

The land that makes up the recreation area was heavily exploited for timber and bituminous coal from the early 1900s through the end of World War II, when resources dwindled and many mining camps and towns were abandoned. You can still visit the old mining town of Blue Heron on the Kentucky side of the park. Black coal seams are visible along trails, and rounded cobbles of coal can be found in the recreation area's rivers and streams.

Resistant Pennsylvanian-age Rockcastle Conglomerate, a medium-to-coarse-grained quartz pebble conglomerate, is exposed about a half-mile east of Leatherwood Ford. Within and below the Rockcastle are shale beds, some of which contain coal seams, and sandstones that are not as well-cemented as the Rockcastle because of their higher clay content. The many interesting landforms of the recreation area, such as cliffs, arches, chimneys, rock shelters, and waterfalls, formed because of differential weathering. Units underlying the Rockcastle Conglomerate are eroded more easily, and this undermines the Pennsylvanian-age sandstone and conglomerate caprock. After a stream cuts through the caprock, the underlying unit readily erodes to form a variety of sculpted-looking geologic features.

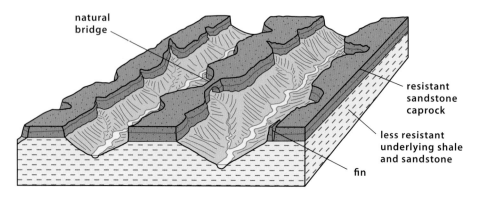

natural
bridge

resistant
sandstone
caprock

less resistant
underlying shale
and sandstone

fin

*Through physical and chemical weathering processes, joints within some of the sand-
stone strata of the recreation area are widened to create isolated and narrow "fins" or
"finger ridges" of sandstone. Over time, natural bridges and arches may develop from
these features as continuing geologic processes, such as freeze-thaw cycles, headward erosion, rockfalls, and groundwater movement, widen and deepen the joints
that are confined to the rock layers beneath relatively unbroken sandstone caprocks.
With continued erosion these bridges and arches may eventually collapse, leaving
behind pillars of rock called chimneys. Finger ridges, natural bridges, arches, and
chimneys are all exposed in the recreation area.* —Modified from Cleland, 1911

Rock shelters are alcoves and amphitheaters that formed in vertical rock faces
where the less resistant rock layers were eroded away, leaving a recess overlain
by more resistant rock. As water falls over a cliff and into a recessed cavity, or
flows through weakly cemented areas of rock, it undercuts softer layers; this is
how rock shelters form. Native Americans used many of the thousands of rock
shelters in the recreation area, and Paleo-Indians used them as early as 10,000
years ago. Rock shelters are found throughout the park.

Over time, rock shelters may become fins if headward erosion eats away at
rock from both sides. Over time headward erosion might cut through the fin,
creating a bridge or an arch. The sandstone that forms an arch or bridge is more
capable of holding its own weight than is the underlying rock, but it will eventually
collapse, sometimes leaving behind columns of rock. The Chimney Rocks, located
on Station Camp Road, are columns of relatively resistant, cross-bedded sandstone with an iron-rich sandstone cap. Chimney Rocks may be the remaining pillar
of a collapsed natural bridge, or they may have formed as erosion ate away at
surrounding rock, leaving a chunk of more resistant, iron-rich caprock protecting
the underlying, less resistant rock.

TN 68

DUCKTOWN—SWEETWATER
55 miles

Between Ducktown and Tellico Plains, TN 68 follows narrow, forested valleys through mountainous terrain. This 33-mile stretch of highway, dotted with small, rural communities, lies entirely within the Cherokee National Forest and the Blue Ridge physiographic province. Along the road are limited exposures of Neoproterozoic-age rocks of the Great Smoky and Walden Creek Groups, both part of the Ocoee Supergroup.

In 1843, a prospector panning for gold near Ducktown accidentally found native copper instead. Unhappy with his find, he left, but Ducktown became a major copper producer, and remained so through the late 1980s. Silver and gold were recovered as a by-product. See the US 64/US 74/TN 40: Cleveland—Ducktown road guide for information about the region's copper mining.

North of Ducktown, the highway leaves the Copper Basin and passes along and over complexly folded and faulted strata of the Great Smoky Group. Scattered outcrops of deeply weathered rocks are visible along the road, with sandy, red soils.

TN 68 crosses several metamorphic isograds, lines on a geologic map that delineate areas that experienced differing degrees of metamorphism, or metamorphic grade. Rocks with metamorphic minerals that formed at a lower temperature and pressure change across an isograd to rocks containing minerals formed at a higher temperature and pressure. Just south of the US 64/TN 68 junction at Ducktown, the area's highest metamorphic grade is marked by the occurrence of the mineral staurolite. At and north of Ducktown, staurolite disappears and garnet occurs in rocks of lower metamorphic grade. At

Staurolite is commonly found in the Ducktown area. Single crystals are typical, but the mineral sometimes forms 90-degree or 60-degree crosses in which two crystals grew together (largest crystal at right). The geologic term for this type of mineral growth is "penetration twins," but many rock hounds call them "fairy crosses." The presence of staurolite indicates regional-scale metamorphism and mountain building occurred.
—Allen R. Trotter photo

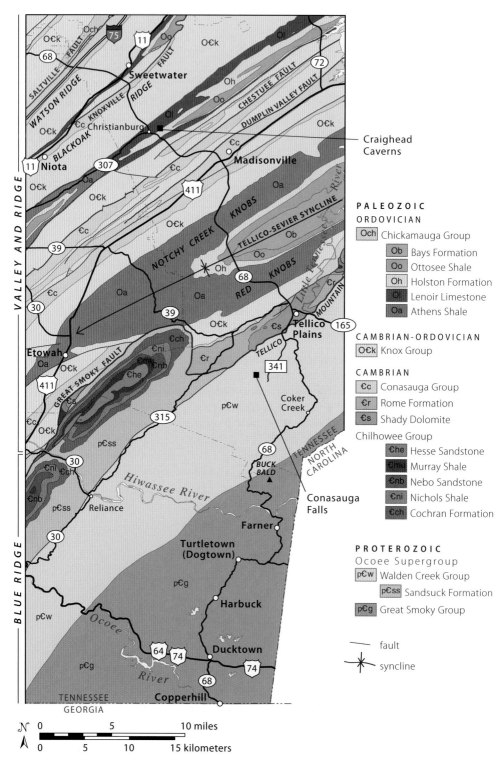

Geology along TN 68 between Ducktown and Sweetwater.

Harbuck, the road crosses another isograd, where garnet disappears and lower-grade biotite is present. The chlorite/biotite isograd crosses the southeast slope of Buck Bald about 3 miles (as the crow flies) northwest of Farner. The Buck Bald Overlook, which provides expansive views of surrounding area from more than 2,300 feet of elevation, is located about 3 miles southeast of TN 68 on Buck Bald Road/Old TN 68.

Among the many popular hiking trails in this part of the Tennessee Blue Ridge is the John Muir National Recreation Trail, a 21-mile-long-trail between the town of Reliance and the North Carolina state line. Part of the trail follows the north side of the Hiwassee River. Named for naturalist John Muir, the trail follows a section of the footpath he traveled during his walk from Kentucky to Florida. He wrote about his experience in his first memoir, *A Thousand-Mile Walk to the Gulf*, published in 1916. An excerpt of the memoir highlights his geologic wonder as well as the beauty of the Hiwassee River:

> My path all to-day led me along the leafy banks of the Hiwassee, a most impressive mountain river. Its channel is very rough, as it crosses the edges of upturned rock strata, some of them standing at right angles, or glancing off obliquely to right and left. Thus a multitude of short, resounding cataracts are produced, and the river is restrained from the headlong speed due to its volume and the inclination of its bed.
>
> All the larger streams of uncultivated countries are mysteriously charming and beautiful, whether flowing in mountains or through swamps and plains. Their channels are interestingly sculptured, far more so than the grandest architectural works of man. The finest of the forests are usually found along their banks, and in the multitude of falls and rapids the wilderness finds a voice. Such a river is the Hiwassee, with its surface broken to a thousand sparkling gems, and its forest walls vine-draped and flowery as Eden. And how fine the songs it sings!

Near Coker Creek, gold was more plentiful. The gold comes from the Neoproterozoic-age metasedimentary rocks of the Walden Creek Group of the Ocoee Supergroup. Hot, metallic-rich fluids circulated through the rock and deposited the gold, probably during Paleozoic time. Tennessee's gold was part of a narrow, 50-mile-long belt of gold deposits between Virginia and Alabama. It runs across Monroe, Blount, and Polk Counties near the North Carolina state line. Tennessee's gold rush was short-lived and lasted only between 1831 and 1854. Numerous shafts were sunk all over the mountains to explore quartz-bearing veins, but underground mining attempts were largely unsuccessful. Placer deposits in stream terrace sediments and alluvium were the most successful producers, but even these had a relatively low economic potential. Sadly, the discovery of gold in this belt played a role in the removal of the Cherokee Indians via the Trail of Tears.

Today, opportunities for guided recreational prospecting abound on TN 68 between Tellico Plains and Ducktown. Several local outfitters sell mining and panning supplies. For more information, visit the web page for the Coker Creek chapter of the Gold Prospectors Association of America. The Coker

Most of Coker Creek's gold is gold dust (in vial, top right corner), but reportedly nuggets up to 1.25 pounds have been found.
—Allen R. Trotter photo

Creek Heritage Group operates a small welcome center, museum, and gift shop located on TN 68 at Hot Water Road in Coker Creek.

North of Coker Creek, the road gains elevation for the next few miles. Deformed, gray thick-bedded sandstones and quartzites of the Walden Creek Group are well exposed along the top of Tellico Mountain just south of Tellico Plains. The road crosses the Great Smoky fault at the northwest foot of Tellico Mountain, where the Walden Creek Group was thrust over shales of the Cambrian-age Rome Formation and Shady Dolomite. The Great Smoky fault forms the geologic and topographic boundary between the Blue Ridge and Valley and Ridge physiographic provinces.

Between Tellico Plains and Sweetwater, TN 68 crosses the eastern Valley and Ridge physiographic province. Broad valleys and narrow ridges have been eroded into folded and faulted Cambrian- and Ordovician-age strata. Between Tellico Plains and Madisonville, TN 68 crosses the Tellico-Sevier syncline that formed during the Alleghanian orogeny on the Chestuee–Dumplin Valley thrust sheet. The syncline extends from Etowah northeastward to near DuPont. The Athens Shale, part of the Chickamauga Group, forms a distinctive ridge known as the Red Knobs near milepost 18 and another ridge, called the Notchy Creek Knobs, near milepost 21. These ridges are limbs of the northeast-plunging Tellico-Sevier syncline. Other Chickamauga Group units, including the Holston Formation, Ottosee Shale, and Bays Formation, are all present in the valley at the interior of the syncline.

Northwest of the Notchy Creek Knobs, the highway crosses upper Knox Group strata, which have deeply weathered into low rolling hills and ridges and

Strata belonging to the Walden Creek Group are exposed along TN 68 where it crosses Tellico Mountain. (35.324614N, 84.298192W) —Chuck Sutherland photo

Conasauga Creek flows over the Walden Creek Group at Conasauga Falls, about 3 miles south of TN 68. The falls are accessible via a short trail from Forest Road 341. (35.304310N, 84.331666W) —Alan Cressler photo

broad valleys. At Madisonville, the highway crosses the Dumplin Valley fault, along which Cambrian-age Maynardville Limestone, part of the Conasauga Group, was thrust over the Knox Group. About 1 mile northwest of Madisonville, the Chestuee thrust fault repeats the upper Knox Group section.

Lost Sea Adventure, a commercial cave that offers daily tours, is part of an extensive cave system called Craighead Caverns that is between Madisonville and Sweetwater. The cave developed in the southeast-dipping Holston Formation. Although there is a natural entrance, the official entry point is a tunnel that was excavated about 50 feet below the natural entrance. The main cave passage roughly parallels the northeast strike of the formation; it is 0.5 mile long, averages 100 feet wide, and is 30 feet high. A network of pits and fissures links a lower level with the main level. One pit is 90 feet deep. At the southwest end of the main level is a large lake that's 600 feet long, 200 feet wide, and up to 65 feet deep. The water level fluctuates seasonally. In addition to containing stalactites, stalagmites, columns, and flowstone draperies, fragments of a Pleistocene-age jaguar have been excavated from the lower level of the cave. The animal's tracks were also preserved in the soft mud of the cave's floor.

Folds and minor faults are visible in the Lenoir Limestone for 0.25 mile north of the caverns. At the TN 307 junction, TN 68 crosses the Middle Ordovician post-Knox unconformity. For millions of years no sedimentation occurred throughout eastern North America, and the surface of the Knox Group was heavily eroded before deposition resumed. Scattered outcrops of Lenoir Limestone mark the Ordovician-age Chickamauga Group section that overlies the unconformity. The lack of outcrops north of the Lenoir marks the presence of the older Knox Group.

The mostly hidden ponds on both sides of TN 68 north of the TN 307 junction are old, partially reclaimed barite pits of the Sweetwater district. Barite is the principal mineral ore of barium. The pits mark the general location of the contact between the Mascot Dolomite and Kingsport Formation, both part of

In the New Room at Lost Sea Adventure are hundreds of anthodites, or cave flowers, in which clusters of tubular calcite and aragonite needles radiate from a central point.
—Lost Sea photo

the Knox Group. Test mining and exploration for fluorspar also occurred in the Sweetwater district, but the area was a better barite producer due to residual concentrations in soils. Barite has a relatively high specific gravity, which makes it a useful additive in drilling muds.

About 2.5 miles north of the pits, the highway passes through a gap on Blackoak Ridge and descends into Sweetwater Valley. The rocks holding up the ridge are dolostones of the Copper Ridge Dolomite, also part of the Knox Group. Conasauga Group is present along the ridge's northwestern base. The road crosses the Knoxville fault and enters the valley of Sweetwater Creek near the junction with US 11. North of the junction, TN 68 gently gains elevation toward I-75 while crossing deeply weathered and poorly exposed Knox Group carbonates. Copper Ridge Dolomite is exposed at the crest of Watson Ridge. The northwest slope of the ridge is composes of Conasauga Group shale and limestone that overrode Knox Group rocks along the Saltville fault just northwest of I-75.

TN 165 (CHEROHALA SKYWAY)
Tellico Plains—North Carolina State Line
23 miles

TN 165, which connects Tellico Plains and Robbinsville, North Carolina, is nicknamed the Cherohala Skyway for the combination of the Cherokee and Nantahala National Forests through which the road passes. Most of the road follows the high ridges of the Unicoi Mountains, a subrange of the Tennessee Blue Ridge, often at more than 5,000 feet. The Cherohala Skyway is a narrow, two-lane national scenic byway with many turnouts and overlooks, several of which are conveniently outfitted with picnic tables. The high elevation makes for a lovely drive during summer months when temperatures can be up to 20 degrees cooler than in the Valley and Ridge. For information on local history, and highway and weather conditions, visit the Cherohala Skyway Visitor Center in Tellico Plains, located about 0.25 mile east of the TN 68 junction on the north side of the road.

Tellico Plains is built on the floodplain of the Tellico River at the eastern margin of the Valley and Ridge physiographic province. Here the elevation is close to 900 feet. At the junction with TN 360, the highway crosses the Great Smoky fault, along which Neoproterozoic-age Walden Creek Group strata of the Blue Ridge were thrust over the Cambrian-age Rome Formation, Shady Dolomite, and other younger, Paleozoic-age strata of the Valley and Ridge.

East of the TN 360 junction, TN 165 follows the narrow gorge of the Tellico River for about 4 miles. The river is famous for trout fishing and whitewater. Brown, layered metasedimentary rocks of the Walden Creek Group are well exposed along the road just east of the bridge. Layers of deformed metasandstone form cascades in the Tellico River.

The River Road offers a worthwhile side trip to Bald River Falls. The road leads up the steep and narrow gorge of the Tellico River. Strata of the Walden

Creek and Great Smoky Groups are exposed throughout the gorge. At the falls, Bald River, a major tributary to the Tellico River, spills 100 feet over strata of the Great Smoky Group. River Road also connects with TN 165 via Turkey Creek Road.

At the junction with River Road, Cherohala Skyway leaves the Tellico River gorge and climbs to nearly 5,000 feet of elevation by the time it reaches the North Carolina state line. From the Caney Branch/Oosterneck Creek Overlook you can look south across Caney Branch and the Tellico River gorge. The Tennessee–North Carolina state line runs along the high ridge on the horizon.

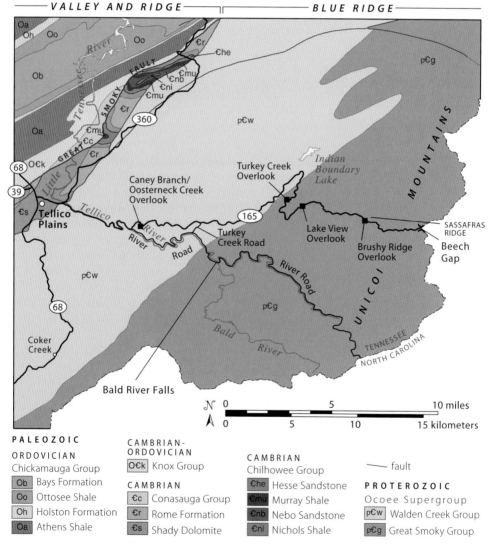

Geology along TN 165 between Tellico Plains and the North Carolina state line.

PALEOZOIC

ORDOVICIAN
Chickamauga Group

	Bays Formation
Ob	Bays Formation
Oo	Ottosee Shale
Oh	Holston Formation
Oa	Athens Shale

CAMBRIAN-ORDOVICIAN
| OЄk | Knox Group |

CAMBRIAN
Єc	Conasauga Group
Єr	Rome Formation
Єs	Shady Dolomite

CAMBRIAN
Chilhowee Group
Єhe	Hesse Sandstone
Єmu	Murray Shale
Єnb	Nebo Sandstone
Єni	Nichols Shale

—— fault

PROTEROZOIC
Ocoee Supergroup
| pЄw | Walden Creek Group |
| pЄg | Great Smoky Group |

The contact between the Walden Creek and Great Smoky Groups is east of the Indian Boundary Lake turnoff, and good exposures of Great Smoky Group strata continue to the state line. The Turkey Creek Overlook offers expansive views southwestward, essentially over the route of TN 165 toward Tellico Plains. The rolling hills of the Valley and Ridge physiographic province are visible on clear days. The Lake View Overlook offers a view northward across the western Citico Creek Wilderness toward Indian Boundary Lake. The Little Tennessee River and Valley and Ridge lie in the distance.

Between milepost 21 and the state line, the Cherohala Skyway winds along the narrow highway. Several overlooks that provide expansive views across the southern Blue Ridge Mountains. Brushy Ridge Overlook lies on Sassafras Ridge and faces southward, offering a view across the upper Tellico River watershed. The Tellico River rises in the high mountains along the Tennessee–North Carolina border just a few miles to the southeast. Two parking areas on the north side of the road east of the Charles Hall Bridge offer nice views and access to trailheads.

At Beech Gap, Cherohala Skyway enters North Carolina. For about 7 miles eastward, the highway winds amongst several high peaks at about 5,000 feet of elevation before descending into the valley of Santeetlah Lake.

Rocks of the Great Smoky Group exposed about 1 mile east of Lake View Overlook. (35.358538N, 84.103204W)
—Marcy Davis photo

Fancher Falls plummets 80 feet over the Mississippian-age Fort Payne Formation. Waterfalls are common in Middle Tennessee, especially along the steep transition between the resistant rocks that cap the Highland Rim and the more easily eroded limestones of the Central Basin. —Chuck Sutherland photo

MIDDLE TENNESSEE
Interior Low Plateaus

Middle Tennessee, the area between the western edge of the Cumberland Plateau and the Tennessee River, is topographically transitional between the flatlands of West Tennessee and mountainous East Tennessee. Over the last 300 million years, Middle Tennessee rivers and their ancient predecessors have eroded through a broad structural upwarp known as the Nashville Dome. The result of this erosion is the oval-shaped depression called the Central (or Nashville) Basin that lies in the middle of the state. A prominent plateau called the Highland Rim encircles the basin about 500 feet above the basin floor. Some of the best rock exposures of Middle Tennessee's Ordovician-to-Mississippian-age marine carbonates and shales are in the topographical transitional areas between the highly dissected Central Basin and the relatively flat plateaus of the Highland Rim. Waterfalls, caves, springs, and sinkholes are well developed in carbonates, especially on the eastern Highland Rim, where water flowing off the Cumberland Plateau exacerbates dissolution.

The Central (Nashville) Basin

The Central Basin, an oval-shaped depression 100 miles long and 60 miles wide, is centered southeast of Nashville at Murfreesboro. The basin sits about 500 feet below the elevation of the surrounding Highland Rim, so you can easily see the basin as you approach it on various roads. Its mostly gently rolling to hilly terrain is rich in grasslands and agriculture. The Central Basin is subdivided into an inner and outer basin. The division of these two areas roughly corresponds to the contact between the Ordovician-age Hermitage Formation (outer basin), part of the Nashville Group, and the Carters Limestone (inner basin), part of the older Stones River Group. The inner basin is comparatively flat, has thinner soils, and contains more sinkholes; limestones of the outer basin contain more caves.

Although a topographic lowland today, the Central Basin formed on the Nashville Dome; through differential erosion the dome was reduced, producing a case of inverted topography. The Nashville Dome, part of a structurally controlled high area, was superimposed on a broad regional uplift called the Cincinnati Arch. The Nashville Dome formed between the Ordovician Period and the Cenozoic Era, with most uplift occurring during the Alleghanian orogeny in late Paleozoic time. As different continental fragments interacted with North America's east coast, the direction of crustal stresses changed, too. Eastern mountain building caused the orientation of the Nashville Dome to shift over time, parallel to structures that formed in East Tennessee.

STRATIGRAPHIC COLUMN FOR MIDDLE TENNESSEE

EON	ERA	PERIOD / EPOCH	GROUP	FORMATION	DESCRIPTION	DEPOSITIONAL ENVIRONMENT
PHANEROZOIC	CEN. (CENOZOIC)	QUATERNARY / HOLOCENE		alluvial and colluvial deposits	silt, clay, sand, conglomerate	sediments deposited along rivers and streams
PHANEROZOIC	MESOZOIC	CRETACEOUS		Eutaw Formation	glauconitic sand, clay	shallow and nearshore marine; exposed in southwest Middle Tennessee
				Tuscaloosa Formation	chert gravel, silt, sand	eastward-flowing streams and shallow marine environments; deposition occurred on paleokarst surface of the western Highland Rim
PHANEROZOIC	PALEOZOIC	MISSISSIPPIAN		Ste. Genevieve Limestone / St. Louis Limestone / Warsaw Limestone / Fort Payne Formation / Maury Formation	chert, silicastone, limestone, shale	shallow marine shelf with a carbonate ramp or platform that persisted throughout the Mississippian Period
				Chattanooga Shale	black shale	shallow sea, oxygen-poor environment, highly organic
		DEVONIAN		Pegram Formation	limestone, sandstone, chert	mixed carbonate and clastic shelf, nearshore, sand bar
		SILURIAN	Wayne Group	Dixon Formation / Lego Limestone / Waldron Shale / Laurel Limestone / Osgood Formation	limestone, shale	mixed carbonate and clastic shelf; Waldron Shale is green and highly fossiliferous
				Brassfield Limestone	limestone, shale	shallow carbonate shelf, nearshore, fossiliferous
		ORDOVICIAN		Sequatchie Formation / Fernvale Member	limestone, shale, siltstone	tidal flats, shallow marine, fossiliferous; Fernvale Member was mined for iron
				Leipers-Catheys Formation	limestone	shallow carbonate shelf, fossiliferous
			Nashville Group	Bigby-Cannon Limestone / Dove-Colored Member	limestone, sandstone	beach, nearshore, lagoon, fossiliferous, mined for phosphate
				Hermitage Formation	limestone, sandstone, siltstone, shale	nearshore, shelf, fossiliferous
			Stones River Group	Carters Limestone / Lebanon Limestone / Ridley Limestone / Pierce Limestone / Murfreesboro Limestone	limestone, shale	shallow carbonate shelf, fossiliferous; Carters Limestone contains layers of bentonite that were once volcanic ash generated by the Taconic Orogeny and zinc mineralization

Generalized stratigraphic section of Middle Tennessee. —Compiled from various sources

Oceans covered Middle Tennessee during most of the Paleozoic Era. Middle Tennessee's sedimentary layers thickened and dipped gently away from the dome in the direction of deeper marine areas. Periodic sea level drop and tectonic uplift occasionally exposed the dome to erosion, sometimes for millions of years. Such depositional gaps are preserved in Middle Tennessee's geologic record as disconformities, erosional surfaces with flat-lying sedimentary rocks both above and below.

At the end of the Paleozoic Era, nearly 14,000 feet of strata covered basement rocks across Middle Tennessee, but the area has been mostly above sea level since then, subject to erosion. Most Pennsylvanian-age layers had been eroded by the end of the Cretaceous Period. By about 6 million years ago, younger Mississippian-age units had been almost completely eroded from Middle Tennessee, and the Fort Payne Formation had been eroded through at the dome crest. At least 7,500 feet of Mississippian and younger strata have been completely removed from the basin by erosion. Less resistant and more soluble underlying limestone layers were exposed once the dome was breached, further enhancing the development of the Central Basin. The current landscape developed fully during the end of the Neogene Period and into the Quaternary Period.

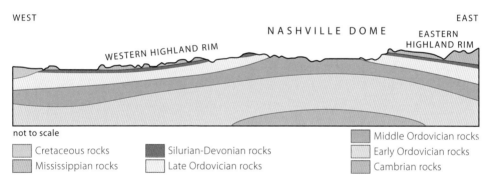

WEST EAST

NASHVILLE DOME

WESTERN HIGHLAND RIM EASTERN HIGHLAND RIM

not to scale

Cretaceous rocks

Mississippian rocks

Silurian-Devonian rocks

Late Ordovician rocks

Middle Ordovician rocks

Early Ordovician rocks

Cambrian rocks

This schematic cross section shows Middle Tennessee's topography and the underlying structure of the Nashville Dome. Paleozoic units were once continuous across Middle Tennessee. —Modified from Lloyd and Lyke, 1995

Ordovician-age rocks of the Stones River and Nashville Groups, and the Leipers-Catheys Formation, are well exposed in the Central Basin. These units are made up of relatively pure limestones that contain thin interbeds of shale. The inner part of the Central Basin, the area surrounding Murfreesboro, includes the flattest terrain and oldest exposed units of the Stones River Group. Ages of exposed units become younger away from the inner basin. Extensive stream incision has exposed Ordovician-to-Devonian-age carbonates and shales in steep-sided valleys along the pronounced erosional escarpment between the Central Basin and Highland Rim, except along the southern edge where erosional remnants of the Highland Rim create a less linear boundary.

MIDDLE TENNESSEE: INTERIOR LOW PLATEAUS

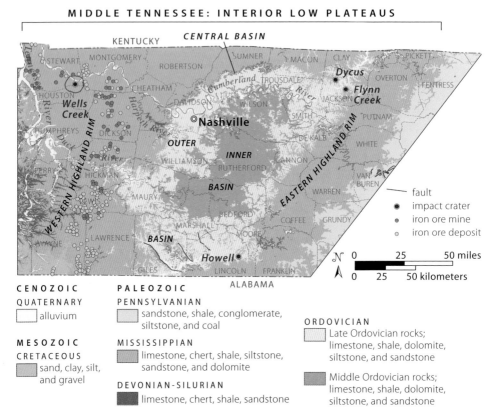

The iron belt includes areas of Wayne, Lawrence, Lewis, Hickman, Dickson, Montgomery, and Stewart Counties and is arcuate; it roughly parallels the outline of the Mississippi Embayment. Two proven impact sites, the Wells Creek and Flynn Creek structures, and two possible impact sites, the Dycus and Howell structures, are preserved in Middle Tennessee.

The Highland Rim

The Highland Rim, which encircles the Central Basin, is a tableland standing intermediate in elevation between the higher Cumberland Plateau and the lower Central Basin. Some undulating plains and hills reflect underlying karst development in the Mississippian-age carbonates that cap the nearly 13,000 square miles of the Highland Rim. The strata dip imperceptibly, only about a quarter of a degree, away from the Central Basin in all directions. Outcrop exposures are limited due to deep weathering and thick, residual cherty soil derived from the rocks.

Mississippian-age units that cap the Highland Rim are rich in chert, a micro-crystalline quartz. Also called flint, chert is commonly found as layers and in nodules in Middle Tennessee strata, especially in that of Mississippian age. Chert's hardness and durability make it resistant to weathering and erosion.

Karst is well developed along the eastern Highland Rim where streams have cut down through the Cumberland Plateau. This region of Tennessee is referred to locally as "sinkhole alley" for the high density of karst features. Here, a stream disappears underground through a swallet in Mississippian-age limestone at Spring Creek in Overton County. —Chuck Sutherland photo

Chert is produced several ways, one of which is through biological means. Some sponges build structures of microscopic silica called spicules. Similarly, diatoms, a type of unicellular algae, form cell walls, called frustules, from silica. Over time, spicules and frustules can accumulate in great numbers on the seafloor and form chert beds or nodules once they are transformed into stone. Chert may also form chemically, precipitated directly from silica-rich seawater. In this process, which usually occurs in deep, cold waters, a silica gel forms on the seafloor. Fine-grained volcanic ash or silica-rich dust particles that fall into shallow waters can also become chert. They are transported to deeper parts of the sea, where they dissolve and are redeposited on the seafloor as silica-rich calcareous ooze that later recrystallizes as chert. Replacement processes can also form chert. Fluids made silica rich by volcanic ash, for example, can percolate through rock layers, filling in pore spaces or replacing other material with chert. When silica-rich fluid replaces wood with silica, for example, chert forms as petrified wood. Beds of chert nodules can form when silica-rich carbonates weather, dissolving the carbonate and concentrating the silica in pores and voids.

Two parallel lines of caves along the eastern Highland Rim correspond to the boundaries between the rim and Cumberland Plateau and the rim and

Chert is a very hard sedimentary rock made almost entirely of microcrystalline quartz that comes in a variety of colors. It is easy to recognize by the smooth, arcuate shapes that develop on broken surfaces, a characteristic known as conchoidal fracture. Across the state, chert was the preferred material for knapping by Native Americans. It is still used as road metal in some areas.
—Ryan Parish photo

Central Basin. Both the Cumberland Plateau and the Highland Rim are capped by resistant rocks underlain by more soluble limestone. Caves develop where high-energy waterfalls and streams cascade up to several hundred feet off the plateau and rim and undercut more resistant units. Most caves have developed in the Bangor, Monteagle, and St. Louis Limestones at the boundary between the Cumberland Plateau and the eastern Highland Rim. Sinkhole plains have developed on the Highland Rim in the Mississippian-age Ste. Genevieve and St. Louis Limestones where stream runoff and rain increase dissolution. Many local streams disappear underground into sinkholes and emerge elsewhere as springs.

Together, these processes erode the western edge of the Cumberland Plateau while effectively expanding the eastern side of the Highland Rim by way of escarpment retreat. Similar processes occur between the entire Highland Rim and the Central Basin; however, the effects are less pronounced due to the smaller amount of elevation change between the regions. Rivers spilling over the Highland Rim into the basin once powered numerous mills, including Falls, Evins, and Spencer Mills.

Many caves underlying the eastern Highland Rim, as well as many areas of East Tennessee, contain nitrate-bearing minerals such as nitrocalcite or, to a lesser extent, nitromagnesite. These minerals were mined from cave floors and walls and placed into hoppers with wood ash to make niter, a potassium nitrate known as saltpeter. Water was percolated through the mixture, and the extract was drawn off and heated in kettles, which evaporated the water and left niter residue. The niter was collected and mixed at nearby powder mills with other materials to make black powder. Niter was mined from before the Revolutionary War to after the Civil War. During the Civil War, black powder made from Tennessee cave earth was a major munition source for the Confederacy, and the powder mills were a major target of the Union.

Western Iron Belt

Tennessee's western iron belt is a 10-mile-wide zone of iron-rich rock that spans from Kentucky to Alabama on the western Highland Rim. Karst is well developed in Mississippian-age limestones in the iron belt, mainly of the Warsaw and St. Louis Limestones, both of which contain an abundance of the mineral limonite, a relatively soft, reddish-brown iron oxide mineral. This limonite, which was mined from small, shallow deposits, supplied Middle Tennessee's ironworks during the nineteenth century.

Middle Tennessee's first ironworks were in Dickson County at Cumberland Furnace, which was operated by Nashville founder James Robertson starting in 1796. By 1835, twenty-seven smelting furnaces operated on the western Highland Rim, many of which supplied cannonballs during the Civil War. In the

The Great Western Iron Furnace, located on the Trace in the Land Between the Lakes National Recreation Area, was built in the 1850s. Made from local limestone, the furnace smelted brown iron ore, primarily from the mineral limonite that was dug from local shallow pits. (36.640655N, 87.975572W) —Chuck Sutherland photo

early 1900s Middle Tennessee's iron industry crashed due to an increasing lack of furnace fuel; local trees had been harvested too quickly and weren't replanted. Also during this time, high-grade iron ore discovered in the Lake Superior region became more desirable than the brown ore of the western Highland Rim, which wasn't good for making steel due to sulfur and phosphorous impurities. Remains of furnaces, forges, pits, and associated mills are open to the public over much of the western Highland Rim, including at Montgomery Bell State Park, Cumberland Furnace, and Land Between the Lakes National Recreation Area. Several town names, such as Iron City, reflect Middle Tennessee's iron legacy.

Highland Rim iron ore was often mined from puddingstone, a conglomerate of mainly angular chert pebbles and cobbles cemented together with the iron oxide mineral limonite. The rock was named for its resemblance to plum pudding. —Chuck Sutherland photo

The shape of the iron belt and the limited nature of its presence suggest the iron developed along an ancient shoreline. In this scenario, first karst developed between the Mississippian and Cretaceous Periods as rocks were exposed to erosion following the Alleghanian orogeny. By Late Cretaceous time nearly all Mississippian-age strata and younger Pennsylvanian-age rocks had been removed from Middle Tennessee. As Late Cretaceous seas advanced into Tennessee, iron-rich clay and sand were deposited across the karstic area that is now the western Highland Rim. These sediments contained the mineral glauconite, an iron-rich mineral in the mica group. During Tertiary time, Cretaceous-age strata were exposed as sea level fell and the shoreline retreated westward. Fluids percolating through these strata became iron rich before flowing through the underlying limestone, where the iron was precipitated as the mineral limonite in the karst networks of the Mississippian-age St. Louis and Warsaw Limestones. The limonite cemented together angular fragments of chert and other karst rubble in these units.

Impact Craters

Several unusual circular features are preserved on the Highland Rim of Middle Tennessee. Geoscientists are now certain that at least two, the Wells Creek and Flynn Creek structures, are impact craters, locales of fractured rock where cosmic debris, such as an asteroid or comet, struck the Earth. Such space detritus, known generically as impactors, comes in a variety of shapes and sizes. They can weigh hundreds of metric tons and can strike the Earth at speeds of up to several miles per second. Two other possible impact sites, the Dycus and Howell structures, are also preserved in Middle Tennessee.

Geologists have identified several periods in Earth history when life was significantly altered or even stamped out by the effects of a major impact. Dinosaurs, for example, became extinct following a large impact in the Gulf of Mexico at the end of the Cretaceous Period. Dust and ejecta from the impact, now preserved in a thin layer in rocks all over the world, severely changed global climate and the ecosystems that supported dinosaurs. A large impact today would likely have cataclysmic consequences for life on Earth as we know it. Scientists speculate that a prolonged, multiyear period of cold and darkness, decimating plants, animals, and the entire food chain, could follow such an impact.

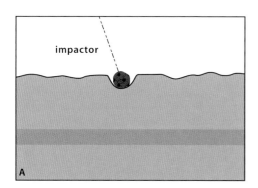
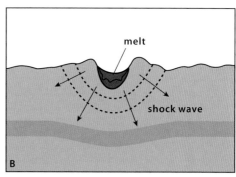
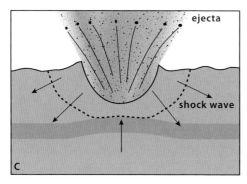
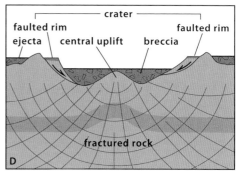

Both the Wells Creek and Flynn Creek structures contain a central uplift with deformed strata, a depression containing breccia that encircles the central uplift, and an outer faulted rim. —Adapted from Willsey, 2017

When a large comet or asteroid strikes Earth's surface, it generates an essentially instantaneous explosive event that creates a crater. Shock waves compress surrounding rock on impact, moving it downward and outward. The impactor is also highly compressed and commonly vaporizes, along with some surface rock, and other rocks may melt. Shattered rock debris is thrown from the impact area and settles around the impact zone as breccia, a rock composed of angular fragments fused together. Large impact structures may have a raised rim, radial faults, or a series of concentric, normal faults around the crater. Strata may slump and collapse in and around the crater in response to gravity and faulting. Large craters typically feature a central uplift of rock that rebounded after the impact, finding a new position above its original position on the crater floor.

Vegetation, erosion, burial, and deformation modify ancient craters, often complicating their recognition and identification. Suspected depressions must be carefully mapped to determine their general shape and size. Geologists also look for evidence of faulting, brecciation, and products of shock-induced changes in rock, including shatter cones; high-pressure quartz minerals, such as coesite and stishovite; shock lamellae, planar features that develop in some

Deformed layers of the Ordovician-age Knox Group mark the Wells Creek structure's central uplift near Erin. Such outcrops are anomalous in Middle Tennessee, where most strata are nearly horizontal. These strata are more than 2,000 feet above their original stratigraphic level as the result of an impact. —Jana Ruth Ford photo

Shatter cones have a telltale conical shape and form where an impactor subjected rocks to great pressure. The orientation of shatter cones from Wells Creek suggests that a meteor pierced the Highland Rim to nearly 2,000 feet of depth before exploding. Shatter cones in dolomite of the Knox Group are found in the center of the structure. The rocks are pictured here following a snowstorm. —Andrew F. Tischler photo

mineral grains; and impact melt glass. Without at least some of these shock features, a structure suspected to be of impact origin cannot be positively classified as such.

Tennessee's largest impact structure, the Wells Creek structure, is located southwest of Clarksville at the confluence of Wells Creek and the Cumberland River near Erin. The center of the impact crater, currently used largely for farming, pastureland, and quarrying, is highly dissected. It doesn't look much like an impact crater to the casual observer, but geologists determined that a 20-million-ton stony meteor, about 200 to 1,000 feet in diameter and traveling up to 90,000 miles per hour, created the circular, about 10-mile-wide basin. The shock from impact forced rocks downward and outward. Two concentric normal faults ring the crater; the outermost ring passes through Erin 4 miles from the crater center. Strata of the Knox Group were originally about 2,500 feet below the crater floor but were uplifted to about 2,000 feet above the crater floor. Much of this material has since been eroded, so the crater floor now has a total relief of about only 350 feet.

The age of the Wells Creek structure is difficult to determine. The Mississippian Period is the age of the youngest rock deformed by the impact. Gravels of the Cretaceous-age Tuscaloosa Formation were deposited atop the western Highland Rim and the deformed structure 75 million years ago. Therefore, the Wells Creek impact is between 325 and 75 million years old.

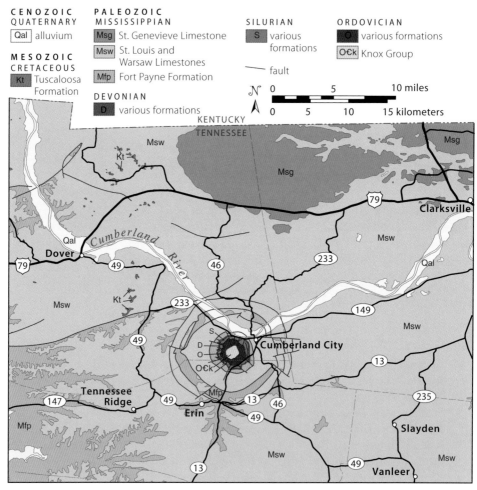

Impact craters may be difficult to see in aerial or satellite photography due to erosion and vegetation, so scientists must look to the geology on the ground to determine if an impact occurred. The Wells Creek structure, located 70 miles northwest of Nashville, forms a diagnostic geologic bull's-eye on the Tennessee state geologic map. The crater is approximately 10 miles in diameter. Rock layers are broken and offset along radial and concentric faults that resulted from the impact. Deformed dolomite of the Ordovician-age Knox Group marks the Wells Creek structure's central uplift.

ROAD GUIDES IN MIDDLE TENNESSEE

I-24
CLARKSVILLE—NASHVILLE
50 miles

Interstate 24 runs northwest-southeast across Middle Tennessee. Outcrops are relatively scarce between the Kentucky state line and Nashville, except in transitional areas between the Highland Rim and Central Basin, and in urban settings along the main highways where there are roadcuts.

I-24 crosses the Mississippian-age Ste. Genevieve Limestone between the Kentucky state line and Rossview Road at exit 8. This limestone once covered Tennessee but is now only exposed over a relatively small area of northern Middle Tennessee between the Fort Campbell Military Reservation and Springfield. The Ste. Genevieve Limestone is massive and gray, only 70 feet thick, and very fossiliferous, with horn and colonial corals, crinoids, and brachiopods. It was deposited at the same time as the Monteagle Limestone but farther west in deeper water.

Ooids help distinguish the Ste. Genevieve Limestone from other limestones. Ooids are sand-sized, oval grains most commonly made of layers of calcium carbonate that accrete around something that serves as a nucleus, such as a sand grain or shell fragment. They form on the shallow tropical seafloor where waves and currents are strong enough to continuously move the nuclei, and they grow larger as carbonate material either physically accretes to them or precipitates directly from the water. The ooids in the Ste. Genevieve Limestone nucleated around shell fragments of different shapes and sizes, which gives them round to elongate shapes.

The highway crosses the Red River near milepost 9. Its confluence with the Cumberland River is on the north side of Clarksville. The Red River is named for the red color of the surrounding soils that are common throughout Middle and East Tennessee where carbonates are at the surface.

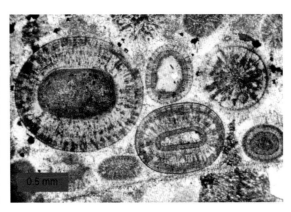

Ooids nucleate around sand grains or shell fragments and grow as mineral layers are added concentrically as they roll along the ocean floor. The internal structure of the ooids is visible in thin section and under magnification. —Mark A. Wilson photo

0.5 mm

Ooids are a distinguishing feature of the Ste. Genevieve Limestone and look similar to these modern ooids from Joulter Cays in the Bahamas. These formed in a relatively warm, shallow, and high-energy beach environment. —Mark A. Wilson photo

0.50 mm

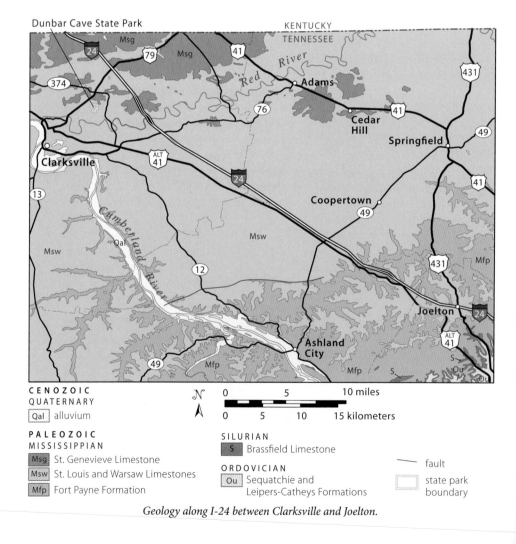

Dunbar Cave State Park

CENOZOIC
QUATERNARY
Qal alluvium

PALEOZOIC
MISSISSIPPIAN
Msg St. Genevieve Limestone
Msw St. Louis and Warsaw Limestones
Mfp Fort Payne Formation

N

0   5   10 miles
0   5   10   15 kilometers

SILURIAN
S Brassfield Limestone

ORDOVICIAN
Ou Sequatchie and
     Leipers-Catheys Formations

— fault

state park
boundary

Geology along I-24 between Clarksville and Joelton.

Karst topography is well developed in and near Clarksville because the St. Louis and Warsaw Limestones underlie the city. Many karst features can be seen in local parks, including Dunbar Cave State Park. New karst features can form rather quickly and without much warning. Local roads are often closed due to sinkhole mitigation. In May 2014, a 40-foot sinkhole opened up inside Governors Stadium on the campus of Austin Peay State University in Clarksville, swallowing one corner of an end zone on the football field. Remediation efforts have since stabilized the sinkhole, and there was no damage to the stadium.

Residual cherty soils weathered from the St. Louis and Warsaw Limestones are exposed in the surrounding farmland and at new construction sites between Clarksville and Joelton. The Warsaw Limestone is exposed in drainages, whereas the St. Louis Limestone forms the higher areas. The two units can look so similar that they are often mapped together; however, there are some notable differences. On fresh surfaces, the Warsaw Limestone is dark steel-blue in color, is coarse-grained, and contains more sand than most of the Mississippian-age carbonates. This massively bedded limestone is about 130 feet thick, is cross-bedded, and contains bryozoans and crinoids. Crinoids are made of a harder material than the surrounding matrix, so they often stand out from the rock. The Warsaw Limestone is also silica rich; in places

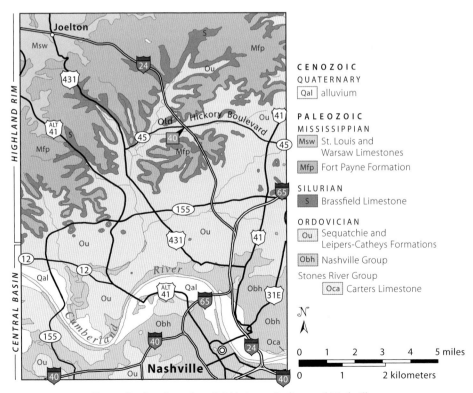

Generalized geology along I-24 between Joelton and Nashville.

DUNBAR CAVE STATE PARK

Dunbar Cave, located off exit 8 near Clarksville, formed about 2 million years ago as surface water percolated downward through northwest-southeast-trending joints into the Mississippian-age St. Louis Limestone. The joints created a pathway by which water could move into and through the rock and dissolve it along bedding planes.

The park is located within an abandoned meander loop in the Red River, a tributary to the Cumberland River. The path to the cave mouth from the visitor center follows the abandoned channel north of Swan Lake. The Red River flowed through here during the Pleistocene Epoch but is now located about 1 mile south of the park.

The first humans known to have used the cave are thought to have lived in Middle Tennessee from about AD 800 to AD 1400. They left more than thirty petroglyphs, pictographs, and mud glyphs on the cave walls. The cave may have been a sacred place or may have provided shelter to seasonal hunters during times of inclement weather. The cave entrance became a popular hot-weather music venue in the early twentieth century due to the cool temperatures surrounding the entrance. When air conditioning became commonplace in the 1950s, Dunbar Cave became less popular as a venue. The park offers ranger-guided cave tours May through August, and interpretive programs occur year-round.

During the early-to-mid-1900s, summertime community events, such as concerts and dances, were held at the mouth of Dunbar Cave, where pleasantly cool, always-58-degree-Fahrenheit air comes to the surface. The Dunbar Cave system has more than 8 miles of known passageways that developed in flat-lying, Mississippian-age St. Louis Limestone.
—Alan Cressler photo

where carbonate material has been dissolved or replaced by silica, masses of fossiliferous chert remain in a dark-red residuum of sandy clay. The St. Louis Limestone is a fine-to-medium-grained, thin-to-thick-bedded fossiliferous limestone. This brown-gray rock contains dolomite and chert and may be up to 150 feet thick.

The St. Louis Limestone contains crinoids, bryozoans, corals, and foraminifera. Where heavily weathered, the unit is often covered by a thick blanket of dark-red, residual sandy clay and chert that often contain molds of crinoids and bryozoans. The St. Louis Limestone also contains "cannonballs," rounded lumps of chert that may be up to several inches across. Karst topography is well developed in areas where the St. Louis Limestone is at the surface, particularly on the northern part of the western Highland Rim near Clarksville. The underlying Warsaw Limestone resembles the St. Louis Limestone, but it's a more-coarse-grained, thickly bedded, sandy limestone that commonly contains crossbeds.

South of Joelton, the landscape becomes hillier along the dissected edge of the Highland Rim. The Mississippian-age Fort Payne Formation is exposed in the Sycamore Creek drainage near milepost 28. The Mississippian-age Warsaw Limestone underlies the highway at Joelton.

The terrain is highly dissected along the edge of the Highland Rim for several miles south of Joelton. A noticeable change in elevation of about 300 feet occurs along the narrow valley of Claylick Creek as it crosses from the Mississippian-age strata of the western Highland Rim to the Ordovician-age strata of the Central Basin. Yellowish-gray, thick-bedded Fort Payne Formation, the most prominent cliff-forming unit of the Highland Rim, is well exposed at the top of the grade. The Fort Payne Formation consists of calcareous and dolomitic siltstone with some shale. Lenses, beds, and blebs of dense chert make the unit highly resistant to erosion. In some areas, most of the original carbonate material has been dissolved from the Fort Payne Formation so that only chert and brownish residual soils remain. Consequently, many geologists refer to the Fort Payne Formation as silicastone. Cherty soils (called Dellrose soils) form at the foot of areas capped with this formation, and they tend to move slowly, or creep, downslope under the forces of gravity. The only visible evidence of this slow type of soil movement is the tilting of trees, light posts, and fences. When water saturated, however, such as after a large storm, these soils may move quickly and cause a sudden slope failure in which a large accumulation of material moves downslope at once, an event that can be catastrophic for roads, utilities, and buildings.

The green Maury Formation is only a few feet thick and separates the Fort Payne Formation from the underlying Chattanooga Shale. Because it is so thin, the Maury is mapped as part of the Fort Payne Formation. (The Chattanooga Shale is also quite thin in parts of Middle Tennessee, so sometimes it is also mapped with the Fort Payne Formation.) Elongate phosphate nodules are common in the base of the Maury Formation along the front of the western Highland Rim. These nodules may be up to 3 feet long and are typically brownish in color in contrast to the green shale and mudstone of the formation itself.

North and south of Old Hickory Boulevard (exit 40), I-24 crosses eroded spurs of the western Highland Rim. Many such vestiges remain near the edges of the Central Basin, so the landscape north and west of downtown Nashville is quite hilly. Look for the Maury Formation underlying the Fort Payne Formation that caps the hills. The black Chattanooga Shale, which typically underlies the Maury Formation, is absent here, probably because this area was above sea level when the Chattanooga Shale was being deposited.

The Silurian-age Brassfield Limestone underlies the Maury Formation here. It is the oldest Silurian-age unit in Middle Tennessee and was deposited at the same time as East Tennessee's Rockwood Formation. The Brassfield Limestone once extended across Middle Tennessee but, along with other Silurian units, has been eroded between eastern Davidson County and Sequatchie Valley. The gray limestone is up to 40 feet thick and composed of thin to medium beds; it contains many coral species as well as other marine invertebrates.

The Brassfield Limestone overlies green-gray shales of the Ordovician-age Sequatchie Formation. This formation was deposited as part of a tidal flat complex during Late Ordovician time, so it also contains shallow marine and river deposits.

Limestones of the Ordovician-age Leipers-Catheys Formation are well exposed at exit 40. The Leipers-Catheys Formation is actually two units, but they're generally mapped together as a single unit throughout Middle Tennessee because they look very similar and contain many of the same rock types and fossils. The Leipers-Catheys Formation also looks similar to the bottom part of

Calcareous shales of the Ordovician-age Sequatchie Formation are exposed about 0.5 mile north of exit 40 near milepost 40. The reddish color comes from the iron oxide mineral hematite, which was precipitated directly from seawater. The greenish color comes from the mineral glauconite. (36.35311N, 86.719614W) —Marcy Davis photo

the Fernvale Member of the Sequatchie Formation. Geologists often distinguish the two based on the amount and type of fossil material each contains. The Fernvale Member contains fragments of marine invertebrate fossils, whereas the Leipers-Catheys Formation contains a rich marine invertebrate fauna with many intact whole shells.

I-24 crosses the Cumberland River east of downtown Nashville. The Cumberland River enters Tennessee northeast of Nashville near Celina and flows southward along the northwestern edge of the Central Basin. West of Nashville, the river flows northwestward across the Highland Rim through Clarksville and the Land Between the Lakes National Recreation Area to its confluence with the Ohio River at Smithland, Kentucky. The Obey, Caney Fork, Stones, Harpeth, and Red Rivers are all tributaries of the Cumberland River.

Strata of the Ordovician-age Stones River and Nashville Groups and Leipers-Catheys Formation underlie Nashville's downtown, as well as areas north of the river. The Stones River and Nashville Groups are generally found at lower elevations throughout Nashville, and the Leipers-Catheys Formation at higher elevations.

I-24
NASHVILLE—MURFREESBORO—MONTEAGLE
85 miles

Between Nashville and Murfreesboro, I-24 crosses from the outer to the inner Central Basin, the boundary roughly corresponding to the contact between Nashville Group strata and underlying Stones River Group strata, all Ordovician in age. Middle Tennessee's oldest rocks are at the surface near Murfreesboro at the center of the basin. Younger units encircle the Stones River Group, creating a bull's-eye on geologic maps and reflecting the structure of the ancient Nashville Dome.

The brownish-gray Bigby-Cannon Limestone, part of the Nashville Group, is exposed along both sides of the highway between exits 212 and 213, where I-24 runs concurrently with I-40. At the interchanges with I-40 and I-440 (exit 53), look for exposures of the Hermitage Formation, also part of the Nashville Group. It is relatively easy to spot due to its characteristic light-and-dark banding.

Strata of the Stones River Group are exposed south of the interchanges. This group includes the Murfreesboro, Pierce, Ridley, Lebanon, and Carters Limestones, all relatively pure limestones that contain very little clastic sediment and have alternating thin and thick beds. While each unit does have distinguishing characteristics, the depositional environment was fairly consistent the whole time the Stones River Group was being deposited. The limestones were deposited in a warm, shallow sea far from any sources of clastic sediment, and the sea's relatively gentle currents brought minimal amounts of detrital material from elsewhere.

For the several miles south of the interchanges, the interstate dips between the Carters Limestone in the low areas and the overlying Hermitage Formation

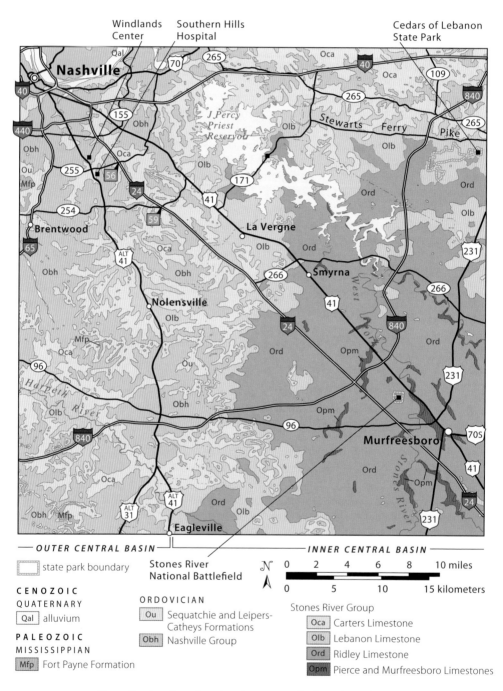

Generalized geology along I-24 between Nashville and Murfreesboro.

in higher areas. You can find gastropods in the Carters Limestone near the Southern Hills Hospital in south Nashville, and you can hunt for the brachiopod *Resserella fertilis* in the Hermitage Formation behind Windlands Center on Nolensville Pike (Alternate US 41) near the zoo. You can see the Carters Limestone between exits 57 and 62; it's exposed under the Hermitage Formation at exit 60. This area is well-known for cedar glades, unusually open and rocky areas that commonly form on strata of the Stones River Group, especially on the Lebanon Limestone, which lies below the Carters Limestone.

The Ridley Limestone, a thick-bedded, brownish-gray rock, underlies the highway at Smyrna, as well as most of the inner Central Basin. The unit contains fossilized brachiopods, bryozoans, corals, sponges, gastropods, trilobites, ostracods, stromatoporoids, and cephalopods. Karst topography, with sinkholes and caves, is well developed in the Ridley Limestone and is common throughout the inner basin. Look for exposures of this limestone near Murfreesboro.

Cedar glades and karst topography played a significant role during the Civil War at the Battle of Stones River, where the Union and Confederate armies fought for control of agricultural land and transportation routes. Though the open glades of the Stones River Group allowed for visibility, the rough karstic terrain and dense clusters of cedar forests made moving troops and supplies difficult.

The thick-bedded Ridley Limestone contains less shale than units above and below, making it more prone to karstification than other Stones River Group strata. At Stones River National Battlefield, outside Murfreesboro, and

In the Slaughter Pen at Stones River National Battlefield, karrens played a pivotal role in the Battle of Stones River by severely hindering the movement of Union troops, artillery, and wagons. —Trista Thornberry-Erlich photo

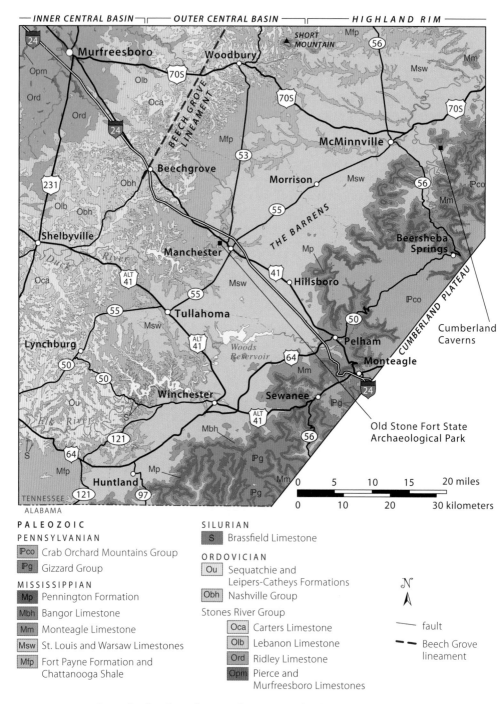

Murfreesboro

Woodbury

SHORT MOUNTAIN

Beechgrove

McMinnville

Morrison

THE BARRENS

Beersheba Springs

Shelbyville

Manchester

Hillsboro

Cumberland Caverns

Tullahoma

Pelham

CUMBERLAND PLATEAU

Lynchburg

Monteagle

Woods Reservoir

Winchester

Sewanee

Old Stone Fort State Archaeological Park

Huntland

TENNESSEE
ALABAMA

Duck River

Elk River

| 0 | 5 | 10 | 15 | 20 miles |
| 0 | 10 | 20 | 30 kilometers |

PALEOZOIC

PENNSYLVANIAN

- Pco   Crab Orchard Mountains Group
- Pg   Gizzard Group

MISSISSIPPIAN

- Mp   Pennington Formation
- Mbh   Bangor Limestone
- Mm   Monteagle Limestone
- Msw   St. Louis and Warsaw Limestones
- Mfp   Fort Payne Formation and Chattanooga Shale

SILURIAN

- S   Brassfield Limestone

ORDOVICIAN

- Ou   Sequatchie and Leipers-Catheys Formations
- Obh   Nashville Group

Stones River Group

- Oca   Carters Limestone
- Olb   Lebanon Limestone
- Ord   Ridley Limestone
- Opm   Pierce and Murfreesboro Limestones

— fault

– – Beech Grove lineament

Generalized geology along I-24 between Murfreesboro and Monteagle.

over much of Middle Tennessee, dissolution features called karrens are up to 3 feet deep in the flat-lying Ridley Limestone. Karrens develop along two sets of bedrock joints that are oriented at 90 degrees to each other. As the joints widen, limestone pinnacles become more pronounced, and the terrain becomes more challenging to navigate. Abandoned cannons still lie amongst the karrens at the battlefield.

For a nice break from the road, visit Earth Experience at the Middle Tennessee Museum of Natural History in Murfreesboro, accessible via exit 80. Displays include some of Tennessee's most beautiful mineral and fossil specimens. The oldest exposed rocks in Middle Tennessee are located in and near Murfreesboro in the inner Central Basin along the highest structural point of the Nashville Dome.

A monument to Tennessee's geographic center stands on Old Lascassas Road north of Middle Tennessee State University in Murfreesboro. In 1834 the State of Tennessee tasked Nashville University mathematics professor James Hamilton with determining the geographic center of Tennessee for the purpose of establishing the capital as close as possible to the center of the state. To do so, he divided the state map into four sections and calculated the center of each by making each section a triangle or parallelogram. He then calculated the common center of these points to find Tennessee's geographic center. Politics kept the capital at Nashville, but the geographic marker remains.

The small town of Woodbury, known for its geodes, lies about 20 miles east of Murfreesboro off exit 81 at the eastern edge of the Central Basin along the highly dissected margin of the eastern Highland Rim. The geodes, which may be up to 2 feet in diameter but are usually smaller, come primarily from dolostones in the Mississippian-age Warsaw Limestone and Fort Payne Formation. Typically, quartz crystals fill the geodes. Quartz is a secondary mineral, having replaced the original mineral anhydrite, an evaporite mineral commonly found in arid environments such as tidal flats. Often the quartz crystals developed around a nucleus, such as a crinoid, sponge, or bryozoan fossil, and the spheroidal geode grew larger as silica replaced the anyhdrite.

Open, flat pastureland eventually replaces suburban development south of Murfreesboro. The Ridley Limestone underlies the highway for 7 miles across the southeastern inner Central Basin. Older Pierce and Murfreesboro Limestones are exposed in local drainages, while higher areas are made of the Lebanon Limestone.

Between Buchanan/Epps Mill Road (exit 89) and Manchester (exit 111), I-24 gradually ascends out of the Central Basin and onto the eastern Highland Rim. Eroded knobs of the southern Highland Rim are visible from southbound lanes near milepost 90. These hills are capped with silicastone of the Mississippian-age Fort Payne Formation. Thinly bedded limestones and shales of the Lebanon Limestone are exposed along the northbound lanes at milepost 91. The Lebanon and Carters Limestones and overlying Hermitage Formation are exposed along the road to Beechgrove.

In 1976, using satellite imagery scientists identified a northeast-trending linear feature that is 1.2 miles wide and stretches more than 100 miles between

Woodbury geodes are irregularly shaped with an outer quartz rind that encases quartz crystals. Some geodes may be partly hollow, while others may be dense with crystals that grew together completely. Other minerals, such as anyhdrite, calcium sulfate, and pyrite, are also commonly found inside. —Albert Ogden photo

Lincoln and Smith Counties. Named for the town of Beechgrove, where I-24 crosses the structure, the Beech Grove lineament is a series of parallel fractures that formed as joints in the limestone bedrock dissolved. No evidence of displacement has been discovered along the fractures, so it is not a fault. The zinc ore mineral sphalerite fills many holes and fractures near the Beech Grove lineament, and the Central Tennessee zinc district lies at the northern end of its surface trace (the main mine of the zinc district is within 2 miles of the lineament at Carthage). This suggests that the lineament may have been one of the primary conduits through which mineral-rich fluids flowed to near the surface in Middle Tennessee.

The area surrounding Beechgrove, along the edge of the Highland Rim, is highly dissected. The Bigby-Cannon Limestone of the Nashville Group and the Leipers-Catheys Formation are exposed near milepost 99, and also along Panhandle Branch, where the highway climbs to the Highland Rim.

The Cumberland Plateau comes into view from southbound lanes near Manchester. Pennsylvanian-age shales, sandstones, and conglomerates cap the upper third of the plateau, and Mississippian-age limestones and calcareous shales form the lower slopes. Water flowing off the Cumberland Plateau and into Highland Rim carbonates forms many springs in the region. TN 55 east from Manchester leads to Cumberland Caverns, a popular show cave eroded in the limestone.

The Mississippian-age Warsaw Limestone underlies the highway at Manchester. The older Fort Payne Formation is exposed along the Duck River, while the St. Louis Limestone caps higher areas. The 100-to-275-foot-thick Fort Payne Formation contains an abundance of chert beds and nodules. In fact, much of the original limestone has been completely silicified or eroded away so that the unit is called a silicastone. In some areas chert is present as small, irregularly shaped pieces within shale layers. When weathered, the more resistant chert stands out from the more easily eroded carbonate surface, a characteristic that gives the rock a speckled look that local geologists describe as "scraggy." Chert makes the Fort Payne Formation relatively insoluble and very resistant to weathering and erosion. Streams have difficulty carving down very far into the Fort Payne, so water typically flows along its resistant beds until reaching a well-established stream.

The Warsaw and St. Louis Limestones underlie the highway between Manchester and exit 127 near the Coffee-Grundy county line. This part of the Highland Rim is known as the Barrens. Barrens are similar to Tennessee glades. Like glades, barrens are open areas with few trees and underlain by limestone. Barrens are larger than glades and typically have thicker sandy and loamy soils where glades have little soil at all. Barrens are likely the result of periodic controlled burning by Native Americans hundreds of years ago. Controlled burns held back the forest so that open areas could be used for gathering native grains and for hunting and grazing animals. Tennessee's first European settlers continued to clear and burn the barrens to encourage the growth of grasses for

The Little Duck River cascades over silicastone of the Fort Payne Formation at Step Falls in the Old Stone Fort State Archaeological Park near Manchester. —Michael Hicks photo

Legend has it that the iron-free spring water and cool caves in Lynchburg provided Jack Daniel with an ideal location for making whiskey. The spring flows at 800 gallons per minute from the Ordovician-age Leipers-Catheys Formation and remains a constant 56 degrees Fahrenheit. The Jack Daniels Distillery is in Lynchburg via TN 55 at exit 111. (35.283664N, 86.366228W) —Chuck Sutherland photo

their grazing animals. This is the largest area of barrens in Tennessee, although other barrens are well developed on the northwestern Highland Rim near Clarksville.

I-24 climbs the north side of Monteagle Mountain, part of the Cumberland Plateau, between the Elk River and Monteagle, gaining about 1,000 feet. Travelers in northbound lanes will receive an expansive view of the Highland Rim, while those traveling in southbound lanes will get an impressive view of the Cumberland Plateau from the bottom up. The lower 700 feet of Monteagle Mountain is made up mostly of Mississippian-age limestone and shale and has a more gentle topography than the steep upper 300 feet, composed of resistant Pennsylvanian-age conglomerate, sandstone, and shale.

St. Louis Limestone underlies the valley of the Elk River south of Pelham. Light-colored, medium-to-thick beds of the Mississippian-age Monteagle Limestone are exposed at the base of Monteagle Mountain. Sandstones of the Hartselle Formation separate the Monteagle Limestone from the overlying, darker-gray Bangor Limestone. The Pennington Formation crops out about 1 mile south of the Grundy County rest areas. These thin dolomite beds interbedded with maroon and green shales were deposited in a broad tidal flat complex. The Pennington Formation shales are prone to slides, so they are

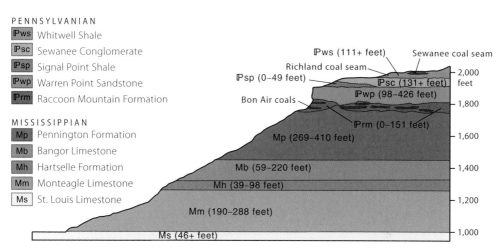

PENNSYLVANIAN

ℙws	Whitwell Shale
ℙsc	Sewanee Conglomerate
ℙsp	Signal Point Shale
ℙwp	Warren Point Sandstone
ℙrm	Raccoon Mountain Formation

MISSISSIPPIAN

Mp	Pennington Formation
Mb	Bangor Limestone
Mh	Hartselle Formation
Mm	Monteagle Limestone
Ms	St. Louis Limestone

ℙws (111+ feet)
Sewanee coal seam
Richland coal seam
ℙsp (0–49 feet)
ℙsc (131+ feet)
ℙwp (98–426 feet)
Bon Air coals
ℙrm (0–151 feet)
Mp (269–410 feet)
Mb (59–220 feet)
Mh (39–98 feet)
Mm (190–288 feet)
Ms (46+ feet)

2,000 feet
1,800
1,600
1,400
1,200
1,000

Generalized stratigraphic section near Monteagle. —Modified from Knoll et al., 2015

covered with wire mesh and sprayed with gunite, a thin coat of cement, sand, and water.

The contact between the Mississippian-age Pennington Formation and the overlying Pennsylvanian-age Raccoon Mountain Formation, part of the Gizzard Group, is exposed along the southbound lane west of the rest areas. The contact, an erosional surface called a disconformity, has more than 40 feet of topographic relief in the Monteagle area and can be traced throughout the southern Appalachian Basin. The Pennington Formation was exposed as regional uplift at the beginning of the Alleghanian orogeny. The paleochannels of ancient streams are well developed in the formation in some places. These contain a coarse basal conglomerate up to 3 feet thick that's stained red by the iron oxide mineral hematite. Paleosols and paleokarst have also developed on the upper part of the Pennington Formation.

The sediment composing the shales, siltstones, and sandstones of the overlying Raccoon Mountain Formation were deposited at the mouth of a very large river system in a tidal flat and tidal-delta environment, just barely above sea level. Lenses of coal are found throughout the unit, some with impressions of ancient plants, including *Lepidodendron*, *Calamites*, and *Sigillaria*.

The Warren Point Sandstone, also part of the Gizzard Group, overlies the Raccoon Mountain Formation. The unit's thick beds are the primary cliff-former of the southern Cumberland Plateau. Fresh surfaces of it are light gray, and it weathers to a yellowish brown. Large crossbed sets are common in the sandstone and indicate that it was deposited in a southwest-flowing braided river system with headwaters in and parallel to the developing Appalachian Mountains. The Warren Point Sandstone also contains plant-rich zones, coal seams, and horizons of *Lepidodendron*, *Calamites*, and *Sigillaria*. The quartz-rich Sewanee Conglomerate of the Crab Orchard Mountains Group caps Monteagle Mountain.

The erosional surface between the Pennington Formation and the overlying Raccoon Mountain Formation is visible along the highway west of the Grundy County rest areas. The disconformity represents a major environmental change, from the mostly marine conditions of most of the Paleozoic Era to the mostly nonmarine conditions that have existed in Tennessee since Pennsylvanian time. (35.239373N, 85.863322W) —Marcy Davis photo

I-40
COOKEVILLE—LEBANON—NASHVILLE
80 miles

I-40 makes a dramatic descent from the Cumberland Plateau east of Cookeville, passing through Pennsylvanian-age sandstones and Mississippian-age shales and limestones. Thin sandstone of the Hartselle Formation forms the topographic bench approximately halfway down the plateau's western escarpment. The city of Cookeville sits on the eastern Highland Rim, made of flat-lying Mississippian-age strata, mainly the Warsaw and St. Louis Limestones. The Monteagle Limestone, Hartselle Formation, and Bangor Limestone cap higher areas on the east and south sides of town. Erosional outliers of the Cumberland Plateau, benches and plateaus capped by sandstone of the Hartselle Formation, are also present near Cookeville.

Karst is well developed along northeast-oriented joint sets in and around Cookeville. Sinkholes, disappearing streams, springs, and caves are abundant, including Big Spring, City Spring, Trog's Sink, Warehouse Sink, and Ensor Sink. Living in a karst landscape presents some challenges. For one, sinkholes are prone to flooding, a problem commonly exacerbated by illegal dumping, which clogs the sinkholes. Surface water and runoff enters sinkholes and cave passages quickly and without sufficient filtration. Because these waters may reemerge elsewhere as springs, it's important to keep this dynamic system clean. Human activities such as salting roads in winter, fertilizing lawns, illegal dumping, and paving all heavily impact groundwater quality and recharge in karstic areas.

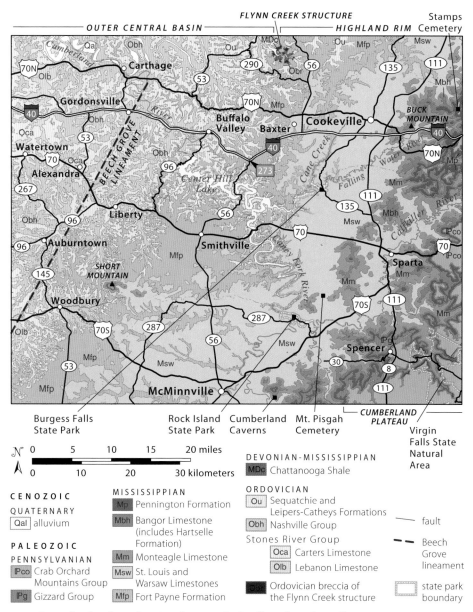

Generalized geology along I-40 between Cookeville and Gordonsville. See map on page 256 for section between Lebanon and Nashville.

The comb grave tradition began in the early nineteenth century, and comb graves such as these, in Mt. Pisgah Cemetery in White County, can be found throughout White, Putnam, and Overton Counties. Comb graves are primarily made of the Mississippian-age Hartselle Formation, which is quarried from a 30-foot-thick sandstone along the western front of the Cumberland Plateau. Stamps Cemetery, a quick side trip in the Cookeville area (it's 10 miles east of downtown on Buck Mountain Road), is a great place to see comb graves.
—Chuck Sutherland photo

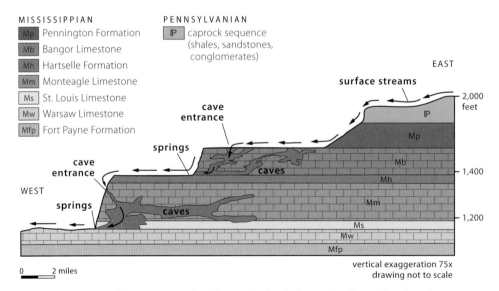

MISSISSIPPIAN

Mp	Pennington Formation
Mb	Bangor Limestone
Mh	Hartselle Formation
Mm	Monteagle Limestone
Ms	St. Louis Limestone
Mw	Warsaw Limestone
Mfp	Fort Payne Formation

PENNSYLVANIAN

| ℙ | caprock sequence (shales, sandstones, conglomerates) |

EAST

surface streams

cave entrance

cave entrance

springs

springs

caves

caves

WEST

2,000 feet

ℙ

Mp

Mb

Mh

Mm

Ms

Mw

Mfp

1,400

1,200

vertical exaggeration 75x
drawing not to scale

0   2 miles

Energetic streams flowing westward off the Cumberland Plateau dissolve and erode carbonates, particularly the Bangor and Monteagle Limestones. Water is channeled underground through these units and resurfaces again at the contacts with the Hartselle Formation and St. Louis Limestone, which are less soluble. This dynamic creates a high density of karst features, such as caves and springs, along the western edge of the Cumberland Plateau and eastern edge of the eastern Highland Rim. Virgin Falls State Natural area near Sparta offers a good look at these processes in action. —Modified from Pride et al., 1988; Wolfe et al., 1997

Blue Spring Cave, located near Sparta, is Tennessee's longest cave at more than 38 miles long. Cumberland Caverns, the region's most popular show cave northeast of McMinnville, offers an up-close look at a local cave. Concerts take place underground in the cave's Volcano Room.

The Flynn Creek structure is located on the eastern Highland Rim about 15 miles north of Baxter and south of Gainesboro. It has been identified as an

BURGESS FALLS STATE PARK

Plunging waterfalls, such as Big Falls (115 feet), are typical features of rivers that descend from the Highland Rim to the Central Basin. Waterfalls form where rivers cut through the resistant Mississippian-age Fort Payne Formation. Once the caprock of the formation is breached, the underlying limestone dissolves, leading to the upstream migration of the falls. The contact between the Fort Payne Formation and the Chattanooga Shale is about halfway down the cliff at the left. (36.045510N, 85.599560W) —Chuck Sutherland photo

About 1 mile east of the junction with US 70 (exit 290), I-40 crosses Falling Water River. The river flows southwestward and spills over the eastern Highland Rim into the Central Basin about 6 miles south of Cookeville. Three waterfalls at Burgess Falls State Park descend more than 130 feet in Falling Water Gorge through the Fort Payne Formation and Chattanooga Shale to the Ordovician-age Leipers Formation, the oldest rock in the park.

Falling Water River may have changed its course relatively recently. About 1 mile southeast of its confluence with Cane Creek is Tibbs Hollow, a small valley occupied by a 2-mile-long stream. At Tibbs Hollow there's a large meander, too large to have been made either by the stream that occupies it now or by Cane Creek, so it was likely created by an ancestral channel of Falling Water River. An excellent display at the park's visitor center explains the river changed course.

impact structure based on the presence of shatter cones, unique microscopic features in quartz minerals, and microscopic crystalline deformation. About 200 feet of Devonian-to-Mississippian-age Chattanooga Shale filled the crater shortly after it formed, before erosion could erase the evidence of the event. The Chattanooga Shale is only about 20 feet thick outside the crater.

The Flynn Creek structure is a little more than 2 miles in diameter, is nearly 500 feet deep, and features a central uplift and collapsed crater rim. The asteroid that created it struck flat-lying carbonates of the Knox and Stones River Groups that were covered by a shallow sea about 380 million years ago, in Late Devonian time. The carbonates were deformed and fractured to a depth of more than 1,600 feet! About 0.5 cubic mile of fractured rock was ejected and fell back into the hole, covering the deformed rocks with more than 365 feet of brecciated material. The strata rebounded 30 to 100 feet along the rim and 1,000 feet at the central uplift. Subsequently, karst developed throughout the depression and created at least ten caves. One of these, Hawkins Cave, is located in the central uplift.

About 8 miles northwest of the Flynn Creek structure is the Dycus structure, an oval-shaped depression that's about 0.5 mile wide. Erosion and vegetation obscure any indisputable geologic evidence that the Dycus resulted from an impact; however, its shape and location suggest that there may have been an impact coincident with the Flynn Creek structure. The origins of the Dycus remains unproven and debated.

Both the Flynn Creek and Dycus structures are difficult, if not impossible, for the casual traveler to see because they have been buried by younger strata, dissected by streams, and covered by vegetation. An official historic marker highlights the feature where Flynns Creek Road crosses the central uplift west of the hamlet of Center Grove.

Between Cookeville and Baxter, the Fort Payne Formation is exposed in some of the larger drainages. West of Baxter on I-40, the landscape becomes heavily dissected along the transition between the eastern Highland Rim and Central Basin, as the elevation drops about 500 feet. Waterfalls spill over the Fort Payne Formation along the western escarpment of the rim. Streams undercut more resistant units of the Fort Payne and erode the underlying and less resistant Devonian-to-Mississippian-age Chattanooga Shale and Ordovician-age carbonates, forming overhangs that eventually break off. Over time, the falls have migrated upstream and eastward, thereby slowly eroding the eastern Highland Rim. Springs and caves are common along the interface between the eastern Highland Rim and Central Basin, as are historic mills that harnessed the water power of these natural falls for a number of applications. Great Falls Cotton Mill at Rock Island State Park, located about 30 miles south of the McMinnville/Smithville exit (exit 273), is one such example.

West of exit 273, I-40 follows the Buffalo Branch, a tributary to the Caney Fork River. Excellent exposures of Mississippian-to-Ordovician-age units occur between milepost 272 and exit 168, mainly on the north side of the road. Look for the thick-bedded Fort Payne Formation at milepost 271. Ordovician-age units are exposed over the next couple of miles to Buffalo Valley.

The I-40 Welcome Center Smith County (milepost 267) is one of Tennessee's most picturesque rest stops. Stretch your legs by the Caney Fork River while looking at cliffs of Ordovician-age limestone. (36.143110N, 85.807691W) —Chuck Sutherland photo

I-40 parallels the Caney Fork River for several miles west of Buffalo Valley. The interstate crosses the river five times in a 4-mile stretch due to the many twists and turns the river makes in its floodplain. The Caney Fork River is a popular trout-fishing destination for many anglers, as the water is kept cold by discharge from Center Hill Lake. The Leipers-Catheys Formation and Bigby-Cannon Limestone crop out at lower elevations, especially in the bluffs along the river north of the interstate. The Hermitage Formation is exposed along the lower Caney Fork River. The surrounding hills are isolated erosional remnants of the eastern Highland Rim capped by the Fort Payne Formation.

A major zinc deposit was discovered in 1969 on the east side of the Central Basin near Gordonsville. Exploration revealed several economically viable deposits that collectively became known as the Central Tennessee zinc district, which can be traced northward into southern Kentucky. These deposits, along with three economically important East Tennessee zinc deposits, are classic Mississippi Valley–type deposits that consist of zinc and lead within carbonate rocks. Ore minerals typically include sulfide ore minerals such as sphalerite (the only ore mineral mined in Central Tennessee) and galena, with associated minerals such as marcasite, pyrite, fluorite, barite, celestine, dolomite, calcite, and quartz. The rare earth mineral germanium, which has optical and electronics applications, is found in the sphalerite here and is recovered as a by-product during the zinc smelting and refining process.

In the Central Tennessee zinc district, mineralization occurred within the Knox Group, a thick marine carbonate sequence exposed at the surface in Middle Tennessee only within the Wells Creek and Flynn Creek impact structures. Except for these places, the nearly flat-lying, 3,000-foot section is deeply buried, forming the base of Paleozoic-age units directly overlying the

Proterozoic-age granitic basement and underlying the Stones River Group of Middle Ordovician age. As it is in the East Tennessee zinc districts, the mineralization occurred within the Mascot Dolomite, a fine-grained dolomite that is the uppermost formation of the Knox Group. Ore is mined from open spaces within collapse breccias, the rock rubble that resulted from the ancient solution and collapse related to karst development. The mineral emplacement happened when relatively low-temperature, metal-rich, mineralized brines flowed through karstic limestone and dolomite. Many scientists believe this happened at the end of the Paleozoic Era; however, the exact timing remains unclear. The Beech Grove lineament is a conspicuously linear surface feature that extends southwestward about 50 miles from Carthage. It may have been the conduit through which these mineral-rich fluids reached the breccia zones within the Knox Group.

The large size of mineral specimens from the Central Tennessee zinc district makes them popular with collectors. The dark reddish-brown zinc ore mineral sphalerite occurs with calcite, fluorite, barite, and galena or by itself in masses up to 4 feet thick. Individual sphalerite crystals up to 2 inches long, fluorite crystals as wide as 6 inches, barite spheres up to 12 inches in diameter, and calcite crystals longer than 18 inches have all been found in large pockets along the edge of large mineralized breccia bodies at the Elmwood Mine near Carthage. Sphalerite is the only valuable ore mineral; the other minerals are separated, along with rock, from the sphalerite and sent to tailings dumps.

Gordonsville is built on the floodplain of the Caney Fork River, which joins the Cumberland River a few miles north of the interstate at Carthage. The Caney Fork begins on the Cumberland Plateau, flows through Scott Gulf, across the Highland Rim to Center Hill Dam, and then through Buffalo Valley. The Caney Fork is an energetic river, particularly where it flows off the Cumberland Plateau and Highland Rim; it has many waterfalls and rapids. Early Tennessee settlers tried to harness its energy for various kinds of mills, especially following the Civil War to the early 1900s, but frequent flooding was a problem.

I-40 crosses the hilly and highly dissected eastern Central Basin between Gordonsville and Nashville. Mississippian-age units cap small, isolated remnants of the eastern Highland Rim near Gordonsville. Nashville Group strata of Ordovician age are exposed along the highway from Gordonsville to the Smith-Wilson county line (0.25 mile west of milepost 251). Look for the medium-bedded, gray-brown limestone of the Bigby-Cannon Limestone immediately west of Gordonsville and again west of milepost 251. In between are exposures of the underlying Hermitage Formation, a thinly bedded, sandy limestone interbedded with shale. The Carters Limestone, the uppermost unit of the Stones River Group, is present in drainages. The Leipers-Catheys Formation caps nearby hills.

Short Mountain lies about 28 miles south of Gordonsville, via TN 264, on the western edge of the eastern Highland Rim in northeastern Cannon County. Although Short Mountain rises 800 feet above the surrounding area, it's tough to see from the interstate. It is a distant outlier of the Cumberland Plateau that is capped with Pennsylvanian-age sandstone. The presence of the sandstone

Minerals from the Central Tennessee zinc district are known for their large size, particularly those from the Elmwood Mine.

White masses of barite on sphalerite. —Albert Ogden photo

A large calcite crystal. —Albert Ogden photo

A single fluorite crystal that is 6 inches on each side. —Travis Paris photo

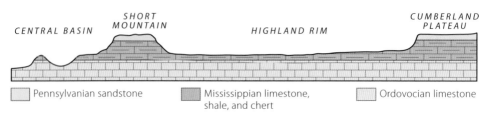

WEST   EAST

CENTRAL BASIN   SHORT
                   MOUNTAIN   HIGHLAND RIM   CUMBERLAND
                                                            PLATEAU

| Pennsylvanian sandstone | Mississippian limestone, shale, and chert | Ordovocian limestone |

Mississippian- and Pennsylvanian-age strata once extended across Middle Tennessee between Short Mountain and the Cumberland Plateau but have been eroded. Short Mountain is about 30 miles west of the Cumberland Plateau. —Modified from Miller, 2014

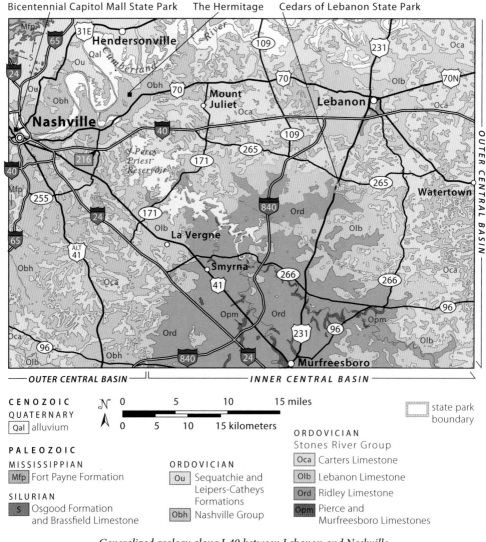

Bicentennial Capitol Mall State Park   The Hermitage   Cedars of Lebanon State Park

CENOZOIC
QUATERNARY
Qal alluvium

PALEOZOIC

MISSISSIPPIAN
Mfp Fort Payne Formation

SILURIAN
S Osgood Formation
and Brassfield Limestone

ORDOVICIAN
Ou Sequatchie and
Leipers-Catheys
Formations
Obh Nashville Group

ORDOVICIAN
Stones River Group
Oca Carters Limestone
Olb Lebanon Limestone
Ord Ridley Limestone
Opm Pierce and
Murfreesboro Limestones

state park boundary

Generalized geology along I-40 between Lebanon and Nashville.

CEDARS OF LEBANON STATE PARK

Cedars of Lebanon State Park, located about 7 miles south of Lebanon, protects 900 acres of open, rocky areas of the cedar glade ecosystem. Cedar glades typically develop on Paleozoic-age limestones, as they have at the park. In the Central Basin, glades have developed where weathered Ordovician-age limestones create areas of thin, acidic soils. The fine-grained and thinly bedded Lebanon Limestone of the Stones River Group is the primary glade-former in Cedars of Lebanon State Park. Glades are also well-developed on Mississippian-age carbonates of the eastern Highland Rim and in the Western Valley of the Tennessee River south of Parsons, where the Silurian-age Brownsport Group is at the surface.

Glades form on the thinly bedded limestones of the Ordovician-age Lebanon Limestone in Cedars of Lebanon State Park. Glades conspicuously lack soil cover and are known for their rare and endemic plant species. —Alan Cressler photo

Unique to the southeastern United States, glades support endemic flora particularly suited to the rocky, limy soils. Many plants found in Middle Tennessee glades are rare or endangered. Glade microclimates are harsh—wet in winter with poor drainage and dry in summer with little soil to hold moisture. Most trees find glades a difficult place to grow, with the exception of red cedars. These "cedar" trees, which are actually junipers, are adept at securing their roots in cracks in the platy, thinly bedded rock. Glades once comprised more than 5 percent of the Central Basin, but expanding cities have destroyed much of the habitat. Fossil collecting is not permitted in the state park, but glades not under the such protection are often good places to look for invertebrate fossils, such as sponges, crinoids, corals, and brachiopods.

Karst features are also common throughout the park. Sinkholes and caves are well developed along joints and bedding planes in strata of the Stones River Group throughout the Central Basin.

on the eastern Highland Rim is evidence that it once extended across Middle Tennessee.

The fossiliferous Lebanon Limestone of the Stones River Group underlies the city of Lebanon. Look for a few exposures of the thin, platy limestone between exits 239 and 238. Many sinkholes have developed in the Lebanon Limestone throughout Middle Tennessee because its thin beds collapse into caves that developed in the underlying Ridley Limestone.

There are good exposures of the Carters Limestone west of Lebanon. Near exit 232 for TN 109, reddish soils cover the light-colored, medium-to-thick-bedded limestone. In this area, dissolution has widened vertical joints to such a degree that stacked limestone blocks have been used to mitigate further dissolution and erosion. The Carters Limestone contains four layers of ancient volcanic ash, as well as coral reefs and zinc, lead, fluorite, and barite minerals that were deposited in veins during the mineralization of the Central Tennessee zinc district.

Near Nashville, the exposures are mainly of Carters Limestone with the thinly bedded Hermitage Formation at higher elevations. A thin layer of decomposed volcanic ash, now bentonite clay, separates the two units in same areas.

The Hermitage Formation weathers into distinctive light- and dark-gray bands due to alternating layers of darker shale and lighter sandy limestone. The formation is well exposed along interstates, at major highway junctions, and around downtown Nashville. The unit was first described in the area that is now

The thinly bedded Carters Limestone, the youngest unit in the Stones River Group, is exposed near exit 216 for the Nashville International Airport. The outcrop pictured here, which no longer exists, shows the contact (the line of rusty patina) between the light-colored Carters Limestone and the overlying, light and dark banded Hermitage Formation. —Steven M. Holland photo

the neighborhood of Hermitage, which is also the location of a historic planta-
tion by the same name and the home of President Andrew Jackson, which lies
north of I-40 off US 70. The Bigby-Cannon Limestone is also well exposed in
most of the lower-elevation areas around Nashville and along I-40. Local hills
are capped by the Leipers-Catheys Formation.

NASHVILLE GEOLOGY

*The Tennessee State Capitol stands on a hill capped with the Ordovician-age
Leipers-Catheys Formation. This view looks down Bicentennial Capitol Mall
State Park across the northwestern Central Basin toward the western Highland
Rim escarpment. (36.165875N, 86.784269W)* —Chuck Sutherland photo

Long before humans settled the Nashville area, ice age mammals, including
mastodons, mammoths, camels, horses, deer, saber-toothred cats, and ground
sloths, frequented its mineral springs and associated salt licks. The remains of
these Pleistocene-age animals, along with human artifacts, are found at several
sites near Nashville. In the mid-1700s, Native Americans built villages nearby to
facilitate active trading with French-Canadian hunters who established permanent settlements near springs on the south bank of the Cumberland River. These
settlements collectively became known as French Lick. A marker in Bicentennial
Capitol Mall State Park sits atop McNairy Springs, one of the springs that fed
Old French Lick Creek. Sulphur Dell baseball park (now First Tennessee Park),
once located between Fourth and Fifth avenues, was named for and built near
Sulphur Spring, another of Nashville's mineralized springs. On the northeast side

of Nashville, spring water allegedly began flowing near the Hermitage, President Andrew Jackson's former home, the same night in December 1811 that the first of the New Madrid earthquakes happened. It became the Fountain of Health resort and served customers for fifteen years. Springs are found throughout Middle Tennessee, especially where water-saturated limestones of the Highland Rim intersect the Central Basin.

The area surrounding Nashville is hilly, particularly north and west of downtown where the Cumberland River has excavated a path through the Central Basin and Highland Rim. The best rock exposures in Nashville are along highways (including the interstates), in drainages, and in areas of new construction. (See the guides in this book for the roads that pass through Nashville.) Stones River Group strata are exposed in drainages to the southeast. Highly fossiliferous strata of the Middle Ordovician Nashville Group underlie lower elevations in downtown Nashville and surrounding areas. The Carters Limestone is exposed in major drainages, and the younger Leipers-Catheys Formation forms higher areas around town.

The relatively pure limestones of the Stones River Group were deposited in Ordovician time when a sea covered the central part of North America. The Nashville Dome was uplifted and eroded at this time, and when the sea returned the dome remained a low island. The oldest unit of the Nashville Group, the Hermitage Formation, was deposited around 450 million years ago on eroded beds of the Carters Limestone, the youngest formation of the Stones River Group, along the flanks of the exposed dome. Sea level fluctuated throughout this period, often in conjunction with recurrent uplift of the Nashville Dome, and the sediments that were deposited reflect this. Nashville Group strata contain more silt and clay, as well as more coarse-grained, fossiliferous limestones, than the underlying Stones River Group strata.

The Hermitage Formation of the Nashville Group grades upward into the Bigby-Cannon Limestone, a complex unit made up of three members: the Bigby and Cannon Limestones and the Dove-Colored Member, each of which represents a

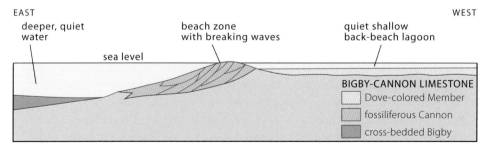

The Bigby-Cannon Limestone consists of three members: the Bigby and Cannon Limestones and the Dove-Colored Member, a light-gray and very dense limestone. All three members are exposed in the Nashville area. They grade into each other laterally and vertically and reflect a complicated mix of contemporaneous depositional environments that existed in Middle Tennessee during Middle Ordovician time. —Modified from Miller, 2014

different depositional environment that existed concurrently near the Nashville Dome. While this unit was being deposited, the Nashville Dome was not exposed, but the Central Tennessee Bank, a relatively higher submarine area, existed beneath the surface in shallower water. This carbonate bank resembled those found today in places such as the Bahamas or the Yucatán Peninsula. In deeper waters on the west side of the bank, the relatively homogeneous Cannon Limestone was deposited. Waves rolling over the submerged reef broke up shells that are preserved in limestones made entirely of shell detritus, of which the typically cross-bedded Bigby Limestone is one. Reefs formed in shallower waters and protected low-energy lagoons located on the east side of the bank, where algae precipitated a limy ooze that became the Dove-Colored Member.

The Tennessee State Capitol was originally faced with Bigby Limestone, originally named the Capitol Limestone by James Safford in 1869. Unfortunately, the weathering of crossbeds caused unsightly flaking and dangerous rockfall potential. The stone was replaced with a limestone from Indiana that contains some interesting sedimentary features and fossils, including the shells of cephalopods, straight-shelled marine animals in the same family as squids and octopuses. The Bigby Limestone was also used in the foundations of many of Vanderbilt University's older buildings. Much of the stone came from a quarry that was located at Pearl Street and Sixteenth Avenue North.

Nashville area strata are highly fossiliferous and contain abundant Middle Ordovician sponges, corals, bryozoans, brachiopods, pelecypods, gastropods, cephalopods, trilobites, echinoderms, and ostracods. Gastropods from the Carters

The Bigby-Cannon Limestone is exposed along I-40 and at the Demonbreun Street exit ramps. This section of the unit formed in a high-energy shallow water environment. Look for crossbeds in the thick-bedded limestone. (36.152396N, 86.786955W)
—Anand Raghunathan photo

Limestone, part of the Stones River Group, may be found near the Southern Hills Hospital in south Nashville. You can hunt for the brachiopod *Resserella fertilis* in the Hermitage Formation behind the Windlands Center on Nolensville Pike (Alternate US 41) near the zoo, or look for bryozoans, such as *Constellaria*, in the Catheys Formation on Rosa L. Parks Boulevard between Clay Street and Vantage Way. *Constellaria* is named for the star-shaped openings in which the tiny, filter-feeding animals lived. Brachiopods can be found in the Leipers Formation on US 70 west of Red Caboose Park in Bellevue. Just about any outcrop in and around Nashville is likely to contain fossils. (The website tennesseefossils.com includes detailed fossil photos and a printable guide on Nashville fossils and fossil locales by local teacher Nancy Stetten. Ms. Stetten's printable guide is also available at the Tennessee Department of Environment and Conservation's website.)

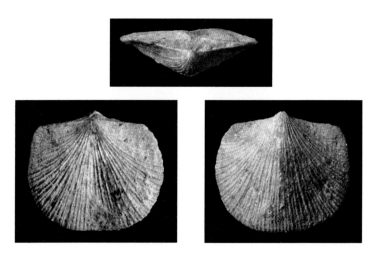

The 0.5-inch-wide brachiopod Resserella fertilis *was small but mighty. Beds composed of both whole and fragmented shells are up to 30 feet thick and cover many square miles of the western Central Basin. These animals lived in shallow water along the western flank of the Nashville Dome. Imagine the entire seafloor covered with these shells!* —Jim Davison photo

Beautiful rivers, lakes, woods, and geologic features can be enjoyed at many Nashville parks. Bicentennial Capitol Mall State Park has a variety of good geology-related displays that are accessible on foot. In addition to the McNairy and Sulphur Springs memorials, the mall contains an excellent display on Tennessee rivers. The Rivers of Tennessee Fountain (also a splash pad) contains thirty-one vertical fountains, one for each of Tennessee's main waterways. Tennessee Map Plaza, located adjacent to James Robertson Parkway, has a 200-foot-long granite map of the state. If you walk up the hill from the Tennessee State Capitol you can have a look at the thinly bedded shaley limestone of the Leipers-Catheys Formation exposed along Seventh Avenue.

Nashville is prone to flooding due to the relatively pure, dense, impermeable lime-stones that underlie the city. Intense spring storms, such as those that occurred in 2010 when more than 14 inches of rain fell in just 48 hours, bring more water than the ground can absorb. The view here is northward from the John Seigenthaler Pedestrian Bridge, with a flooded Riverfront Park. The Cumberland River is on the right side of the photo. (36.161188N, 86.773625W) —Rachael Moore photo

I-40
NASHVILLE—DICKSON—TENNESSEE RIVER
55 miles

Ordovician-age strata are present along I-40 through downtown Nashville and for several miles west of the city to where the interstate crosses the northwestern Central Basin. The medium-to-thick-bedded Bigby-Cannon Limestone is well exposed between exits 210 and 208B. Keep an eye out for a light-gray bed that is a couple of feet thick near exit 209B. This distinctive layer, known as the Dove-Colored Member, is a convenient identifier of the Bigby-Cannon Limestone. There are good exposures of the Leipers-Catheys Formation at the I-440 interchange (exit 206) where the interstate cuts through a couple of small hills.

A few erosional remnants of the Highland Rim form hills along the city's north, west, and south sides. Look for these erosional outliers west of the Charlotte Pike (exit 201). Lower hills are capped with Silurian-age units, while Mississippian-age strata cap higher hills. Percy Warner and Edwin Warner Parks, collectively known as the Warner Parks, are located near Bellevue, and Radnor Lake State Natural Area, located in the Brentwood neighborhood west of I-65, are erosional remnants of the Highland Rim with exposures of Ordovician-to-Mississippian-age units. Along the self-guided Geology Trail at Percy Warner Park, visitors can learn about the geology of Nashville and Middle

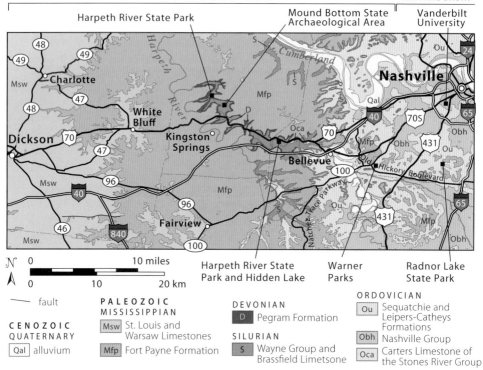

Harpeth River State Park

Mound Bottom State
Archaeological Area

Vanderbilt
University

Harpeth River State
Park and Hidden Lake

Warner
Parks

Radnor Lake
State Park

N
0   10 miles

0   10   20 km

— fault

CENOZOIC
QUATERNARY
Qal alluvium

PALEOZOIC
MISSISSIPPIAN
Msw St. Louis and
Warsaw Limestones
Mfp Fort Payne Formation

DEVONIAN
D Pegram Formation

SILURIAN
S Wayne Group and
Brassfield Limetsone

ORDOVICIAN
Ou Sequatchie and
Leipers-Catheys
Formations
Obh Nashville Group
Oca Carters Limestone of
the Stones River Group

Generalized geology along I-40 between Nashville and Dickson.

The Leipers-Catheys Formation is exposed near the Charlotte Pike/US 70 exit and underlies much of the interstate westward to Bellevue. (36.132173N, 86.898877W) —Anand Raghunathan photo

HARPETH RIVER STATE PARK

For a slower but geologically rich pace, you can take US 70, which parallels the interstate, from Nashville. Silurian-age strata are well exposed along the highway in the Harpeth River valley, and several sites along the river, managed by Harpeth River State Park, are worth visiting. Mound Bottom State Archaeological Area, situated in a tight bend in the river, hosts platform and burial mounds built between AD 950 and AD 1300. In the Narrows section of the park, hikers can explore the Pattison (also called Montgomery Bell or Patterson) Forge Tunnel project, spearheaded by industrial entrepreneur Montgomery Bell. Between 1818 and 1820, slave labor excavated the tunnel through 300 feet of solid rock. The tunnel diverted water from the Harpeth River to power the Pattison Iron Forge where wrought iron was made from pig iron mined and smelted on the western Highland Rim.

The Pattison Forge tunnel cuts through nearly 300 feet of the Silurian-age Lego Limestone in a narrow meander neck of the Harpeth River. Mudstone of the Dixon Formation, also part of the Wayne Group, and the Devonian-age Pegram Formation overlie the Lego Limestone. (36.147080N, 87.122389W) —Chuck Sutherland photo

At Hidden Lake, also located in Harpeth River State Park, are two old quarries where the Laurel and Lego Limestones, both part of the Silurian-age Wayne Group, were quarried between 1914 and 1918. During the 1940s, the site was turned into a resort, but old stone steps that lead up to a marble dance floor are all that remain.

Tennessee. The Interactive Guide to Warner Park smartphone app contains a section on local geology and a useful interactive map.

In Bellevue, I-40 crosses the floodplain of the Harpeth River, which meanders northward to its confluence with the Cumberland River west of Ashland City, zigzagging under the highway for the next few miles.

I-40 climbs about 200 feet in elevation over a distance of about 10 miles through the transition between the Central Basin and the western Highland Rim. The topographic change is most dramatic when traveling eastbound and descending into the Central Basin and Nashville from Kingston Springs.

Silurian-age strata of the Wayne Group, with a maximum thickness of about 70 feet, are exposed along I-40 at the base of the hill west of Bellevue and overlie the older Silurian-age Brassfield Limestone. Most of Middle Tennessee was an island when sediments of these rocks were deposited, so the Wayne Group is limited to western Middle Tennessee and eastern West Tennessee.

Look for exposures of the green-gray Waldron Shale, part of the Wayne Group, near the top of the hill at about mile 193.2. The Waldron Shale separates the underlying Laurel Limestone from the overlying Lego Limestone, both also of the Wayne Group. The Waldron Shale, only 3 to 5 feet thick, consists of calcareous shales and thin limestones with abundant and well-preserved

Eucalyptocrinites, an extinct crinoid genus, is the most famous fossil from the Waldron Shale and is prized by collectors. These specimens, all crinoid cups, were found near Newsom Station and exit 192 of I-40. The cup on the right is upside down; the central depression is the stem attachment point. The cup on the left is right-side up but filled with mud prior to fossilization; the crinoid's arms connected to the outer margin of the cup. In the center is a small cup on its side. The arms would have extended to the left and the stem to the right. —Michael Gibson photo

The Fort Payne Formation overlies Devonian units and is exposed along the westbound lane west of exit 192, where the highway splits, although it is difficult to see due to vegetation. (36.0860086N, 87.0485401W) —Chuck Sutherland photo

small marine invertebrate fossils, including crinoids, colonial and horn corals, bivalves, bryozoans, gastropods, and trilobites. The fossils sometimes show pyritization, meaning that shell material was partly replaced by the mineral pyrite, a gold-colored iron sulfide.

The Mississippian-age Fort Payne Formation overlies the Chattanooga Shale and underlies the town of Kingston Springs. Look for exposures along the Harpeth River east of exit 188 and along the interstate west of the exit.

I-40 crosses the western Highland Rim between Kingston Springs and the Tennessee River. From Kingston Springs to the junction with I-840 at exit 176, cherty residuum of the Fort Payne Formation underlies the interstate, but exposures are mostly limited to drainages. The Mississippian-age Warsaw Limestone caps the hill at milepost 186 and at exit 182. Red soils derived from this limestone are visible for a couple of miles west of the I-40/I-840 junction.

The topography west of Dickson is relatively featureless except for a few isolated hills. On this part of the western Highland Rim, red soils are derived from the Warsaw Limestone that underlies the highway to near milepost 157. The St. Louis Limestone caps higher areas, while the Fort Payne Formation is present in major drainages, such as that of the Piney River.

North of the interstate at exit 163 is a line of hills capped with Cretaceous-age strata, mainly nonmarine Tuscaloosa Formation, which was deposited by

Hugh Link Farm State Archaeological Area

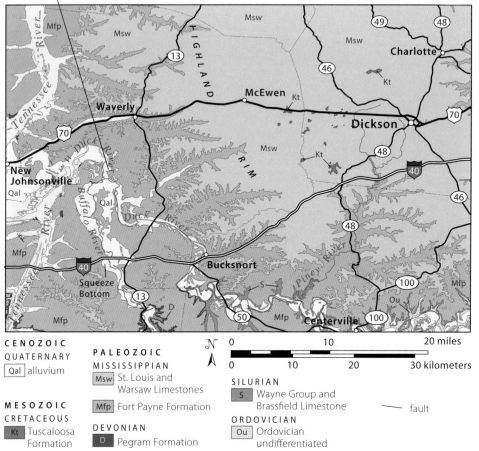

Generalized geology along I-40 between Dickson and the Tennessee River.

east-flowing rivers on the eroded surfaces of Devonian-to-Mississippian-age strata. The Tuscaloosa is preserved in discontinuous patches up to a few feet thick, as well as in ancient karst features, such as sinkholes, in underlying limestones. The Tuscaloosa Formation contains light-colored chert gravel eroded from the Devonian-age Camden Formation and local Mississippian-age units, including the Fort Payne Formation and Warsaw and St. Louis Limestones. The western Highland Rim represents the eastern limit of the Tuscaloosa Formation, where a delta formed at the edge of a shallow sea.

The St. Louis Limestone underlies the highway for about 5 miles west of exit 163, and the Warsaw Limestone and the Fort Payne Formation underlie the valley of Sugar Creek to Bucksnort. Near Bucksnort, there are scattered exposures of the Fort Payne Formation along the road.

The interstate crosses the Duck and Buffalo Rivers west of Bucksnort. Farms are developed in Quaternary-age alluvium in both river valleys. The confluence of these popular canoeing rivers is about 5 miles north of the interstate at Hugh Link Farm State Archaeological Area. From the confluence the Duck River loops in a large meander southward to the Tennessee River.

From Squeeze Bottom on the west side of the Buffalo River floodplain, I-40 follows the North Fork, a small tributary to the Tennessee River. Mississippian-age Fort Payne Formation crops out on both sides of the Tennessee River.

I-65
ALABAMA STATE LINE—COLUMBIA—NASHVILLE
84 miles

The landscape of Middle Tennessee between Alabama and the Marshall-Maury county line south of Columbia is typical of the transitional zone between the Central Basin and Highland Rim. Brownish-gray, medium-bedded Bigby-Cannon Limestone of the Nashville Group and shaley limestone of the overlying Leipers-Catheys Formation are exposed intermittently along the highway. Streams and tributaries to the Elk and Duck Rivers have dissected the area, leaving behind rounded hills, erosional outliers of the Highland Rim. Younger Ordovician- and Silurian-age strata make up lower slopes of these outliers, which are capped by the resistant Mississippian-age Fort Payne Formation. Strata dip slightly southward here along the south side of the Nashville Dome.

At the Alabama state line, the interstate cuts through an erosional knob of the Highland Rim that is capped by cherty carbonates of the Fort Payne Formation. North of the road to Elkton (exit 6), the highway crosses Ordovician-age carbonates. The Silurian-age Brassfield Limestone overlies these units, and the Fort Payne Formation is exposed at the top of the hill. This stratigraphic section is repeated between mileposts 8 and 9 and again between mileposts 12 and 14 as I-65 crosses more erosional outliers of the Highland Rim.

Ancient river channels, preserved near Pulaski and Fayetteville, formed in the Leipers-Catheys Formation at the end of the Ordovician Period when the Nashville Dome was above sea level and eroding. This area was low and featureless, probably a little higher to the west with a broad plain that sloped gently southeastward. The river channels developed on the southern flank of the dome and met the ocean in an estuary near the Tennessee-Alabama state line. The former channels are up to 1,500 feet wide, and in some places the rivers cut down 100 feet through the Leipers-Catheys Formation into the underlying Bigby-Cannon Limestone. The channels are filled with river-deposited clastic sediments, including a conglomeratic sandstone that forms the base of the depositional sequence.

The Howell structure, an oval depression about 1.5 miles in diameter, is located a few miles north of Fayetteville in Lincoln County. Although the structural disturbance resembles an impact crater, many scientists think it's a

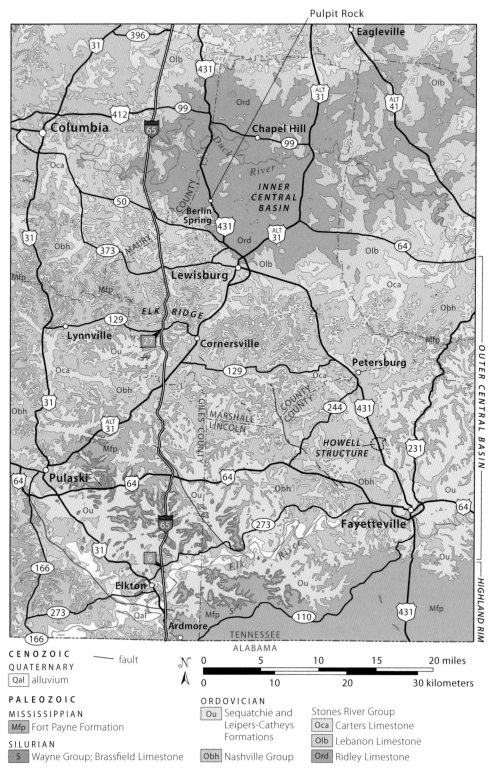

Pulpit Rock

Eagleville

396
31
Olb
431
Olb
ALT 31
ALT 41
412
99
Columbia
65
Ord
Chapel Hill
99
Oca
DUCK
INNER
CENTRAL
River
BASIN
50
Berlin
431
Spring
Ord
ALT 31
Olb
64
Obh
373
MAURY
Lewisburg
Olb
Mfp
Oca
Mfp
Obh
ELK RIDGE
129
Ou
Lynnville
27
Cornersville
Petersburg
Oca
Obh
129
Oca
Mfp
31
LINCOLN COUNTY
MARSHALL COUNTY
244
431
Obh
ALT 31
GILES COUNTY
HOWELL
231
STRUCTURE
Mfp
64
64
64
Pulaski
64
Obh
Ou
Ou
65
273
Fayetteville
6
31
ELK
River
Ou
166
Ou
Elkton
Ou
Mfp
Qal
S
431
273
ALABAMA
110
166
Ardmore
TENNESSEE

OUTER CENTRAL BASIN

HIGHLAND RIM

CENOZOIC   —— fault
QUATERNARY
Qal alluvium   N

0   5   10   15   20 miles

0   10   20   30 kilometers

PALEOZOIC
MISSISSIPPIAN   ORDOVICIAN
Mfp Fort Payne Formation   Ou Sequatchie and   Stones River Group
                                    Leipers-Catheys   Oca Carters Limestone
SILURIAN   Formations   Olb Lebanon Limestone
S Wayne Group; Brassfield Limestone   Obh Nashville Group   Ord Ridley Limestone

Generalized geology along I-65 between the Alabama state line and Columbia.

upland region of moderate
elevation on the southeast
flank of the Nashville Dome

N 0   5   10 miles

0   10   20 kilometers

GILES
COUNTY

Pulaski

Pulaski

LINCOLN
COUNTY

Fayetteville

Fayetteville channel

Elkton

channel

estuaries with an
encroaching sea

TENNESSEE
ALABAMA

The ancient Pulaski and Fayetteville Rivers forged channels on the southern flank of the exposed Nashville Dome following the deposition of the Leipers-Catheys Formation. The more than 30-mile-long Pulaski channel had a sinuous path between Pulaski and Elkton, whereas the Fayetteville channel was shorter and not as meandering. Both channels met the ocean not far from the Tennessee-Alabama state line. —Modified from Miller, 2014

collapsed reef structure. The Howell structure likely formed during the Devonian Period; Ordovician and Silurian strata are deformed within it.

The interstate crosses more erosional knobs of the Highland Rim at mileposts 19 and 20 and north of exit 22 (US 31A). Resistant beds of the Fort Payne Formation are exposed at the top of the hills. Older Brassfield Limestone, Sequatchie Formation, and Leipers-Catheys Formation underlie the Fort Payne Formation and are exposed on lower slopes.

The interstate crosses Elk (Persimmon) Ridge north of exit 27. Thinly bedded calcareous shale and limestone of the Leipers-Catheys Formation crop out along the lower part of the ridge. Near the top of the ridge, weathering of the Chattanooga Shale creates rust stains on the underlying Leipers-Catheys Formation on both sides of the ridge. Look for thick beds of the Fort Payne Formation at milepost 29.

Middle Tennessee, especially south of Lewisburg between I-65 and I-24, is similar geologically and topographically to the Blue Grass area of Kentucky. Native grasses that are loved by Tennessee Walking Horses grow on the thin limy soils.

Lewisburg sits at the southern end of the inner Central Basin. Strata of the Stones River Group are exposed along the highway between Lewisburg and Nashville. Nashville Group strata generally form higher-elevation areas.

North of Lewisburg look for the Lebanon and Carters Limestones exposed in the Duck River valley. Higher ridges are capped with the Hermitage Formation. The thick-bedded Ridley Limestone is exposed along the banks of the

Berlin Spring at Courthouse Park is located off Old Berlin Road about 7 miles north of Lewisburg via US 431. The natural amphitheater and watering hole, developed in Ridley Limestone of the Stones River Group, was a popular location for campaign speeches between 1844 and 1925. Presidents, senators, congressmen, governors, and judges used a stone, known as Pulpit Rock, as a lectern. —Brent Moore photo

river. The terrain tends to be more level where the Ridley Limestone underlies the valley.

The Duck River drains a relatively large part of Middle Tennessee. This still fairly wild river's headwaters are in the Barrens on the eastern Highland Rim in Coffee County. The river flows northwestward through the Central Basin city of Columbia and into Kentucky Lake north of I-40. The Duck River is the longest river entirely in the state of Tennessee and one of the longest dam-free and most biologically diverse rivers in North America.

Graptolites are carbonized fossils of colonial filter-feeding animals that formed rafts and floated through Paleozoic seas. Graptolite fossils are present in many of Tennessee's shale and carbonate rocks. This sample came from the Lebanon Limestone near Caney Spring, located several miles east of I-65 on TN 99. The graptolites pictured here are approximately 0.25 inch wide. —Mark A. Wilson photo

Columbia, located a few miles west of the interstate off exit 46 (US 412), was the center of Tennessee's phosphate mining industry, which began with the mineral's discovery near the city in Ordovician-age Bigby-Cannon Limestone in the late 1800s. The region south and west of Columbia, especially between Mt. Pleasant and the Duck River, was one of the major phosphate-producing areas of the United States. In the early days, mining was done by pick and axe. Mule-drawn wagons took the phosphate to local processing plants where it was weighed, washed, and processed. For about a hundred years, phosphate mining around Columbia supplied several local fertilizer plants and a ferrophosphate plant, which made steel used for armor plating on guns and battleships during World War I. A few local companies refined elemental phosphorus, detergents, and chemical products until 1991.

The "largest phosphate rock mined in Middle Tennessee" is on display at Maury County Park in Columbia. At 30 tons, this rock is a testament to Columbia's dominance as one of the leading producers and refiners of phosphate during the twentieth century. —Brent Moore photo

Phosphate rock contains high concentrations of the mineral apatite (calcium phosphate). Individual apatite crystals are difficult to see with the naked eye, but en masse the crystals can impart color to their host rock. Phosphate rock may be brown, gray, blue, white, or black, depending on the phosphate quality. Black, dark-blue, and brown phosphate rocks are usually richer in phosphate than the lighter-gray and white rocks, which generally contain more fossil material. Commercial phosphate deposits in Middle Tennessee come mainly from high-grade brown rock that occurs as "blanket deposits," layers 30 to 100 feet thick in the Ordovician-age Bigby-Cannon Limestone. Economically viable phosphate deposits are concentrated in Maury and Giles Counties in a northeast-southwest-trending belt that follows the western side of the Central Basin. The concentration of phosphate material decreases north of Mt. Pleasant.

Phosphate was concentrated in the Bigby-Cannon Formation by tiny organisms (mostly the gastropod *Cyclora minuta*) that extracted it directly from seawater and incorporated it into shells and reef structures. Much of this material was broken up by high-energy currents and waves and later collected on the seafloor. Over time, other minerals were replaced by phosphorous-rich seawater, and thick accumulations of this phosphatic material were preserved in limy mud and sand. During the Pliocene Epoch, these phosphate-rich beds were exposed at the surface, where soils developed and much of the remaining carbonate material was dissolved, a process facilitated by extensive joint systems. Groundwater leached phosphate out of the weathered rock and concentrated it in the bedrock joints and as layered deposits.

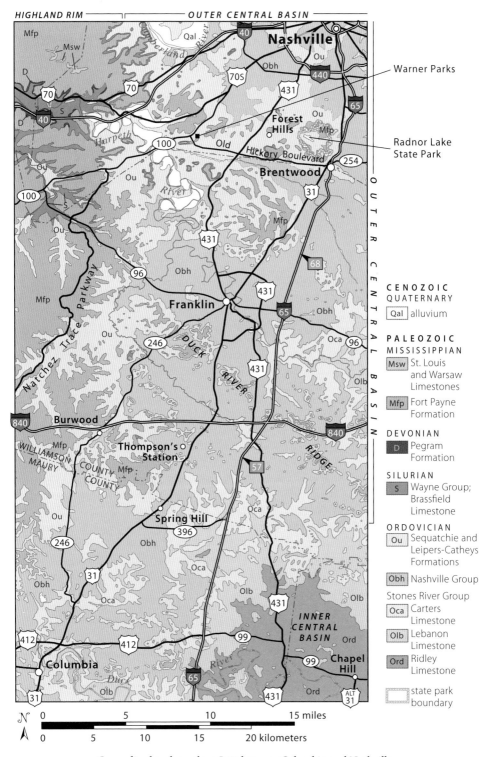

Warner Parks

Radnor Lake State Park

CENOZOIC
QUATERNARY
Qal | alluvium

PALEOZOIC
MISSISSIPPIAN
Msw | St. Louis and Warsaw Limestones
Mfp | Fort Payne Formation

DEVONIAN
D | Pegram Formation

SILURIAN
S | Wayne Group; Brassfield Limestone

ORDOVICIAN
Ou | Sequatchie and Leipers-Catheys Formations
Obh | Nashville Group

Stones River Group
Oca | Carters Limestone
Olb | Lebanon Limestone
Ord | Ridley Limestone

| | state park boundary

Generalized geology along I-65 between Columbia and Nashville.

Strata belonging to the Ordovician-age Bigby-Cannon Limestone are well exposed at the I-65/I-840 junction, where the highway passes through an erosional remnant of the Highland Rim called Duck River Ridge. The Fort Payne Formation caps the highest areas. (35.825438N, 86.833469W) —Marcy Davis photo

Near milepost 57, I-65 crosses the Tennessee Valley Divide. Rivers and their tributaries south of the divide drain to the Tennessee River, whereas those north of the divide flow to the Cumberland River.

Exposures of the Hermitage Formation and the Bigby-Cannon Limestone, both of the Nashville Group, are intermittent between the Duck River Ridge and Old Hickory Boulevard. North of Franklin there are more erosional outliers of the western Highland Rim. These hills, on both sides of the highway, are capped with the Fort Payne Formation.

In 1977 archaeologists discovered Pleistocene-age fossils and human tools during the construction of a golf course east of the interstate off Cool Springs Boulevard (exit 68). Since then, the remains of four mastodons and other ice age animals, including horses, deer, and muskrats, have been found at the site, now known as the Coats-Hines site. Many of the bones were separated and had cut marks indicative of butchering. Blades, scrapers, chisel-like devices, and flakes of stone used as sharpening tools have also been found at the site, some of which were made from Fort Payne Formation chert. Soil studies at the site indicate that a large pond attracted humans and animals to the area. The site's butchered mastodon bones are on display at the McClung Museum of Natural History and Culture at the University of Tennessee in Knoxville.

Look for spectacular exposures of the Bigby-Cannon Limestone and Leipers-Catheys Formation at Old Hickory Boulevard (exit 74). West of the interstate in Radnor Lake State Park, Leipers-Catheys Formation forms the lower slopes and Fort Payne Formation caps the hills, which reach 1,000 feet in elevation. (36.03685N, 86.782669W) —Chuck Sutherland photo

Luke Lea Heights Overlook, located at Percy Warner Park, provides views of the Nashville skyline and the northwestern Central Basin. The Warner Parks (which includes both Percy Warner and Edwin Warner Parks), as well as Radnor Lake State Park, are built on erosional outliers capped by up to 200 feet of the Mississippian-age Fort Payne Formation. —Michael Hicks photo

The Bigby-Cannon Limestone and the Leipers-Catheys Formation are exposed intermittently between exit 74 and the I-40 junction. Look for several small normal faults in the Bigby-Cannon Limestone at the I-40 junction. The faults are most easily seen in the offset of the unit's distinctive light-gray Dove-Colored Member.

I-65

Nashville—Kentucky State Line

39 miles

Northwest of Nashville, I-65 crosses the Cumberland River and merges with I-24 for about 2 miles. Leipers-Catheys Formation is exposed periodically to exit 98 north of Goodlettsville. Erosional outliers capped by the Mississippian-age Fort Payne Formation come into view along the northwest side of the highway where streams have heavily dissected the edge of the Highland Rim. The transition between the Central Basin and the Highland Rim occurs between the Davidson-Sumner county line (near exit 97) and Sumner-Robertson county line (near exit 104). The elevation difference between the two boundaries is about 400 feet over about 6 miles.

The interstate crosses an erosional knob of the Highland Rim north of Goodlettsville. Leipers-Catheys Formation is overlain by shale and fossil-rich limestone of the Sequatchie Formation. The more thickly bedded Brassfield

Green and red shales and limestone of the Ordovician-age Sequatchie Formation are well exposed north of exit 98. The reddish color results from the mineral hematite, an iron oxide. These beds belong to the Fernvale Member, which was mined near Goodlettsville for iron, lead, and zinc until the late 1950s. —Marcy Davis photo

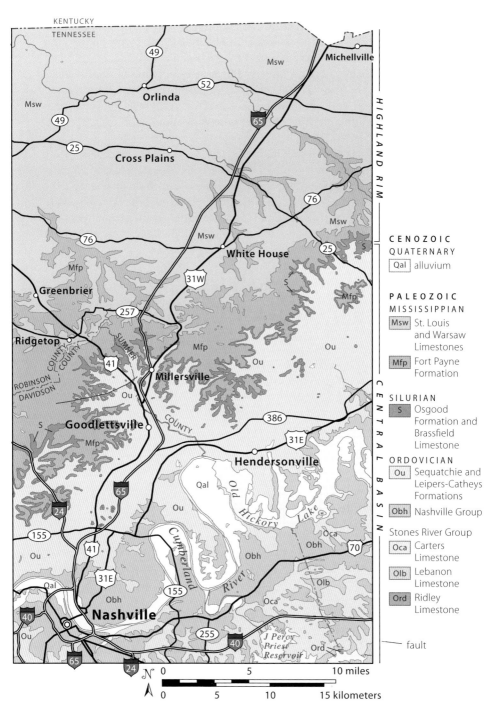

Generalized geology along I-65 between Nashville and the Kentucky state line.

Limestone overlies the Sequatchie Formation, and the unit's distinguishing light-colored cherts are well exposed here and are overlain by the Silurian-age Wayne Group. The Fort Payne Formation caps the hill.

The valley narrows north of Millersville along Slaters Creek as the interstate climbs through the Sequatchie Formation, Brassfield Limestone, Chattanooga Shale, and the Fort Payne Formation. Look for Ordovician-age units near milepost 100 and lengthy roadcuts of Fort Payne Formation uphill from milepost 103 to exit 104 for TN 257.

I-65 is atop the Highland Rim at Ridgetop (exit 104). The red soils are derived from resistant cherty units of the underlying Mississippian-age Warsaw Limestone, which is exposed at road level in some places in small outcrops. The Fort Payne Formation is present in larger streambeds, and the St. Louis Limestone caps higher areas. The St. Louis Limestone underlies the area between exit 117 and the Kentucky state line, and the Warsaw Limestone is present within major drainages.

TN 52

Portland—Livingston

86 miles

TN 52 between Portland in Robertson County and Livingston in Overton County offers a scenic country drive through Mississippian-age limestones of the northeastern Highland Rim. This winding two-lane highway, with plenty of diversions both natural and human (the annual TN 52 Yard Sale, for example), is a pleasant alternative to interstate travel.

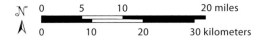

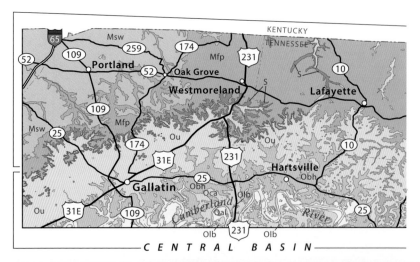

Near Portland, the topography is relatively flat pastureland and farmland. Many northern Middle Tennesseans are trying their hand at viticulture, with wineries popping up in Portland, Lafayette, and Livingston. Dark red soils developed on Mississippian-age Warsaw and St. Louis Limestones support a region rich in soybeans, corn, tobacco, and strawberries. The Fort Payne Formation is present in larger drainages.

Between Oak Grove (at the TN 174 junction) and Red Boiling Springs, the Fort Payne Formation underlies the highway along the edge of the Highland Rim. Deeper drainages near Lafayette and eastward have cut downward into Ordovician-age strata of the Leipers-Catheys Formation. Major streams on this part of the Highland Rim flow northward.

The Fort Payne Formation is well exposed about halfway between Lafayette and Red Boiling Springs at the intersection of TN 52 and Smalling Road. Alternating shale and massive silicastone layers a few feet thick give the rocks a striped appearance. Silicastone occurs where the original carbonate rock dissolved, leaving behind mainly chert.

Karst is well-developed along this section of the northern Highland Rim. Several towns, including Westmoreland and Red Boiling Springs, capitalized on natural mineral springs during the early-twentieth-century search for healing and therapeutic waters. The Devonian-age Chattanooga Shale,

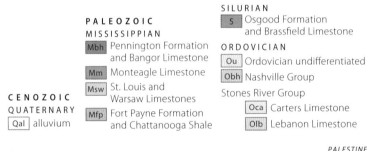

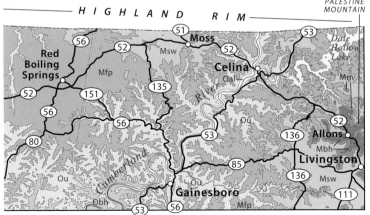

Generalized geology along TN 52 between Portland and Livingston.

Horn corals can be found about 1.5 miles east of the hamlet of Oak Grove in green-gray calcareous shales of the Fort Payne Formation. These corals, a type referred to as rugose, *meaning "wrinkled," thrived in Mississippian-age seas but are now extinct.* —Marcy Davis photo

which underlies Mississippian-age units here, may be the mineral source for these waters. During the early 1900s, tourists arrived via railroad to visit the Epperson Springs Hotel and Resort a couple of miles northeast of Westmoreland. The many different spring waters at Red Boiling Springs, which refers to the movement of natural spring water rather than temperature, varied in mineral content and, consequently, color, taste, and alleged healing properties. Celebrities and politicians reportedly visited the springs. A couple of Red Boiling Springs hotels established during this era remain operational. Many of the town's mineral spring locations are marked by old red water pumps.

Look for dipping beds of limestone in the Fort Payne Formation east of Red Boiling Springs. These beds dip not because they are folded layers but because they are part of a bioherm, a feature constructed through biological processes. Also called mud mounds, bioherms are common to Mississippian-age strata throughout the world. They formed in relatively calm, shallow waters, typically less than 300 feet deep, where animals living on dome-shaped mounds had plenty of light and were also protected from most storm energy. The mounds may be up to several hundred feet wide and 50 feet high.

Tennessee's bioherms are made of siliciclastic mud, broken shells, and other biological material, and they formed during periods of lower sea level when northern Middle Tennessee was at the northern edge of a very shallow sea. Bryozoans, brachiopods, sponges, crinoids, trilobites, bivalves, and algae helped trap and stabilize sediment, and the mounds grew. When the animals died, their debris accumulated on the sides of the mound. In some areas this debris is up to 15 feet thick. Fossiliferous green shales drape over these mounds and

Gray-green shales of the Fort Payne Formation are full of crinoid ossicles at and near the junction of TN 52 and TN 151 in Red Boiling Springs. Ossicles are round plates of calcium carbonate that were stacked and held together by connective tissue. They composed the stem that attached the crinoid animal to a holdfast on the ocean floor. —Larry Knox photo

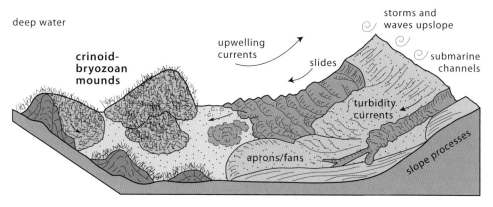

Bioherms are found in the Fort Payne Formation in northern Middle Tennessee and southern Kentucky. The area was a shallow marine shelf that was southwest of a delta during the Mississippian Period. Strong currents created a lumpy seafloor topography. Mud mounds grew between channels on the seafloor. Siliciclastic sediments came from the delta complex; sediments richer in carbonate came from slopes located north and northwest of the bioherms. As sea level rose, sediment supply decreased. Marine animals helped stabilize available sediment, which caused the bioherms to grow. —Modified from Khetani and Read, 2002; Greb et al., 2008

thicken outward along mound flanks. TN 52 crosses through several bioherms in the Fort Payne Formation between Red Boiling Springs and Livingston.

A couple of miles east of Moss, the highway turns southeastward toward Celina, following New Hope Branch and Proctor Creek, both tributaries to the Cumberland River. Numerous roadcuts line the highway as it descends to the Cumberland River. The Fort Payne Formation forms the higher areas here, and the valley has been eroded down into the Ordovician-age Leipers-Catheys Formation.

Celina is located at the confluence of the Obey and Cumberland Rivers. South of Celina, TN 52 follows the south side of Dale Hollow Lake across Mississippian-age strata that are extremely well exposed between Celina and Livingston.

A bioherm is well exposed about 1 mile southeast of downtown Celina at the first large roadcut on the west side of the highway. The dark, organic-rich Chattanooga Shale is exposed at road level. The green Maury Formation forms the core of the bioherm and grades upward into green and tan shales of the Fort Payne Formation that overlie the structure. The reddish layers that are above road level are a bryozoan-and-crinoid-rich limestone. The highway continues to pass through tall roadcuts in the Fort Payne Formation. Just east of the Cecil

The western part of a Mississippian-age bioherm in the Fort Payne Formation is exposed in a large roadcut on the east side of the highway across from a quarry about 4 miles west of Celina. The core of the structure is made of green shale that is mostly covered and out of frame. Light-colored beds of fossiliferous limestone and green mudstone are at road level in the eastern part of the outcrop. The limestone and mudstone slumped along the mound flank during deposi-tion, resulting in a unique, wavelike geometry. Green and tan shales of the upper Fort Payne Formation drape over the mound. Small quartz and gypsum geodes can also be also found here. Orange topsoil weathered from carbonates spills over the roadcut and stains underlying strata. (36.581244N, 85.559195W) —Larry Knox photo

A submarine channel, formed by underwater currents, is preserved in the Fort Payne Forma-tion east of the Cecil and Frances Langford Bridge. A mix of mudstone and carbonate and silica material from deceased marine animals fills the 15-foot-deep channel, in which crinoid ossicles up to 2 inches in diameter have been found. (36.503333N, 85.446736W) —Larry Knox photo

and Frances Langford Bridge, the highway cuts through an ancient submarine channel.

Younger Mississippian-age strata underlie the road east of the Clay-Overton county line. Thick-bedded limestones of the Monteagle Limestone are exposed along the lower slopes of Palestine Mountain, an erosional spur of the Cumberland Plateau west and east of Allons. The Cumberland Plateau escarpment comes into view for eastbound travelers near here. At Allons, the Mississippian-age Hartselle Formation underlies the road, and the Bangor Limestone and Pennington Formation cap higher areas.

Mississippian-age strata form erosional knobs near Livingston, as well as the lower slopes of the Cumberland Plateau escarpment east of Livingston. The St. Louis Limestone underlies the town of Livingston. Several downtown buildings are faced with locally quarried, brown-to-yellow Pennsylvanian-age sandstone.

NATCHEZ TRACE PARKWAY
Nashville—Alabama State Line
108 miles

Natchez Trace Parkway (not to be confused with Natchez Trace State Park of West Tennessee) extends southwestward from Bellevue through Alabama to Natchez, Mississippi. The parkway follows the route of the Old Natchez Trace, a path first used as a game trail by the Chickasaw tribe. European and American pioneers and frontiersmen followed it during the early 1800s, often when

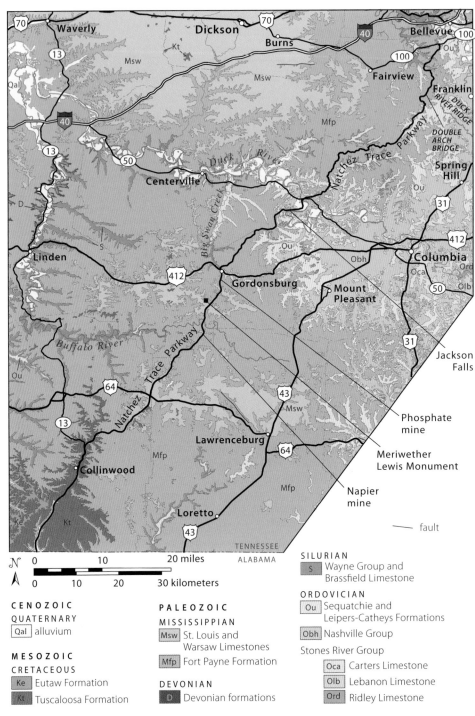

Geology along the Natchez Trace Parkway.

SILURIAN
S Wayne Group and Brassfield Limestone

ORDOVICIAN
Ou Sequatchie and Leipers-Catheys Formations
Obh Nashville Group
Stones River Group
Oca Carters Limestone
Olb Lebanon Limestone
Ord Ridley Limestone

CENOZOIC
QUATERNARY
Qal alluvium

MESOZOIC
CRETACEOUS
Ke Eutaw Formation
Kt Tuscaloosa Formation

PALEOZOIC
MISSISSIPPIAN
Msw St. Louis and Warsaw Limestones
Mfp Fort Payne Formation

DEVONIAN
D Devonian formations

— fault

returning from Natchez, Mississippi, or New Orleans, Louisiana, after selling goods they had floated down the Tennessee, Ohio, and Mississippi Rivers. Use of the Trace declined once steamboats became more common.

Original trail segments remain accessible from the Natchez Trace Parkway at several locations. There are also many scenic trails (several of which allow horses), overlooks, waterfalls, and picnic areas to enjoy along the parkway. The Tennessee part of the Natchez Trace Parkway, from mileposts 444 to 336, follows the western Highland Rim. To reach the parkway from the Nashville area, either take TN 100 west from Bellevue or exit 192 from I-40 and head south for 5 miles on McCrory Lane.

Rock exposures along the parkway are primarily of Mississippian-age carbonates and their associated red residual soils, with Silurian- and Ordovician-age carbonates appearing in larger drainages. South of US 64, some higher areas are capped by Cretaceous-age units.

Thick beds of heavily weathered Fort Payne Formation are exposed about 1 mile south of the TN 100 turnoff along Backbone Ridge. Tree roots have grown deeply into fractures and joints in the rocks.

Double Arch Bridge crosses the Little East Fork of the Harpeth River and is quite spectacular when viewed from below. Take the first turnoff south of the bridge toward Franklin. A viewing area is located at the junction with TN 96. Silurian-age units underlie the valley.

An informational placard at milepost 423.9 on Duck River Ridge marks the Tennessee Valley Divide, the watershed boundary between the streams flowing toward the Tennessee River and those flowing toward the Cumberland River. The Gordon House is located east of the highway on the north side of the Duck River. The brick structure, built in 1818, was home to the family that operated the Duck River ferry before a bridge was built in 1896. Baker Bluff Overlook provides a view across the Duck River valley.

Jackson Falls cascades over Ordovician-age strata at milepost 404.7, about 2 miles south of the Duck River bridge. Jackson Branch once flowed north here but was captured by erosion along a meander bend of the Duck River. The former stream course was abandoned as a new channel was cut through the rock.

The Fort Payne Formation is exposed across from the Fall Hollow Trailhead north of Gordonsburg. Mississippian-age Warsaw and St. Louis Limestones are exposed near the Meriwether Lewis Monument and at higher elevations for a few miles south.

The Natchez Trace Parkway passes through two significant mining operations in Tennessee. Phosphate was mined from the Ordovician-age Bigby-Cannon Limestone during the late 1800s. Most mining operations were between the parkway and Columbia, to the east. You can see a couple of old mine shafts, ore pushcarts, and an abandoned narrow-gauge railbed at the Phosphate Mine at milepost 390.7, south of the US 412 junction.

Iron was mined from Mississippian-age limestone between the 1830s and 1920s in Napier, about 10 miles south of the junction with US 412. The furnace produced pig iron that was then sold to other foundries and mills. The remnants of the mine mill, furnace site, and slag pile are at Metal Ford at the Buffalo River.

At Sunken Trace, milepost 350.5, you can view the original Natchez Trace, widened and deepened here by ruts made by carts and wagons that sank into the mud during wet periods. Frustrated travelers cut new paths around this muddy spot. Three such paths are preserved here.

Iron was mined at Napier from shallow open pits in Mississippian-age limestone. Although now largely overgrown, the rust-colored pit walls are still visible from the Napier Mine overlook, located at the Napier Mine turnoff on Natchez Parkway.
—Marcy Davis photo

WEST TENNESSEE
Gulf Coastal Plain

West Tennessee, the low-lying region between the Mississippi and Tennessee Rivers, is part of the Gulf Coastal Plain. The region is divided into three physiographic districts in Tennessee: the hilly West Tennessee Uplands, the dissected West Tennessee Plain, and the flatlands of the Mississippi River Valley. West Tennessee is largely rural except for Memphis and smaller cities such as Dyersburg, Jackson, Martin, Union City, and Paris. Aggregate, sand, clay, and heavy minerals are mined throughout West Tennessee and contribute substantially to local economies. These materials are extracted from northeast-trending swaths of Cretaceous-age-to-recently-deposited marine and river sedimentary units.

Outcrops are scarce in this part of the state due to the unconsolidated nature of the underlying strata, but subtle changes in topography and soil color reveal clues to the geology. A notable exception is the west-facing edge of the Chickasaw Bluffs lining the Mississippi River, which are up to 100 feet high.

West Tennessee is part of the Gulf Coastal Plain, a low area that includes the Mississippi Embayment (yellow) and extends southward to the Gulf of Mexico.

289

Fossiliferous Silurian-age strata crop out along the Tennessee River near Clifton. The Tennessee River forms the boundary between Middle and West Tennessee. The western Highland Rim of Middle Tennessee is visible in the distance. (35.410822N, 88.051990W) —Chuck Sutherland photo

Eocene-age and younger units are exposed in this pronounced topographic boundary between the Mississippi River Valley and the West Tennessee Plain. Well-indurated Paleozoic-age units are exposed along the Tennessee River and in tributary valleys.

West Tennessee Uplands

The West Tennessee Uplands, the hilly area that forms the drainage divide between the Tennessee and Mississippi Rivers, parallel the western side of the Tennessee River valley. The uplands are about 12 miles wide near the Kentucky border and about 40 miles wide at the Mississippi border. Elevations range between about 400 and 700 feet, roughly 200 feet above the West Tennessee Plain, which lies to the west.

The upland's mainly marine sand, clay, and calcareous shale of Cretaceous age were deposited along a dynamic shoreline, resulting in a sometimes complicated mash-up of unconsolidated coastal and marine sediments. River deltas, tidal flats, lagoons, estuaries, beaches, and nearshore and shelf environments are all preserved in the geologic record of the West Tennessee Uplands. These sediments unconformably overlie Paleozoic-age sedimentary rocks that crop out along the Tennessee River.

West Tennessee Plain

The West Tennessee Plain, the low-lying area between the West Tennessee Uplands and the Mississippi River Valley, is covered with loess, windblown silt. Silt-sized quartz and feldspar minerals dominate the loess, with lesser amounts of carbonate and iron minerals. Over time, the feldspar minerals weather to clay minerals. Fresh exposures are grayish in color while weathered surfaces are shades of yellow, orange, and brown due to the oxidation of iron minerals. Loess forms only during periods of glaciation, so its presence indicates a past cold global climate, in this case that of the Pleistocene ice ages. Tennessee's loess deposits originated as silt along the banks of the early Mississippi River, which was a braided system formed of coalescing meltwater streams flowing from northern ice sheets and choked with sediment. During drier periods, silt deposited along the riverbanks dried out, and westerly winds entrained and redeposited it in a thick mantle across much of middle North America.

Tennessee has three loess layers that are separated by ancient soil layers. These three loess layers correlate with loess deposits found elsewhere in North America, indicating that the Pleistocene ice ages consisted of several pulses of glaciation, wherein North American ice sheets periodically advanced and retreated. The soils developed during warmer intervals between three different glacial stages, or

STRATIGRAPHIC COLUMN FOR WEST TENNESSEE

EON	ERA	PERIOD	EPOCH	GROUP	FORMATION	DESCRIPTION	DEPOSITIONAL ENVIRONMENT
PHANEROZOIC	CENOZOIC	QUATERNARY	HOLOCENE		alluvial deposits	silt, clay, sand, conglomerate	sediments deposited along rivers and streams
			PLEISTOCENE		loess	silt, clay	glacially-derived windblown silt
		NEO.	PLIOCENE		Upland Complex	iron-rich gravel, sand	river terrace deposits
		PALEOGENE	OLIGOCENE		Jackson Formation	silt, clay, sand	coastal and nearshore marine, contains lignite
			EOCENE	Claiborne Group	Cockfield Formation, Cook Mountain Formation, Memphis Sand	silt, clay, sand, lignite	low-gradient streams on a low coastal plain; coastal lakes, swamps, freshwater lagoons; contains abundant fossil plants that are well preserved
			PALEOCENE	Wilcox Group	Flour Island Formation, Fort Pillow Sand, Old Breastworks Formation	silt, clay, sand, lignite	river and deltaic with some marginal marine and nearshore environments; contains fossilized plants
				Midway Group	Porters Creek Clay	clay, sand	shallow marine and sandbars; fossiliferous
					Clayton Formation	clay, marl	offshore to nearshore; fossiliferous
	MESOZOIC	CRETACEOUS			Owl Creek Formation		shallow and nearshore marine; fossiliferous
					McNairy Sand		nearshore, delta, bay, lagoon sediments deposited during regression of the Demopolis Sea; contains heavy minerals
					Coon Creek Formation	glauconitic sand, silt, clay, marl	offshore, environment intermediate to the deeper shelf of the Demopolis Formation and the shallower McNairy Sand; highly fossiliferous
					Demopolis Formation		offshore, relatively deep shelf
					Sardis Formation		offshore
					Coffee Sand		barrier beaches and lagoons in the transgressing Demopolis Sea
					Eutaw Formation		shallow and nearshore marine
					Tuscaloosa Formation	chert gravel, silt, sand	eastward-flowing streams and shallow marine environments; deposition occurred on paleokarst surface of the Highland Rim
	PALEOZOIC	MISSISSIPPIAN			Fort Payne Formation	chert, limestone, silicastone	warm, shallow to deep marine basin with a carbonate ramp or platform that persisted throughout the Mississippian Period
		DEVONIAN			Chattanooga Shale	black shale	shallow sea, oxygen-poor environment, highly organic
					Camden Formation, Harriman Formation	chert	shallow shelf
					Flat Gap Limestone	limestone	shallow shelf
					Ross Formation: Birdsong Shale Member, Rockhouse Limestone Member	limestone, shale	shallow shelf; highly fossiliferous and glauconitic; Rockhouse Limestone contains mud mounds
		SILURIAN			Decatur Limestone	limestone	shallow shelf; highly fossiliferous
				Brownsport Group	Lobelville Formation, Bob Limestone, Beech River Formation	limestone, shale	shallow shelf

Generalized stratigraphic column for West Tennessee. —Compiled from various sources

periods of ice sheet advance. The loess is thickest along the Chickasaw Bluffs and thins eastward across the West Tennessee Plain to about the longitude of Jackson. Many West Tennessee parks, including T. O. Fuller State Park, Meeman-Shelby Forest State Park, and Fort Pillow State Historic Park, are good places to have a look at loess and underlying sedimentary units. The loess forms the bluff along Riverside Drive in Memphis, although it is covered by grass.

Loess bluffs tend to be steep, often between 45 and 90 degrees. In periods of heavy rainfall or during earthquakes, bluff edges are prone to slumping. In agricultural areas surrounding Memphis where slopes are gentle and not heavily vegetated, loess is susceptible to sheet erosion during heavy rains. The runoff removes thin layers of soil from across large areas rather than in discrete channels, resulting in substantial soil loss and degradation.

The loess covers Pleistocene-age sand and gravel, as well as older sediments of Neogene and Paleogene age that record a transition from primarily marine conditions of the Mesozoic to nonmarine conditions of the Cenozoic. The ocean withdrew from the Mississippi Embayment for the last time in the Oligocene Epoch, about 30 million years ago. Although devoid of topographic character, the West Tennessee Plain is agriculturally rich. Row crops of corn, soybeans, cotton, and hay are grown in the fertile soils that have developed on sand, silt, clay, and loess. Several rivers, including the Wolf, Loosahatchie, Hatchie, and Obion, flow sluggishly northwestward across the often swampy region to join the Mississippi River.

Reddish, iron-rich stream deposits of the Pliocene-to-Pleistocene-age Upland Complex are exposed in the Chickasaw Bluffs. Exposures are usually limited to streambanks, construction sites, and quarries, where the unit is mined for aggregate. Up to 100 feet of Upland Complex sand and gravel were deposited by the ancestral Mississippi and Ohio Rivers between Kentucky and Louisiana. Fist-sized cobbles and ancient oxbows two to three times larger than those of the modern Mississippi River indicate that the ancestral Mississippi was a powerful, high-velocity river with a discharge estimated to have been six to eight times that of the modern river. There were multiple sediment sources for the Upland Complex, including the St. Francois Mountains of Missouri, south-central Canada, and Grenville-age rocks of the Blue Ridge. Pliocene sea level was about 300 feet higher than today's, but by about 4 million years ago it was about 25 feet higher than today. During subsequent ice ages, when sea level was even lower, the river incised the floodplain and left behind the ancient stream terrace gravels of the Upland Complex. In West Tennessee, the Upland Complex averages 30 feet thick and is preserved in a discontinuous band along the Mississippi River.

Underlying the Upland Complex is the Jackson Formation, an Eocene-Oligocene-age unit made of silty sand and clay. The Jackson Formation is about 60 feet thick, and in West Tennessee it is exposed only at the base of the Chickasaw Bluffs along the Mississippi River. Jackson Formation sediments were deposited in part by the last sea that extended into the upper part of the Mississippi Embayment.

Mississippi River Valley

The Mississippi River Valley is the low-lying area west of the Chickasaw Bluffs. Only the Amazon and Congo River basins are larger than that of the Mississippi River. The Mississippi transports millions of tons of gravel, sand, silt, and clay from interior North America to the Gulf of Mexico each year. These sediments, called the river's load, include the bed load, suspended load, and dissolved load. The bed load consists of larger particles, such as coarse sand and gravel that roll and bounce along the river bottom. The suspended load is carried in the water column. Gravel, sand, silt, and clay may all be part of the bed load or suspended load, depending on the river's velocity. The Mississippi River's nickname, Big Muddy, reflects the brown coloration imparted to the river when it has a suspended load high in silt and clay particles, typically after large rains. The dissolved load consists of ions dissolved in the water; they come from the chemical weathering of rocks and soil.

During flood events, the river may leave the channel and deposit its sediment on the floodplain. Coarse material settles out adjacent to the river channel to form a natural levee, while silt and clay are carried farther away. These sediments nourish the floodplain and provide the fertile foundation for more than 900 square miles of West Tennessee cropland. Row crops, such as soybeans and cotton, have replaced native cypress swamps and bottomland forest.

The Mississippi River's gradient is low. *Gradient* describes a river's change in elevation divided by the total river channel distance between two points. High-gradient rivers, typically found in the mountains, are characterized by

The Mississippi River floodplain near Richardsons Landing at Drummonds west of US 51. —Marcy Davis photo

narrow, steep-walled valleys with fast-moving water flowing through relatively straight channels that do not have a wide floodplain. Low-gradient rivers develop a wide, flat floodplain over which they slowly meander, shifting their channels from time to time. They also transport relatively high volumes of sediment in their broad, U-shaped channels. Despite being a low-gradient river, the Mississippi is dynamic and responsive to variations in climate, sea level, subsidence, and tectonism. Drought and flood can change the river dramatically within a few days; sandbars may develop or disappear entirely. The river's course is always changing, so in its natural state all features of the river system are temporary.

The Mississippi River has left a chaotic mosaic of abandoned channels across its floodplain. As the river flows around a bend, it erodes the outer edge, called the cutbank, where water velocity and turbulence are greatest. Sediments settle out on the inside of the bend, the point bar, where water velocity slows and turbulence drops. As a result of this continued erosion and deposition, the river begins to bend. Over time the bend becomes more pronounced and S-shaped and migrates laterally across the floodplain as well as downstream. A pronounced bend is called a meander. As meanders migrate, they may leave behind a meander scar where they eroded a cutbank.

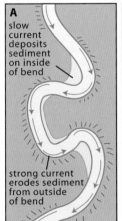
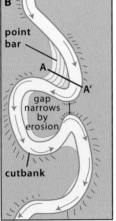
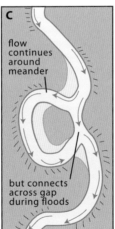
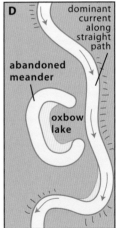

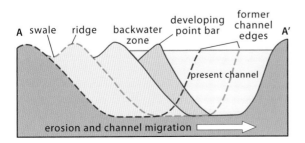

A river erodes a cutbank along the outside of a meander where river velocity is greatest. Sediments are deposited on a point bar in the inside of a meander where velocity slows. The river eventually cuts through a narrow meander neck and abandons the meander, which becomes an oxbow lake.

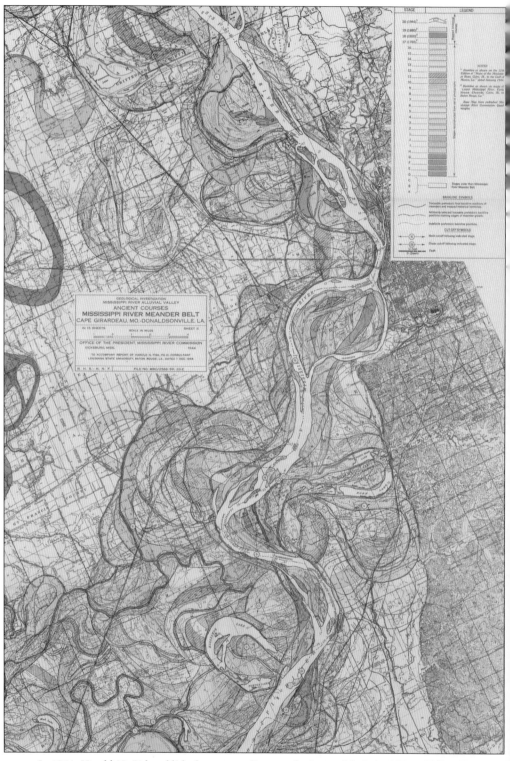

In 1944, Harold N. Fisk published a compendium on the Lower Mississippi River Valley. He used aerial photography, topographic maps, boreholes, well log data, and geological field work to reconstruct the history of the Mississippi River. Fisk's work greatly advanced our understanding of Mississippi River processes. Fisk's plate 22, sheet 5 is pictured here. Colors correspond to abandoned Mississippi River channels. Memphis is at right center. —From Fisk, 1944

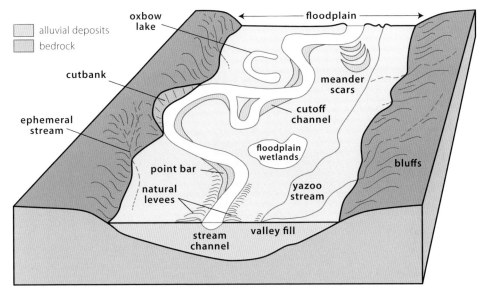

In Tennessee the Mississippi River migrates laterally across its floodplain, leaving behind numerous landforms. Meander scars form during this migration. Oxbow lakes form as the main river channel cuts off narrow meander necks. During flood stage, the river deposits sediment adjacent to the main channel. With multiple flood events, these sediments form a natural levee. Tributary drainages, called yazoo streams, often develop parallel to the main river.

Ridge and swale topography develops on the point bar as meander loop sinuosity increases. When the river channel is stable, sediment builds up along the point bar, forming a subtle ridge. As the river moves, a new point bar and corresponding ridge is created with the swale—a low spot—between them. Eventually, the meander loop may bend back on itself and favor a shortcut across the remaining neck; when it does, it leaves behind ridges and swales and a swampy, horseshoe-shaped lake called an oxbow that often remains for several thousand years before drying out or filling with silt, sand, and fine-grained, sticky black "gumbo" soil. The hundreds of oxbow lakes and meander scars on the Mississippi River floodplain are most obvious when viewed from the air.

New Madrid Seismic Zone

The flat Mississippi River Valley doesn't look like the most active area of seismicity east of the Rocky Mountains, but it is. Earthquakes occur mainly at depths between 2 and 9 miles in the New Madrid Seismic Zone, a 150-mile-long zone of active faulting in the northern Reelfoot rift between Marked Tree, Arkansas, and Cairo, Illinois. The earthquakes here result from intraplate tectonic activity, or forces acting within the North American tectonic plate. This is in contrast to interplate tectonics, forces between tectonic plates, such as the situation along the west coast of North America. Earthquakes resulting

earthquake epicenters of magnitude greater than 2.5 and that occurred 1973 and later

earthquake epicenters of magnitude greater than 2.5 and that occurred before 1973

estimated locations of earthquake epicenters that occurred in 1811 and 1812

Mississippi Embayment boundary

The New Madrid Seismic Zone is a region of active seismicity responsible for four large earthquakes that occurred during the winter of 1811–1812. Three major fault systems and many secondary faults located in the northern Mississippi Embayment make up the New Madrid Seismic Zone. Right-lateral movement along the Axial and the New Madrid North faults creates compression and thrust faulting along the left-stepping Reelfoot fault. —Modified from Csontos and Van Arsdale, 2008; Martin and Van Arsdale, 2017; Martin et al., 2014

from intraplate tectonics are poorly understood, but scientists have a handful of hypotheses about potential causes. One idea is that the seismic zone crust may be thinner, weaker, and higher in temperature, allowing it to stretch and move more easily. Isostatic rebound, a process by which continental crust very, very slowly "bounces back" to a stable position, may also play a role. Following the last glacier retreat during the Pleistocene ice ages, crust rebounded because it no longer bore the weight of the ice. The region of the seismic zone wasn't glaciated, but the crust may be bouncing back due to the erosion of tens of feet of sediment by the Mississippi River over the last 20,000 years.

Regardless of the underlying causes, earthquakes in the New Madrid Seismic Zone result from northeast-southwest-directed compressional forces, or squeezing, that causes movement on old Proterozoic-to-Cambrian-age faults. GPS studies have shown that the ground surface in the New Madrid Seismic Zone is moving surprisingly little despite the region's many earthquakes. More than two hundred earthquakes occur each year in the seismic zone—that's about one earthquake every other day. Most are imperceptible to humans, so geoscientists rely on seismographs, sensitive instruments designed to record earthquake magnitude, location, and depth.

In simplest terms, the New Madrid Seismic Zone consists of two fault zones connected by a third, with each fault zone consisting of one dominant fault and several smaller associated faults. The New Madrid North fault zone extends 60 miles northeast from New Madrid, Missouri. The Axial fault zone is also about 60 miles long, extending from Marked Tree, Arkansas, to near Ridgely, Tennessee. Both of these fault zones are dominated by nearly vertical, right-lateral strike-slip faults. Most of the earthquakes cluster along the third fault zone, the Reelfoot, which connects the other two. The Reelfoot fault was a normal fault during Cambrian time but has been reactivated as a thrust fault. All of these faults, along with rift margin faults, displace Quaternary-age sediments, meaning they have been active during the last 1.8 million years.

Four of North America's largest recorded earthquakes occurred in the New Madrid Seismic Zone during the winter of 1811–1812. With estimated magnitudes between 7.2 and 8.1, the New Madrid earthquakes, along with hundreds of aftershocks, devastated surrounding areas. The first New Madrid earthquake and the second, a large aftershock, both occurred on December 16, 1811, likely in the Axial fault zone near Blytheville, Arkansas. The third earthquake, on January 23, 1812, probably occurred on the New Madrid North fault near New Madrid, Missouri. The fourth earthquake, on February 7, occurred on the Reelfoot fault near Tiptonville, Tennessee. Damage and surface rupture from the shaking were greatest between Memphis and Cairo, Illinois, but the effects were felt over more than 200,000 square miles. The hard, consolidated nature of bedrock underlying the seismic zone allowed earthquake waves to spread out over eastern North America. Witnesses reported ground shaking, ringing church bells, pavement cracks, and lurching buildings as far away as the Atlantic and Gulf Coasts, and even Canadian residents reported ground shaking.

New Madrid resident Eliza Bryan, wrote her account of the earthquakes in an 1816 letter to Methodist evangelist Lorenzo Dow. Her letter was reprinted in his biography. An excerpt of the letter reads:

> On the 16th of December, 1811, about two o'clock, A.M., we were visited by a violent shock of an earthquake, accompanied by a very awful noise resembling loud but distant thunder, but more hoarse and vibrating, which was followed in a few minutes by the complete saturation of the atmosphere, with sulfurious vapor, causing total darkness. The screams of the affrighted inhabitants running to and fro, not knowing where to go or what to do—the cries of the fowls and beasts of every species—the crackling of trees falling, and the roaring of the Mississippi—the current of which was retrograde for a few minutes, owing as it is supposed, to an [eruption] in its bed—formed a scene truly horrible.

Together, the earthquakes produced a number of natural phenomena that terrified local residents over a period of several months. The earthquake waves uplifted, tilted, and cracked trees and opened large cracks, or fissures, through which sand, water, and methane seeped to the surface and into which livestock fell. The earthquakes also generated seiches—large waves—on the Mississippi River that overturned and washed away boats and caused local flooding. Where the land dropped down in response to the faulting, farms became swamps. The upward movement of land along the Reelfoot fault formed a dam on the Mississippi River, causing it to reverse directions north of Reelfoot Lake. Sandbars and islands disappeared as new channels opened and the river changed course. More than two hundred landslides and slumps collapsed riverbanks and created waterfalls and whirlpools along the Mississippi River. Some of these features remain visible in the contemporary landscape.

Severe ground shaking during the New Madrid earthquakes caused water-saturated sand, silt, and clay close to the water table to lose strength and the ability to support weight, a process called *liquefaction*. Friction normally helps sand grains stick together, but during an earthquake water pressure increases and forces sand grains apart. As a result, water is forced up and out, taking some sand with it, and the ground temporarily becomes quicksand. In severe cases, liquefaction may cause buildings, utilities, and roads to sink, thereby destroying a city's infrastructure. In some areas, the alluvial cover along the Mississippi River floodplain and other rivers is only about 100 feet thick and water saturated to within 20 feet of the surface. Consequently, features resulting from liquefaction are found all over the northern Mississippi Embayment, but they are particularly concentrated in northwestern Tennessee, southeastern Missouri, and northeastern Arkansas.

Paleoseismology is the study of sediments and faults in order to find clues about ancient earthquakes. Paleoseismologists estimate that major earthquakes shake the New Madrid Seismic Zone about every five hundred years. Predicting if or when an earthquake will occur and how large it will be is quite difficult. Assuming an earthquake is inevitable, geoscientists model the effects of earthquakes of various magnitudes in an effort to establish smart and efficient public policies, such as building codes and emergency services. Most assumptions about future earthquakes are based on the locations of today's small earthquakes, as well as where large earthquakes are thought to have occurred in the past. Seismologists currently estimate there's a 7 to 10 percent probability that a magnitude 7 or greater earthquake will occur in the New Madrid Seismic Zone sometime in the next fifty years.

A contemporary earthquake comparable in magnitude to the New Madrid earthquakes would cause more damage because of the large urban population and supporting infrastructure that exist today. Ground shaking and surface rupture would damage buildings, particularly those built of the old brick masonry common to the region. Also at risk are levees, utilities, bridges, roads, sewage lines, and communication lines, particularly along creek and river floodplains where liquefaction is more likely.

Road Guides in West Tennessee

I-40
Tennessee River—Jackson
53 miles

I-40 crosses the north-flowing Tennessee River a few miles south of the confluence of the Tennessee and Duck Rivers at Cuba Landing. Here, at the upstream end of Kentucky Lake, the river channel is wide with many islands. Mississippian-age and older strata are exposed along the Tennessee River and its tributary valleys but are covered by younger strata in upland areas.

Between exit 133 and Jackson, I-40 crosses relatively narrow northeast-southwest-trending belts of Cretaceous-to-Paleogene-age marine and nonmarine sedimentary strata. For much of the Cretaceous Period, West Tennessee resembled today's coastal Gulf of Mexico. Barrier islands protected shallow, brackish lagoons and bays teeming with life. Generally sandy sediments were deposited during the transgression and regression of the Demopolis Sea, a small embayment of the Western Interior Seaway that extended from the Gulf of Mexico through the western United States. In general, sedimentary layers thicken southwestward, where the Cretaceous-age ocean was deeper, and thin northward toward what were Cretaceous-age highlands. Because these units were

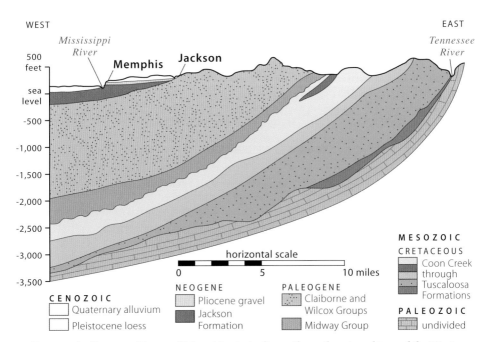

Between the Tennessee River and Memphis, strata dip gently southwestward toward the Mississippi Embayment as a result of subsidence during the Mesozoic and Cenozoic Eras. Cretaceous and younger strata lie unconformably on Paleozoic-age units. —Modified from Wells and Foster, 1933

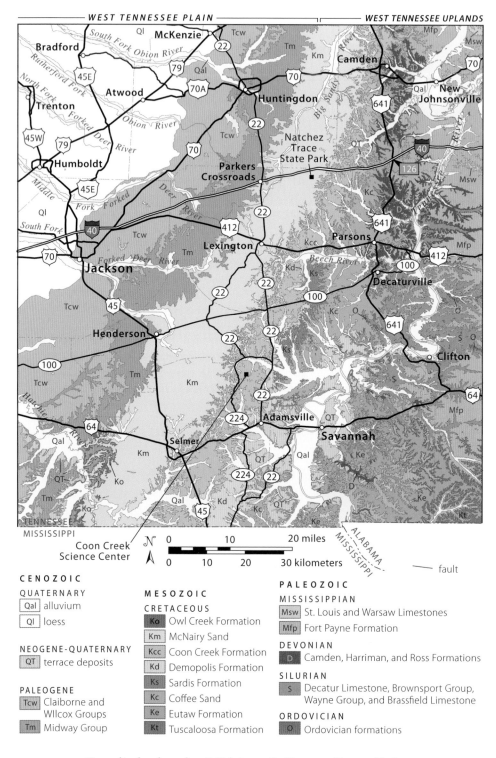

Coon Creek
Science Center

N

0   10   20 miles

0   10   20   30 kilometers

—— fault

CENOZOIC

QUATERNARY
Qal alluvium
Ql   loess

NEOGENE-QUATERNARY
QT   terrace deposits

PALEOGENE
Tcw Claiborne and
     Wilcox Groups
Tm   Midway Group

MESOZOIC
CRETACEOUS
Ko   Owl Creek Formation
Km   McNairy Sand
Kcc Coon Creek Formation
Kd   Demopolis Formation
Ks   Sardis Formation
Kc   Coffee Sand
Ke   Eutaw Formation
Kt   Tuscaloosa Formation

PALEOZOIC
MISSISSIPPIAN
Msw St. Louis and Warsaw Limestones
Mfp Fort Payne Formation

DEVONIAN
D   Camden, Harriman, and Ross Formations

SILURIAN
S   Decatur Limestone, Brownsport Group,
     Wayne Group, and Brassfield Limestone

ORDOVICIAN
O   Ordovician formations

Generalized geology along I-40 between the Tennessee River and Jackson.

never deeply buried, they remain relatively unconsolidated. They are often difficult to distinguish from one another, especially from the highway.

The Cretaceous-age Coffee Sand lies unconformably on the Mississippian-age Fort Payne Formation and crops out in low areas along the interstate between the rest areas (near milepost 132) and exit at 126 for US 641. The Coffee Sand is the remains of a barrier island and lagoon complex that existed during the initial inland push of the rising Demopolis Sea. Streams delivered fine-grained sand, silt, and clay to the shoreline, while the ocean mixed stream sediments with marine sediments brought in by longshore currents. Nearby forests and marshes contributed organic material that is now preserved as lignite in clay lenses within the sand layers. Small nodules of amber, fossilized tree sap, are occasionally found within beds of wood fragments.

Between the US 641 junction and Parkers Crossroads, I-40 crosses the West Tennessee Uplands, an area of noticeably higher elevation and more relief than surrounding areas. Near milepost 122 the interstate crosses an important geomorphic boundary, the drainage divide separating rivers that flow toward the Tennessee River and those that flow toward the Mississippi River.

Lagerstätte, a German word meaning "storage place," refers to a sedimentary deposit with exceptional fossil preservation. There are Lagerstätten representing all geologic time periods, and they can provide a fairly complete picture

Glauconite, a greenish mineral in the mica group, gives sediments a greenish hue. The mineral, present in the sands of most of West Tennessee's Cretaceous-age units, forms on the seafloor through the alteration of clay minerals. Lumps of these greensands and fossilized shell material of the Coon Creek Formation are affectionately called "potatoes" when wrapped in foil by geologists who want to preserve them for future study. —Michael Gibson photo

of the ecology, biodiversity, and animal behavior for a particular time period and habitat. Some Lagerstätten contain high concentrations of well-preserved organic hard parts in disarray, such as in a bone bed. Others are known for the remarkable preservation of fossilized plants and animals, especially soft tissues. Both types of Lagerstätten are present in West Tennessee.

The Coon Creek Formation is a Lagerstätte renowned for the excellent preservation and diversity of marine animals that lived in the shallow waters off then coastal West Tennessee. Look for greenish-tan soils along the I-40 as it crosses the 70-million-year-old Coon Creek Formation between milepost 122 and Natchez Trace State Park at exit 116. Today's Gulf of Mexico, from the coastline to about 90 miles offshore, is a good analog for the paleoenvironment of the Coon Creek. Waves helped oxygenate waters, and currents supplied nutrients, both of which created an ideal habitat for the more than six hundred animal species that lived here. Many animals were burrowers that churned up seafloor sediments, so much of the Coon Creek Formation lacks distinct bedding planes. Snails, clams, oysters, sponges, corals, crabs, lobsters, urchins, fishes, turtles, sharks, and crocodiles all lived in the regressing Cretaceous-age sea. Other predators, such as ammonoids, plesiosaurs, and mosasaurs, also lived in the sea. Fossilized bones, teeth, carapaces, and still-opalescent aragonite shells are found unaltered in the fine-grained, clay-rich marine sand. The number of fossils is staggering, and the relatively unconsolidated nature of the sediments makes collecting and preparing fossils relatively easy.

The Pink Palace Museum in Memphis contains the most extensive collection of Coon Creek fossils, many of which are still being described and studied. The Pink Palace also leads educational tours, by appointment, to the Coon Creek Science Center in Adamsville, where the Coon Creek Formation was first described. The Discovery Park of America, in Union City, and the McClung Museum of Natural History and Culture, in Knoxville, also have Coon Creek fossils on display.

Near milepost 116 the Coon Creek Formation grades into the overlying McNairy Sand, which was deposited where saltwater habitats of the shallow sea and estuaries oscillated with freshwater deltaic environments as the Demopolis Sea regressed. These sands are mined north of the interstate for quartz used in the manufacture of glass, and for heavy minerals.

West of Parkers Crossroads, I-40 crosses the West Tennessee Plain. Brown soils derived from the weathered Midway Group of Paleocene age line the highway between exits 108 and 101. Thinly bedded limestone at the base of the Midway Group marks the initial appearance of the last sea to cover West Tennessee. The lower part of the Midway Group is made mostly of marine sand of the Clayton Formation that grades upward into the Porters Creek Clay, which was deposited during the maximum reach of the sea in Tennessee during Cenozoic time. Porters Creek Clay consists predominantly of montmorillonite, a highly absorbent clay mineral. It swells when wet and shrinks when dry. Porters Creek Clay is mined near Paris, north of here, for use in cat litter and fertilizers, and for products that help remediate chemical spills. The gradational contact between the Midway Group and overlying Wilcox Group marks the

Pterotrigonia (Scabrotrigonia) thoracica from the Coon Creek Formation became Tennessee's official state fossil in 1998. Geology faculty and students of the University of Tennessee at Martin championed the fossil because it is easy to collect and is often found molded in life position within enclosing sediment. The fossil also is a member of Trigoniida, *a family of modern bivalve mollusks currently near extinction. The scale is in centimeters.* —Tammy Braithwaite, Pink Palace Museum photo

transition from the dominantly marine environment of the Cretaceous Period to the dominantly river environment of the Cenozoic Era.

The Paloecene-to-Eocene-age Wilcox and Claiborne Groups underlie about 15 miles of the interstate east of Jackson. These strata preserve the development of a south-flowing, meandering river system that was similar to the modern Mississippi River. The river developed in a humid, warm, swampy lowland following the final southward regression of the sea. The Wilcox and Claiborne Groups are so similar that they are difficult to distinguish. Both consist of thin layers of gray-to-buff-colored sand, silt, and discontinuous lenses of organic-rich clay that are 2 to 9 feet thick. Some circular lenses contain seams or caps of low-quality coal, so they probably formed in lakes and swamps where plants decomposed. Arc-shaped lenses preserve ancient oxbow lakes. Others are elongate or S shaped, and in cross section they are shaped like a river channel—curved along the bottom and flat on top with well-defined boundaries between the clay and surrounding channel sands. Together, these clay lenses mark an ancient river system where clay and organic material accumulated in abandoned river channels, oxbow lakes, and backswamps over a 500-to-1,500-year time frame.

Sand from the Claiborne Group is mined near Jackson for fiberglass and ceramics applications. The clay, typically bentonite and kaolinite, is mined near Paris for ceramics and a number of industrial uses. The Wilcox Group is an important coal-bearing formation in Texas, Louisiana, and Arkansas, but deposits are not economically viable in Tennessee.

The Wilcox and Claiborne Groups together are a Lagerstätte in which fossil soft parts are spectacularly preserved as impressions or casts. Soft-part preservation occurs only in low-energy, low-oxygen environments, such as lake or ocean bottoms, where bacteria cannot survive and thus decompose organic

This leaf fossil from the Claiborne Group is several inches across and so well-preserved that its veins can be traced. Wood, leaf, flower, pollen, seed, and fruit fossils preserved in clay lenses of the Claiborne Group indicate that West Tennessee had a diverse tropical to subtropical flora during Eocene time. (36.282703N, 88.528909W)
—Chuck Sutherland photo

material. This type of preservation also requires relatively large influxes of fine-grained sediment to fall gently to the lake bottom or seafloor and collect in thin layers that preserve plants, animals, and insects. The organic-rich clays of the Wilcox and Claiborne Groups contain some of the best-preserved Eocene-age flowering plant and insect fossils in North America. Wood, leaves, flowers, pollen, seeds, and fruit from walnut, beech, eucalyptus, laurel, tea, oak, coffee, palm, and Chinese hard rubber trees, as well as hornworts and legumes, are fossilized in finely layered clay lenses, fine sand, and lignite coal seams.

I-40

JACKSON—MEMPHIS
85 miles

Jackson sits at the eastern edge of Tennessee's Pleistocene-age loess, glacially derived, windblown silt that covers the West Tennessee Plain. Near Jackson loess is negligible, but its thickness increases westward to the Chickasaw Bluffs, where it is more than 100 feet thick in some areas. The loess overlies Eocene and Oligocene sediments, and in places it covers Pliocene-to-Pliestocene-age gravels of the Upland Complex.

I-40 crosses bottomlands of the Hatchie River west of Jackson. The Hatchie is West Tennessee's only major river that has not been impounded. Some geologists suggest that the Hatchie River valley was the ancestral course of the Tennessee River, which may have flowed in a westerly direction about 5 million years ago.

Soils developed on mineral-rich Pleistocene-age loess provide a fertile foundation for much of West Tennessee's row crops. Jackson is an agricultural center originally founded on cotton grown in surrounding areas.
—Michael Roedel photo

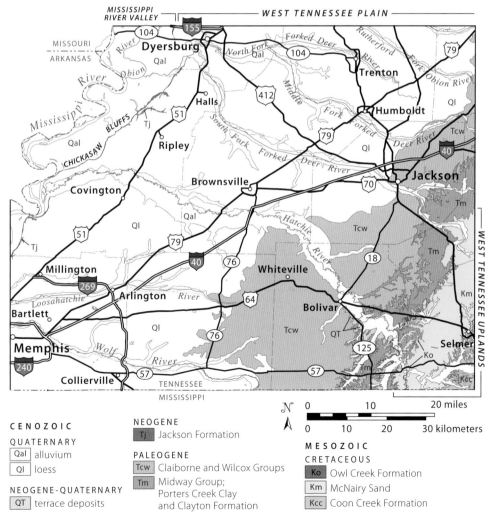

MISSISSIPPI RIVER VALLEY — **WEST TENNESSEE PLAIN**

CENOZOIC

QUATERNARY
Qal alluvium
Ql loess

NEOGENE-QUATERNARY
QT terrace deposits

NEOGENE
Tj Jackson Formation

PALEOGENE
Tcw Claiborne and Wilcox Groups
Tm Midway Group; Porters Creek Clay and Clayton Formation

MESOZOIC

CRETACEOUS
Ko Owl Creek Formation
Km McNairy Sand
Kcc Coon Creek Formation

Generalized geology along I-40 between Jackson and Memphis.

MEMPHIS GEOLOGY

The Wolf River parallels I-40 through downtown Memphis. It has always played an important role in West Tennessee's history. Chickasaw, Spanish, and French settlements existed at the Wolf's confluence with the Mississippi River, despite regular flooding issues. In 1960, the US Army Corps of Engineers dammed the mouth of the Wolf River and diverted its flow into the Mississippi River at the northern end of Mud Island. The original channel, now Wolf River Lagoon, separates Mud Island from downtown Memphis.

I-40 crosses Gayoso Bayou, another important Memphis waterway, near exit 1A, but it is hidden under the city. A map of Memphis, made in 1819, shows that Gayoso Bayou was once a major landscape feature that drained downtown Memphis. Since the late 1800s, it has been steadily diverted through a series of mostly underground concrete channels to the Wolf River. Only a small section remains open to the surface. The containment of Gayoso Bayou was meant to help control flooding and to make room for urban growth. Several streets and buildings north of the highway, including the St. Jude campus, are built on top

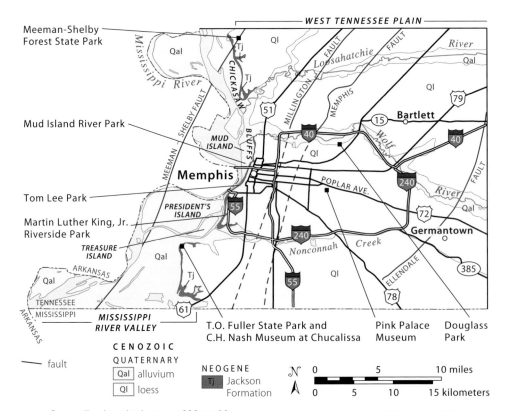

Generalized geologic map of Memphis. —Structural features after Hildenbrand, 1985; Hao et al., 2013; Martin and Van Arsdale, 2017

of a maze of bayou-confining channels. The bayou is completely enclosed under North Lauderdale Avenue. You can see an aboveground section north of A. W. Willis Avenue between North Front and North Fourth streets. The bayou's mouth is now sealed to prevent backwater flooding, and a pumping station releases water into the Wolf River Lagoon at Quincy Bayou.

From the Hernando de Soto Bridge over the Mississippi River, you will get a great view to the south of Memphis and the Chickasaw Bluffs on which the city is built. The east end of the bridge crosses Wolf River Harbor, the former Wolf River channel. Look southward toward downtown at the Cobblestone Landing, where stones were set in the muddy bank of the Wolf River in the late 1800s.

Memphis occupies the fourth Chickasaw Bluff, the southernmost of four 30-to-100-foot-high bluffs that define the boundary between the Mississippi River Valley and the West Tennessee Plain. The bluffs are named for the Chickasaw Indian tribe that lived throughout the area for hundreds of years prior to the European exploration and settlement that began during the sixteenth century. Pioneering Memphians built on the bluff to avoid Mississippi River flooding, as well as the swampy bottoms of the often flooded Wolf River and Nonconnah Creek, which form the northern and southern boundaries of the city, respectively.

Memphis owes its nickname, Bluff City, to its location on the Chickasaw Bluffs. At 100 feet above the Mississippi River, the Memphis area has been a safe haven from flooding for thousands of years. The view is northwestward across downtown Memphis. Wolf River Harbor, Mud Island, the Hernando de Soto Bridge (I-40), and the Mississippi River are in the middle ground. The jetties located on Loosahatchie Bar on the left side of the photo, along with Memphis's pump stations and floodwalls, help protect the city from floodwaters. —Mary E. Phelps photo

Following the Great Mississippi Flood of 1927, the US Army Corps of Engineers began to alter the Mississippi River channel in an effort to better control navigation and flooding. Improvements in engineering and technology continue to be implemented along the Lower Mississippi River Valley, but residents of the now largely urbanized Memphis must still periodically contend with backwater and fast-rising floodwaters despite modern flood-control measures. Heavy spring rains, often in combination with snowmelt upstream, periodically cause the river to flood urban areas. During the 2011 spring floods, the Mississippi River reached its highest level in Memphis since 1937 and began eroding a new channel through President's Island near the Port of Memphis, proving once again that humans cannot entirely tame the Mississippi.

The City of Memphis maintains a flood-protection system of pumping stations, reservoirs, earthen levees, and flood walls. Many of these structures are visible at riverside parks. Concrete flood walls and earthen levees parallel the Wolf River between the Welcome Center at Jefferson Avenue and Douglass Park. Completed in the 1940s, the concrete walls are 1 foot thick and up to 8 feet tall with heavy gates that close during times of high water. Look for a fantastically painted section at Chelsea Avenue between Louisville Avenue and North Evergreen Street. In south Memphis, earthen levees parallel Nonconnah Creek from its mouth just south of Martin Luther King, Jr. Riverside Park to Prospect Street, near the US 61 overpass.

Memphis's city parks, especially those located along Riverside and Island Drives and south of the Memphis-Arkansas Bridge (I-55), are good places to admire the mighty Mississippi River. The river bounds the west side of Memphis and also forms the state line with Arkansas. Across the river, you'll see the rich agricultural farmland of Arkansas, with row crops planted in fertile river alluvium. Abandoned river channels and oxbows typically have more natural vegetation, including trees. A narrow strip of the floodplain on the Tennessee side is farmed north of Meeman-Shelby Forest State Park to the Kentucky state line.

You can step back in history at Cobblestone Landing at Wolf River Harbor, located south of the Tennessee Welcome Center and between Jefferson Avenue and Beale Street. Prior to the 1850s, a narrow, muddy strip of land separated the river from downtown streets that cut through the bluffs. Loading and offloading people and goods was a huge challenge due to the thick, sticky mud. Work began on the Cobblestone Landing in 1859 and continued in three main construction phases through 1881, with one repaving project in the 1930s. The cobblestones include limestone from Illinois, sandstone and syenite from Arkansas, and granite, gneiss, and rhyolite from Missouri. Memphis became a major river port following the landing construction. Cobblestone Landing is still used by riverboats today, and many original cobblestones and old iron moorings remain at the site.

Tom Lee Park is built on the Mississippi River floodplain with downtown Memphis, located on top of the fourth Chickasaw Bluff, just across the street. The paved Riverwalk trail winds along the top of the bluff between Martyrs Park and Union Avenue. Around Memphis, reddish iron-rich stream deposits of the Upland

Complex form the base of the bluff, and Pleistocene-age loess caps it. Loess tends to form vertical cliffs despite its unconsolidated nature. In the past, willow branches were used to protect the bluff from river erosion and landslides. Modern revetments are made of concrete, concrete block mats, or riprap. Vegetation and artificial fill often obscure a complete view of the bluff strata, but glimpses are

Satellite images show the Mississippi River in April 2010 during nonflood conditions and in May 2011 during the second-highest river level ever recorded, when muddy waters spilled over the Mississippi's east and west banks. Floodwaters inundated Mud Island River Park and parks along Riverside Drive. Many local rivers, including the Wolf River and Nonconnah Creek, spilled their banks and flooded nearby suburbs, but downtown Memphis was largely spared from damage due to robust flood-control measures. Flooding occurred north of Memphis in Millington and in Dyersburg where the Forked Deer River ran backward into the city. —NASA's Earth Observatory images

You can walk a five-block-long scale model of the Lower Mississippi River Valley at Mud Island River Park's Riverwalk. The model includes 1,000 miles between Cairo, Illinois, and the Gulf of Mexico. The Memphis section is pictured here, looking downstream, with the Hernando De Soto Bridge and Mud Island in the foreground and the Memphis-Arkansas Bridge to the south. (35.148986N, 90.058784W) —Chuck Sutherland photo sometimes possible. T. O. Fuller and Meeman-Shelby Forest State Parks offer alternative, sometimes better, bluff exposures. You can look for Paleozoic-age fossils in gravel clasts of the Upland Complex along Nonconnah Creek and in gravel bars along the Mississippi River.

Pleistocene-age animals migrated along the Chickasaw Bluffs in and near Memphis. Construction crews first discovered American mastodon bones in Memphis while working at Rhodes College in 1967. Then, in 1976, two fourth-grade boys playing in Nonconnah Creek, west of the Perkins Road Bridge in south Memphis, discovered a piece of a tusk. At the same site local paleontologists later found an ankle, skull, other tusk pieces, and four teeth from a mastodon that lived 17,000 to 23,000 years ago. About 5 feet of Pleistocene-age loess and old channel deposits covered the bones. Insect, snail, and plant fossils (including pollen, nuts, leaves, and logs) found at the site showed that spruce forests once covered Tennessee. A third mastodon skeleton was found in Raleigh, a neighborhood in North Memphis, on an unnamed tributary of the Wolf River. It, too, was found by two fourth-grade boys.

The sandy layers in the Wilcox and Claiborne Groups are important water-bearing units and provide drinking water to many residents of West Tennessee, particularly in Memphis and surrounding areas. The highly productive Memphis

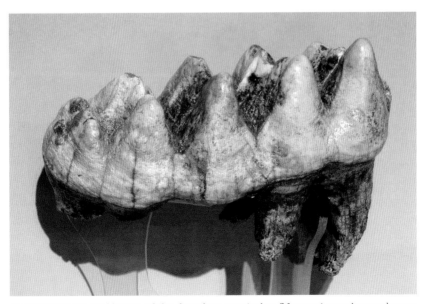

*Fossilized teeth and bones of the American mastodon (*Mammut americanum*) were found in Pleistocene-age loess deposits at the present location of Rhodes College in North Memphis and along Nonconnah Creek in South Memphis. The highly crowned molar is suited to smashing leaves and twigs. The tooth, about the length of a human forearm, is on display at the Pink Palace Museum on Central Avenue in Memphis.*
—Tammy Braithwaite, Pink Palace Museum photo

aquifer, the city's primary water source, resides in the Memphis Sand, part of the Claiborne Group. It is a fine-to-coarse-grained, clean quartz sand that was deposited across an ancient floodplain during Eocene time. The Memphis Sand is about 500 to 800 feet thick; it's located about 500 feet underground, so locals refer to the aquifer as the "500-foot sand." The 225-foot-thick Fort Pillow Sand (or "1,400-foot sand") of the underlying Wilcox Group, also Eocene age, is the city's secondary aquifer. Water from the Fort Pillow Sand is reserved primarily for industrial and military uses. Although Cretaceous-age strata contain water, their depth—nearly 2,000 feet at Memphis—makes withdrawal cost too great. Near-surface aquifers tend to be heavily mineralized, so they are used in agriculture and industry, but that's not the case with the Memphis Sand aquifer. Locals have a great deal of pride for their primary water source, and with good reason—Memphis's water is clean and low in mineral content, which gives it a sweet taste. Even local craft breweries boast about using water from the Memphis Sand aquifer!

Memphis is about 50 miles south of the New Madrid Seismic Zone on the southeastern margin of the Reelfoot rift. Consequently, faults associated with the eastern margin of the Reelfoot rift, and those that lie east of it, are important when

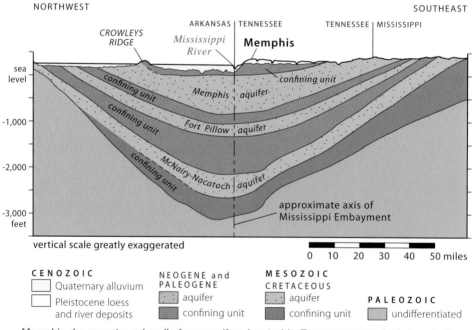

Memphis draws water primarily from aquifers located in Eocene-age sands that underlie West Tennessee and the Mississippi Embayment at depths of 500 and 1,400 feet. Prior to the late 1800s, city drinking water came directly from the Wolf River, but the quality of the water proved unreliable. Following a series of yellow fever epidemics that culminated in 1878 with more than 5,000 deaths, the city modernized its sewage system and tapped underground water sources. Historic and contemporary artesian pump houses are found throughout the city. —Modified from Brahana and Broshears, 2001

Earthquake liquefaction features are found in Memphis-area river and streambanks. Most of these features, including this sand dike, likely formed during the New Madrid earthquakes of 1811–1812. The liquified sand blew through the overlying soil onto the Wolf River floodplain (at knife point location). Sand dikes form as a slurry of sand and water is forced upward through a fracture during an earthquake. This sand dike breached the soil, the dark layer at knife level, and was subsequently buried under Wolf River floodplain sediment near Collierville. Liquefaction susceptibility is high along floodplains of the Mississippi, Wolf, and Loosahatchie Rivers, and in areas of the city with artificial fill. —Roy Van Arsdale photo

evaluating the city's seismic hazards. Although seismicity is relatively low near Memphis in comparison to regions in and near the main part of the New Madrid Seismic Zone, Memphians do periodically receive a magnitude 4 or 5 jolt, and the potential for a moderate to large earthquake exists, given the city's proximity to the seismic zone. In 1843, a serious earthquake rattled Memphis homes, toppled chimneys and walls, and broke windows. People in Nashville and Knoxville reportedly felt the quake, although it did no damage in those cities. Similar damage occurred during large earthquakes in 1865 and 1895. Many liquefaction features found in and near Memphis do not correlate with the age of the large New Madrid earthquakes. Rather, they may be related to faults found outside of, but relatively close and parallel to, the Reelfoot rift. Many such faults extend across West Tennessee.

Quaternary-age sedimentation and urbanization obscure any surface trace of faulting in the Memphis metropolitan area; however, geologists have identified several faults, including the Millington, Memphis, and Ellendale. The Millington and Memphis faults strike northeast and pass beneath the west side of Memphis. The Ellendale fault, also northeast striking, passes beneath east Memphis, Germantown, and the Wolf River.

The Ellendale fault may have been active relatively recently in the geologic sense. Displacement on the fault may have diverted Nonconnah Creek. Prior to the Quaternary Period, Nonconnah Creek flowed from its headwaters near Collierville, Tennessee, northwestward to the Wolf River, but now it flows directly west to the Mississippi River. Strike-slip movement on the Ellendale fault likely created an anticline that geologists found in a cutbank of the Wolf River east of Memphis. Eocene-age and younger sediments are folded in the anticline that is more than 300 feet across. If the fold was created during a single faulting event on the Ellendale fault, it would have created an earthquake of magnitude 7.6! It's estimated that the event happened about AD 400. If so, then the Ellendale fault, and perhaps the Memphis fault, could produce moderate-to-large earthquakes that could decimate Memphis.

US 51
MEMPHIS—DYERSBURG
75 miles

US 51, a two-lane highway, runs along the top of the Chickasaw Bluffs and roughly parallels the eastern margin of the Reelfoot rift between Memphis and Dyersburg. The highway crosses several waterways that flow westward to meet the Mississippi River, including the Wolf, Loosahatchie, Hatchie, and Forked Deer Rivers. The landscape is relatively unremarkable in terms of topographic relief, with many farms and small towns.

Fossils of large animals have been found in the bluffs between Memphis and Dyersburg. All of the species are now extinct, but most have recognizable living descendants. Remains of a giant ground sloth, horse, bison, and a giant beaver (The size of a modern black bear!) were found near Memphis. Mastodons were found on Island 35 west of Munford in 1900, and another was found in Obion County. Eocene-age whale and shark bones and teeth were found near Fulton, between Fort Pillow State Historic Park and the Hatchie River. Fossilized horse teeth along with horse, peccary, bear, and mastodon bones were found in a gravel bar at Richardson Landing about 20 miles north of Meeman-Shelby Forest State Park. Fossils from the site are on display at the Pink Palace Museum in Memphis.

Meeman-Shelby Forest State Park, about 20 miles west of Millington, offers many trails by which to explore the Chickasaw Bluffs and the Mississippi River. The northern end of the Meeman-Shelby fault passes through the Mississippi River floodplain at the park. The high-angle fault has characteristics of both thrust and strike-slip motion. Geoscientists imaged the Meeman-Shelby fault by seismic methods where Jackson Hill Road and River Road meet, finding that the fault extends southward under the floodplain to the Tennessee-Mississippi state line. It may connect with another fault at Porters Gap, located west of Halls about 46 miles to the northeast, but geoscientists still debate this. The Meeman-Shelby fault was active during the Quaternary Period and may be capable of generating a 6.9 magnitude earthquake very close to Memphis.

Geophysical studies of the magnetic and gravity properties of the northern Mississippi Embayment reveal that a pluton, a solidified body of intrusive igneous rock, lies about 0.5 mile beneath the city of Covington. The Covington pluton is approximately 19 miles long and 10 miles wide. Feldspar-rich, coarse-grained intrusive igneous rocks called syenite were encountered in two wells drilled near the Covington pluton. Syenite, which forms from the melting of thick continental crust, is similar in composition to granite but has little to no quartz. The Covington pluton is one of several Cretaceous-age plutons that formed when magma rose along rift-bounding normal faults. The magma was generated during the period of regional uplift associated with the Mississippi Embayment passing over the Bermuda hot spot.

US 51 crosses the Hatchie River north of Covington. The Hatchie remains the only large tributary in the Lower Mississippi River Valley that is not dammed or

Hatchie National Wildlife Refuge, located east of Covington, includes 23 miles of the river's middle reaches that provide important habitat for fish, wildlife, and plants of the Lower Mississippi River. The Hatchie River is West Tennessee's only major river that has not been impounded or channelized and is designated a Scenic River. —Chuck Sutherland photo

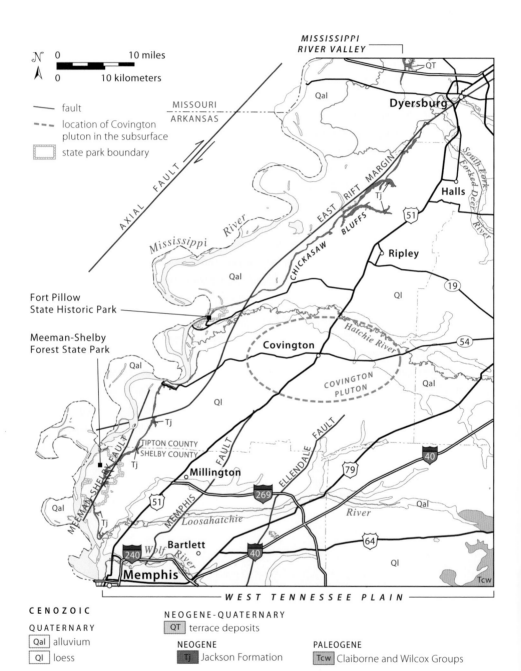

MISSISSIPPI RIVER VALLEY

QT

Qal

Dyersburg

MISSOURI
ARKANSAS

Halls

Tj

51

Mississippi *River*

Qal

Ripley

19

Ql

Fort Pillow
State Historic Park

Qal

CHICKASAW BLUFFS

EAST RIFT MARGIN

Hatchie River

54

Meeman-Shelby
Forest State Park

Covington

Qal

Qal

COVINGTON PLUTON

Ql

Tj

Ql

TIPTON COUNTY
SHELBY COUNTY

Tj

ELLENDALE FAULT

40

Millington

79

269

Qal

Qal

51

MEMPHIS FAULT

Loosahatchie

River

64

Ql

MEEMAN SHELBY FAULT

Tj

Bartlett

240

Wolf *River*

40

Tcw

Memphis

WEST TENNESSEE PLAIN

CENOZOIC

QUATERNARY

| Qal | alluvium |
| Ql | loess |

NEOGENE-QUATERNARY

QT terrace deposits

NEOGENE

Tj Jackson Formation

PALEOGENE

Tcw Claiborne and Wilcox Groups

Generalized geology along US 51 between Memphis and Dyersburg.
—Structural features after Hildenbrand, 1985; Hao and others, 2013; Martin and Van Arsdale, 2017

channelized for flood control or irrigation. The floodplain of the free-flowing Hatchie is heavily forested with hardwoods, biologically diverse, and swampy.

Fort Pillow State Historic Park, located on top of the Chickasaw Bluffs, was built by Confederate troops in 1861 but abandoned in 1862 as the Union Navy progressed along the Mississippi River. The Confederate army took back the fort in 1864 during the Battle of Fort Pillow, a short, bloody massacre of more than 350, mostly African American, Union troops. During the time of the Civil War, a large meander brought the Mississippi River close to the stream-dissected bluffs. Confederate troops constructed earthworks and dug trenches in the unconsolidated loess that caps the bluffs. From this strategic location, they could see river traffic for some distance away, allowing them to control, for a time, transportation and supply routes. Some of the more than 20 miles of hiking trails in the parks parallel the earthworks.

In most areas of West Tennessee, the Chickasaw Bluffs are difficult to see due to vegetation, erosion, and mass wasting (landslides and slumps). Some of the best bluff views are along the trails at Fort Pillow State Historic Park. (approximately 35.626041N, 89.865938W)
—Chuck Sutherland photo

Dyersburg, a historical timber-shipping town, is situated in the Mississippi River Valley where the Forked Deer River cuts through the first and northernmost Chickasaw Bluff. The city's historic downtown is located on the river's north fork. Despite a system of levees built to protect the city, more than six hundred homes and businesses in southern areas of the city were inundated as the Forked Deer River flowed backward during the 2011 Mississippi River floods. Flooding also occurred west of the city where the Forked Deer and Obion Rivers join the Mississippi River.

In addition to flooding, Dyersburg residents might want to worry about earthquakes. The city sits at the eastern edge of the New Madrid Seismic Zone. Magnitude 2 to 3 earthquakes are relatively common, and the potential for a large earthquake in the region exists.

US 641/TN 69
Parsons—Camden—Paris
52 miles

US 641 crosses several tributary drainages to the Tennessee River between Parsons and I-40. Paleozoic-age strata are exposed along the river and in tributary drainages, including Big and Lick Creeks, due to the river's deep incision; in areas, the river is up to 500 feet below surrounding plateaus. The topography provides an opportunity to see units that are not well exposed anywhere else in Tennessee, especially those of Silurian- and Devonian-age.

Sedimentary rocks along US 641 are mostly horizontal, with low, open folds and faulting present in the Paleozoic-age section as a result of mountain building during the Paleozoic Era. In places, minor faulting and folding are the result of groundwater sapping, a process that undermines slopes as seeps and springs dissolve limestone and cause sections of strata to collapse. The region is rural but not agriculturally productive due to the rocky soils weathered from underlying Paleozoic-age limestones. Most larger farms between Parsons and the interstate are developed in the bottoms of tributaries where Quaternary-age alluvium enhances soil fertility.

Parsons was a railroad depot during the late 1800s, built up around a small spring at the head of a small tributary to the Beech River, which meets the Tennessee River a few miles southeast of town. A mural at the US 412 and US 641 junction depicts the town's early history. The Cretaceous-age Coffee Sand underlies most of the city, while Silurian- and Mississippian-age strata underlie drainages east and west of the junction.

Most information about West Tennessee's Silurian- and Devonian-age units comes from exposures of the Decatur Limestone and Ross Formation at a large quarry off US 641 north of Parsons. These units are famous for the variety and abundance of marine fossils that are concentrated in accessible, shale-rich beds, especially in the Birdsong Shale Member of the Ross Formation. West Tennessee's Silurian- and Devonian-age strata are important to scientists and collectors alike, as Tennessee has one of the few exposed sections of this age in North America.

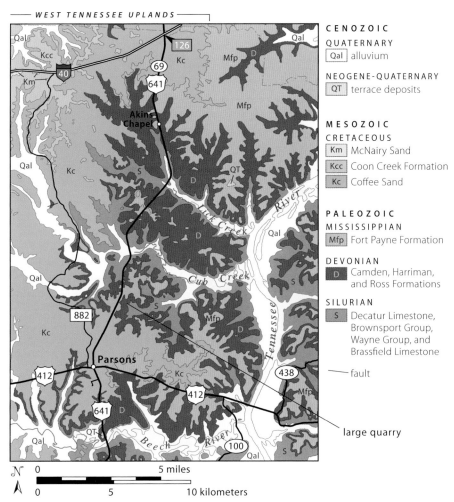

Generalized geology along US 641/TN 69 between Parsons and I-40.
See map on page 326 for section of US 641 north of I-40.

Look for exposures of the Silurian-age Decatur Limestone and overlying Devo-nian-age Rockhouse Limestone Member of the Ross Formation about 4 miles north of Parsons. The Decatur Limestone is loaded with many kinds of marine invertebrate fossils, including sponges, bryozoans, brachiopods, trilobites, ostra-cods, and, most commonly, crinoids. Fossil shells are cemented by calcite that makes the medium-to-thick-bedded rock dense and crystalline. The Decatur Limestone formed from shells that were broken up by high-energy storm waves and accumulated for millions of years along a shallow, carbonate shelf.

The 400-million-year-old Rockhouse Limestone Member contains fossil-iferous, shale-rich limestone beds that form slopes above the more resistant

The Decatur Limestone is exposed north of Parsons at mileposts 32 and 38. The unit is relatively homogeneous and forms resistant medium-to-thick-bedded ledges that are pink on fresh surfaces and pinkish-gray on weathered ones. The rocks at this location were folded into a broad, 0.25-mile-long anticline. (35.775399N, 88.085086W) —Michael Gibson photo

Decatur Limestone. The unit is extremely heterogeneous both laterally and vertically, preserving five depositional environments that coalesced over millions of years as the shoreline of the Devonian sea shifted. The Rockhouse Limestone and Birdsong Shale Members are exposed along and in the vicinity of US 641. Look for a roadcut about 0.5 mile north of the bridge over Lick Creek.

Elongate, parallel mud mounds up to about 50 feet long, 6 feet wide, and 6 feet high, form the base of the Rockhouse Limestone Member. The mud mounds were built by a succession of animal inhabitants. First, as sea level rose, carbonate mud and shell debris collected in shallow depressions on the seafloor. Next, calcareous algae helped bind mud and coarser material together to form a more solid and stable substrate. Reef builders such as corals, sponges, and bryozoans built mounds vertically from this substrate to take advantage of sunlight and nutrient-rich ocean currents. As water became deeper the length and height of the mud mounds increased because anchored animals had to build taller structures to reach the light and nutrients closer to the surface. Their elongate shapes maximized prevailing ocean currents, which deliver oxygen and nutrients. Parsons quarry employees refer to the mounds as "whalebacks" because their shape resembles the back of a swimming whale. Their size and density make them incredibly difficult to bulldoze, so they are a nuisance in quarry operations.

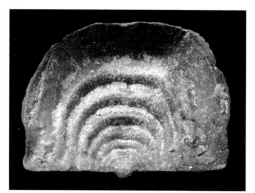 

Brachiopods are well represented in Silurian- and Devonian-age strata. Leptaena, *found in the Birdsong Shale Member of the Ross Formation, was well adapted to life on a muddy sea bottom. The animal had two shells, each about 1 inch wide. By keeping the flatter concave shell (at left) toward the bottom and the convex side (at right) facing upward, the animal was relatively stable in strong currents. The configuration also kept the animal from sinking into the mud. Other animals, such as bryozoans, grew on the shells, creating lacy patterns on the shell surface.* —James Davison photo

The Ross Formation is exposed near Bawcum Cemetery, about 9 miles north of Parsons and about 0.5 mile north of the Lick Creek crossing. Shales and limestones of the Rockhouse Limestone Member are at road level, while the Birdsong Shale Member forms the upper slope. (35.7695841N, 88.0834329W) —Chuck Sutherland photo

The seafloor was soft and muddy while the Ross Formation was deposited. Without solid substrate, many animals had difficulty growing; consequently, many grew on each other. Animals that did this, mainly bryozoans and colonial-type corals, favored the shells of brachiopods, which had a relatively large surface area. They also grew on crinoids, gastropods, and other bryozoans. Bryozoans can be found piggybacking on just about every fossil in the Ross Formation. The Devonian Period is often referred to as the Age of Fishes because of the impressive variety of fishes that emerged during this time, but not one fossil fish or part of a fish has ever been found in these rocks—a geologic mystery!

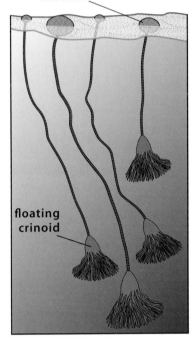

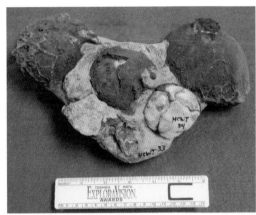

Scyphocrinites *lobolith fossils are found in the Decatur Limestone and Ross Formation. This sample contains three loboliths embedded in limestone.* —Michael Gibson photo

Some crinoids were free swimming. Rather than anchoring to the seafloor with a branching root system, they used air-filled chambers, called loboliths, to bob and float, and their arms filtered food from the water.

The Rockhouse Limestone Member grades into the overlying grayish-green Birdsong Shale Member, the most fossiliferous member of the Ross Formation. The Birdsong Shale contains a diverse fauna of corals and gastropods and high concentrations of brachiopods, bryozoans, and trilobites. An interesting thing about the Birdsong Shale is that its fossilized animals are preserved in separate and distinct beds or zones. Established communities with a dominant animal may have been periodically smothered and preserved by large influxes of sediment brought in by strong storm currents, allowing a different animal to flourish in the aftermath.

The Pink Palace Museum in Memphis, or the museum's website, offers more information about West Tennessee's Devonian-age fossils. The Discovery Park of America in Union City and the Tennessee River Museum in Savannah also have good displays of fossils from these formations.

The Devonian-age Harriman Formation is mined from shallow pits mainly for road materials near milepost 35. The Harriman Formation, also called the Harriman Chert, is made of white novaculite, a dense microcrystalline quartz that is nearly indistinguishable from the Camden Formation, found north of I-40 near Camden. Local soils derived from the Harriman Formation are light colored.

Rolling hills characterize the West Tennessee Uplands landscape north of I-40. The rock layers are unconsolidated, which makes for lots of erosion and

Trilobites were widespread in North American oceans during the Devonian Period. Phaciphacops *trilobites have large compound eyes and a bulging head shield that sets them apart from other genera of trilobites. The head shields (shown here) are the most commonly preserved parts in the Birdsong Shale Member. This sample is about 4 inches wide.* —Tammy Braithwaite, Pink Palace Museum photo

not many outcrops. Light-colored, sandy soils derived from the Cretaceous-age Coffee Sand are visible along the road for a couple of miles north and south of the interstate. Where the highway crosses Birdsong Creek near milepost 3, farms capitalize on the Quaternary-age alluvium of the creek's floodplain. Birdsong Creek flows into the Tennessee River about 6 miles to the northeast.

Tennessee has a long history with freshwater pearls. Native Americans harvested mussels from local waterways as a food source and used the pearls for beads. Global demand for mother-of-pearl buttons fueled a modern industry that began around the turn of the twentieth century and lasted until the 1950s. Mussels were harvested using flat-bottom brail boats. Clusters of three-pronged metal hooks were suspended and lowered into the water on poles, called brails. Underwater sails, called mules, caught the river current and pulled the boat forward. When a hook hit a mussel that was open to feed on river algae and plankton, the mussel closed down on the hook in a reflex reaction. The brailer occasionally pulled up the poles and harvested the mussels.

The American Pearl Farm cultures and farms Tennessee River pearls at the mouth of Birdsong Creek. The farm typically houses 100,000 to 500,000 freshwater mussels at one time, all varieties native to Tennessee, such as washboard and pigtoe. To start the pearling process, technicians implant several calcium carbonate beads of different shapes and sizes into the soft tissue of each mussel. Wire baskets containing a dozen or more of these nucleated mussels are suspended in water on an 18-inch-deep plastic pipe framework, and the mussels

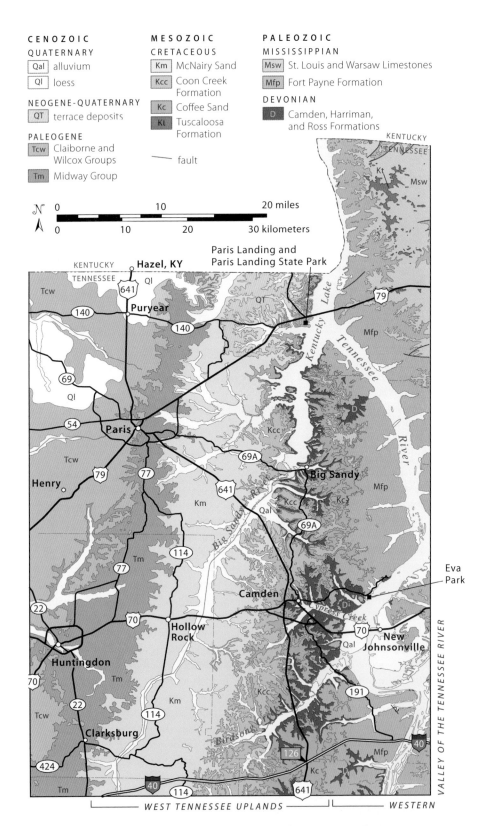

CENOZOIC

QUATERNARY
| Qal | alluvium
| Ql | loess

NEOGENE-QUATERNARY
| QT | terrace deposits

PALEOGENE
| Tcw | Claiborne and Wilcox Groups
| Tm | Midway Group

MESOZOIC

CRETACEOUS
| Km | McNairy Sand
| Kcc | Coon Creek Formation
| Kc | Coffee Sand
| Kl | Tuscaloosa Formation
| — | fault

PALEOZOIC

MISSISSIPPIAN
| Msw | St. Louis and Warsaw Limestones
| Mfp | Fort Payne Formation

DEVONIAN
| D | Camden, Harriman, and Ross Formations

Generalized geology along US 641/TN 69 between I-40 and Paris.

are left to grow for three to five years. As a mussel grows, the animal secretes a lustrous, iridescent, layered calcium carbonate coating called nacre around the irritating beads, turning them into pearls. The farm sells Tennessee River pearls for jewelry once the mussels are harvested. Nuclei beads punched from the harvested shells are sold to other pearl farms all over the world. Approximately 95 percent of the world's round cultured pearls are nucleated with a bead carved from one of Tennessee's freshwater mussels. The Tennessee River Freshwater Pearl Museum and Farm at Birdsong Resort, located off Birdsong Road (TN 191) south of Camden, has more information about this process.

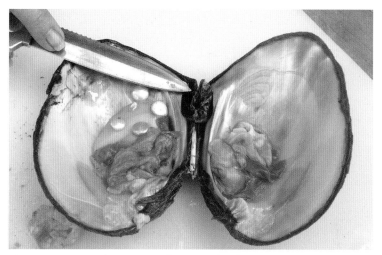

Tennessee River pearls were named Tennessee's official state gem in 1979. Freshwater pearls have been cultured and farmed at the mouth of Birdsong Creek south of Camden since 1983. —Tennessee River Freshwater Pearl Museum and Farm photo

The Cretaceous-age Coffee Sand that underlies Camden lies unconformably on West Tennessee's youngest Devonian-age unit, the fossiliferous Camden Formation. Often called the Camden Chert, it consists of white-to-yellow novaculite, a dense microcrystalline quartz, or chert. The Camden Formation has been quarried locally from small pits for more than a hundred years, especially southeast of Camden between US 641 and US 70 along Cypress Creek.

Near Camden, the lower 200 feet of the Cretaceous-age McNairy Sand contains the ore minerals zircon, leucoxene, staurolite, kyanite, tourmaline, monazite, ilmenite, and rutile. These heavy minerals tend to concentrate due to their high densities and often occur as accessory minerals in quartz sands. These minerals, eroded and weathered from metamorphic rocks in the southern Appalachian Mountains, were transported downstream by a large river to the ocean, where sand rich in heavy minerals accumulated on Cretaceous-age beaches and shallow shelfs. These minerals are mined for the elements titanium and zirconium, which are used in the manufacture of pigments for paint

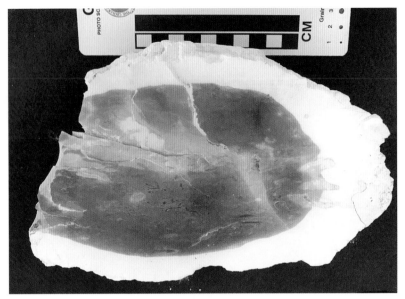

The Devonian-age Camden Formation is made of novaculite, a dense chert that weathers to a chalky white (outer rind in photo). Tools made from the Camden Formation were found at the Eva archaeological site, dated to about 4000 BC, that is now inundated by Kentucky Lake. A monument to the site is located at Eva Park, 6 miles east of Camden on TN 191. —Michael Gibson photo

Hollow Rock, a town about 10 miles west of Camden off US 70, is named after and home to the only hard rock exposed in Tennessee west of the Silurian-Devonian outcrop belt. The rock is made of unusually well-indurated Cretaceous-age McNairy Sand. It has an interior opening that has provided temporary shelter for travelers since prehistoric times. To get to the public park that hosts the rock, head north on TN 114 (Seminary St.), cross the tracks, turn right on High Street to Roundhouse Road, and drive about a half mile to Park Lane. (36.0397994N, 88.2583666W) —Chuck Sutherland photo

and plastics, paper, rubber, cosmetics, pharmaceuticals, metals, ceramics, and a wide range of other products. Quartz sand free of heavy minerals from higher in the McNairy Sand is also mined west of Camden on US 70 for silica and used in glass manufacturing.

Near the turnoff toward Big Sandy (Lower Big Sandy Road), US 641 crosses stream terraces of the ancestral Tennessee River. They consist mainly of gravel deposits that parallel the river but at higher elevations than the current floodplain. Many of the pieces of gravel contain Paleozoic-age fossils.

Near Paris, hills take on enough relief to challenge car engines. The change in elevation corresponds to the transition from the hills of the West Tennessee Uplands (Cretaceous-age sands and clays) to the lowlands of the West Tennessee Plain (Eocene-age clays and sands). Paris straddles the drainage divide between the Mississippi and Tennessee Rivers.

In addition to ball clays, Fuller's earth is mined near Paris. Fuller's earth consists of many kinds of clay minerals and is mined mainly from the Porters Creek Clay, part of the Paleocene-age Midway Group. Fuller's earth is used in cat litters and other absorbents, fertilizers, cosmetics, and to make pretend dust and smoke for movies.

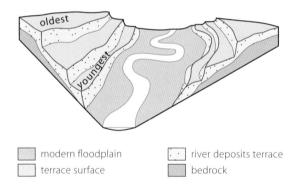

modern floodplain

terrace surface

river deposits terrace

bedrock

When the base level, the lowest point in a river system, is lowered due to sea level drop or tectonic events, the river cuts down into its floodplain, leaving discontinuous deposits, or terraces, of its older floodplain at higher elevations. River terraces form steplike benches along the sides of the valley. —Image modified from Tara N. Jonell work, licensed under Creative Commons, CC-BY-SA

BALL CLAY AT PARIS AND GLEASON

Paris is built on the Paleocene-to-Eocene-age Midway, Wilcox, and Claiborne Groups, which are mined extensively in the area for ball clay, one of Tennessee's most important economic resources. The term originated in England where miners, using hand tools, scooped or cut small pieces of clay from deposits, the edges of which rounded during transport as the pieces were jostled. Tennesseans began mining ball clays near Paris during the late nineteenth century for housewares, such as ceramic water jugs and bricks. Ball clays are currently used in the manufacture of a variety of ceramics, including dinnerware and bricks, and it's used in rubber and as a fertilizer filler.

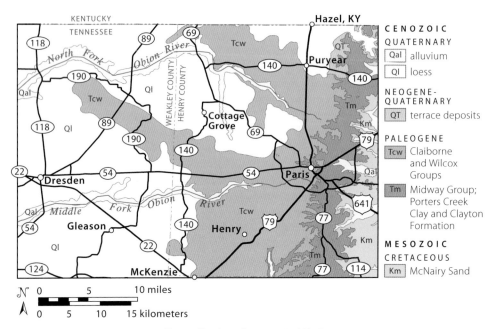

Generalized geology west of Paris.

Ball clays are made of the clay mineral kaolinite, a soft, white mineral created from the chemical weathering of feldspar, which is high in aluminum and silica. West Tennessee kaolinite likely came from an eastern source in the southern Appalachian Mountains where the mineral had weathered from granitic basement rocks. Ball clays are often contaminated with varying amounts of organic material because they were deposited in swamps, along rivers, and in shallow brackish waters along the coast in Paleogene time. Tennessee's highest-quality ball clays come from lens-shaped deposits in which most organic material has decayed in the Paleocene-to-Eocene-age Wilcox and Claiborne Groups. Ball clays are mined in open pits, which often requires the removal of 25 to 80 feet of overlying material.

Gleason, about 20 miles southwest of Paris, is known as the "ball clay mining center of the nation." In 1926, while digging fence posts on a farm 2 miles west of Gleason, a farmer discovered a rich deposit of high-quality clay. He started the Bell Clay Company. After clearing the land, workers blasted and dug clay out with picks and shovels, and it was trucked to the rail yard north of town for shipment. A few clay-mining companies currently operate in Gleason. Bricks are still made from local clay at the Gleason Brick plant, operational since 1910. Bricks from the plant were used to construct many of the town's original buildings. Look for ceramics made from Gleason ball clay in Main Street shops. The Gleason Foundry supplied narrow-gauge rail equipment to local mines and manufactured the Gleason Shredder, an automated tool that homogenized and blended clays.

Ball clay from the Eocene-age Claiborne Group is mined in Weakley, Henry, and Carroll Counties, where the deposits are the most pure found in the state. This clay is highly sought after for its high plasticity and bonding strength. Bulldozers remove overburden, and the clay is then mined by backhoes and front-end loaders. High concentrations of organic material makes the clay dark. (36.282703N, 88.528909W) —Chuck Sutherland photo

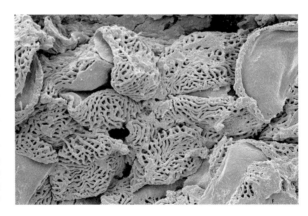

Fossilized pollen is so well preserved in clays of the Claiborne Group that it looks as if it came from a living plant. The pollen's branching pattern is distinctive for this type of plant, a tropical legume. This view is 50 micrometers wide. For comparison, a human hair is about 100 micrometers wide. —Michael Gibson photo

The Claiborne Group is fossiliferous and preserves leaves, flowers, and pollen that provide geoscientists with clues about the climate during Eocene time. A recently discovered fossil species described from Claiborne Group clay deposits near Gleason contains a complete flower with petals and all of its reproductive organs. The fossilized stamen still houses thousands of fossilized pollen grains. The new plant is a legume that grew in a tropical climate. Indeed, Eocene time for most of North America was much warmer than today.

TN 22

SAMBURG—DRESDEN

43 miles

North of Samburg, TN 22 follows the base of the first Chickasaw Bluff, which in places stands more than 100 feet higher than the surrounding floodplain. Vegetation and erosion obscure rock exposures along TN 22, but units can be seen in some steep gullies at road level. The Eocene-Oligocene-age Jackson Formation typically forms the bluff base and underlies the highway. Discontinuous layers of poorly bedded olive-tan clay and silt make up much of the Jackson Formation. In places black stringers of low-grade coal, called lignite, are present, which is indicative of the swampy, near-coastal conditions that existed in northwestern Tennessee during Eocene time. Look for vertical structures up to 3 feet long and 4 inches in diameter; these are attributed to the activity of burrowing mammals. Together, the presence of soil peds (blocky textures that form during weathering) and burrows suggests that part of the Jackson Formation may be a paleosol, an ancient soil.

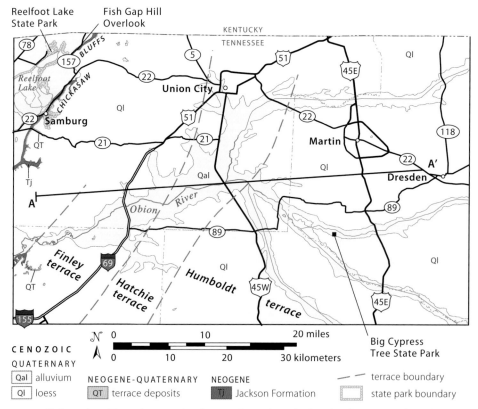

Geology along TN 22 between Samburg and Dresden. The line (A-A') corresponds to the figure on page 336 showing the region's ancient river terraces.

Up to 65 feet of reddish Pliocene-to-Pleistocene-age gravel and sand of the Upland Complex were deposited on an eroded surface of the Jackson Formation. In West Tennessee the Upland Complex, deposited by the ancestral Ohio and Mississippi Rivers, may be absent or may be cemented with iron oxide in beds up to 30 feet thick. The gravels were mined locally off TN 157.

The Jackson Formation is exposed along the base of the Chickasaw Bluffs on TN 22 near Samburg. Blocky soil peds indicate that part of the formation may be a paleosol. (36.4146519N, 89.318676W) —Chuck Sutherland photo

Fish Gap Hill Overlook provides spectacular views southwestward toward Reelfoot Lake State Park from the top of the Chickasaw Bluffs. The overlook is located on Fishgap Hill Road off TN 157. (36.4844191N, 89.2874808W) —Chuck Sutherland photo

Pleistocene-age loess, which overlies the Upland Complex, contains fossilized land snails and occasional vertebrate fossils, mostly of mastodons. In 1964, a gravel quarry operator in Samburg uncovered part of a mastodon jaw with a tooth still attached. The specimen remained in the University of Tennessee at Martin biology teaching collections until 1990. A university paleontologist reexamined the jaw and determined that, based on size and the amount of tooth wear, it came from a young animal. The jaw contained several holes that likely resulted from a disease, such as osteomyelitis, which would have made eating very difficult for the animal.

TN 22 climbs the Chickasaw Bluffs through a low gap created by South Reelfoot and Bogus Creeks at the junction with TN 157. East of the junction, TN 22 crosses the West Tennessee Plain, where Pleistocene-age loess deposits, with their fertile gray-tan soils, have been extensively farmed since the early 1800s. Gently rolling hills are characteristic of the West Tennessee Plain, especially near the edge of the Chickasaw Bluffs, where west-flowing rivers and streams dissect Pleistocene-age loess. Although there is less than 200 feet of relief, the terrain is rugged and prone to flooding, especially in low areas where drainage is slow due to the underlying clay-rich sediments.

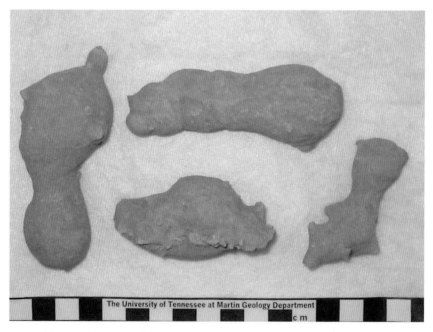

The University of Tennessee at Martin Geology Department

c m

Loess dolls, or loess kindchen, *are concretions that form as groundwater percolates through loess and precipitates calcium carbonate in small holes. These hard, rounded, light-colored mineral masses are left behind as the surrounding material erodes. Their shapes are reminiscent of animal and human dolls. Some loess dolls formed around masses of extinct land snail fossils that lived on the surface 8,000 to 20,000 years ago. Near Memphis, small concretions stained red by the oxidation of iron minerals are called "buckshot."* —Michael Gibson photo

The highly dissected hills with relatively deep gullies and high relief are the result of erosion that stems from early-nineteenth-century farming practices. Bluff sediments are relatively soft and unconsolidated, so they erode easily, particularly during wetter months when saturated bluff sediments are prone to mass wasting. Between 1812 and 1937, sediment input along Indian Creek resulted in a delta that grew westward past Samburg into Reelfoot Lake and out toward Horse Island. The lake contained less foliage and more open water during the 1800s, so the delta was likely visible from the shore. Now the delta is marked by a stand of trees. Since 1937, improved agricultural practices and sediment catchments have reduced erosion in the region. However, Indian Creek, North Reelfoot Creek, and Bayou Du Chien all transport eroded sand, silt, and clay from bluffs and local farms to Reelfoot Lake. This sediment contribution may fill sections of the lake in the next one hundred to two hundred years. Indian Creek continues to introduce sediment; its narrow, elongate delta—an extension of the older one—almost crosses the lake's lower basin to Horse Island, nearly dividing the southern part of the lake into two basins.

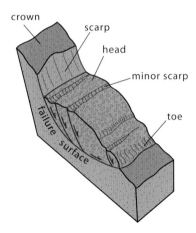

Slumps are common features along the Chickasaw Bluffs. A slump is a form of mass wasting in which a coherent mass of loosely consolidated rock and soil moves slowly downhill along a curved, concave-up surface.

Union City, located where the Nashville & Northwestern Railroad and Mobile & Ohio Railroad meet, began as a railroad town during the 1850s. At that time, small farms of mainly tobacco, corn, and wheat surrounded the city. The railroads turned Union City into a center of commerce in Obion County. The Discovery Park of America, located on Everett Boulevard, has interesting natural history displays, including a dinosaur room and an illuminated, geologic projection globe. The facility also houses an extensive display of Silurian- and Devonian-age fossils from West Tennessee, as well as a fossilized Pleistocene-age peccary herd that was found in the loess bluffs of Kentucky in 1967.

TN 22 crosses the North Fork of the Obion River and its swampy floodplain southeast of Union City. Several wildlife management areas and refuges about 10 miles south of Union City on the Obion River are particularly important to waterfowl, including a large wintering sandhill crane population. Big Cypress Tree State Park is a nice place to access the Middle Fork of the Obion River by trail.

Topographic changes are subtle in the West Tennessee Plain, but if you pay attention you'll notice several slight changes in elevation as you drive west to east or vice versa along any West Tennessee road, including TN 22. Relatively flat floodplains, used mostly as farmland, are marked on their eastern edge with a slight rise in elevation, an escarpment marking the next floodplain. This pattern repeats itself several times between Reelfoot Lake and Dresden, as TN 22 crosses the floodplain of the North Fork of the Obion River and each of the river's tributary floodplains. Each rise marks an elevation gain of up to 20 feet. These flat surfaces are ancient stream terraces that formed on the floodplains of pre-Pleistocene river systems that were at higher elevations. These terraces are older than the stream deposits of the Pliocene-to-Pleistocene-age Upland Complex. In ascending order (youngest and lowest in the west to oldest and highest in the east) they are the Finley, Hatchie, Humboldt, and Henderson terraces. The Finley terrace is named for the town of Finley, west of Dyersburg. Union City is built mostly on the Hatchie Terrace, which is named for the Hatchie River. The community of Midway (halfway between Union City and Martin) is on the Humboldt Terrace, which extends eastward past Dresden. The cities of Humboldt and Jackson are also on the Humboldt Terrace. All the terraces are covered by Pleistocene-age loess.

Martin is home to the University of Tennessee at Martin. The school's GeoClub, a student organization interested in geological and geographical topics and under the mentorship of professor Michael A. Gibson, was instrumental in nominating the Cretaceous-age bivalve *Pterotrigonia (Scabrotrigonia) thoracica* to be Tennessee's state fossil. In 1998 the honor was bestowed upon "Ptero," which won out over ten other fossils because it is easily collected from the Cretaceous-age Coon Creek Formation and represents a group of bivalves that are near extinction. The GeoClub was actually the second student group from Martin to lobby the Tennessee legislature in the name of geology. In 1979

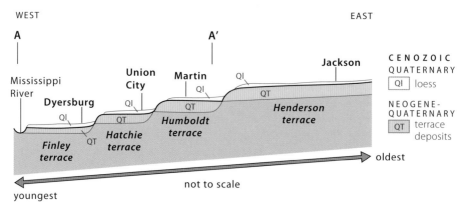

Stream terraces form stairstep-like elevation changes between Reelfoot Lake and Dresden. The terraces formed along the floodplains of older river systems that were at higher elevations. All terraces are capped by 1 foot or more of Pleistocene-age loess. See the road guide map on page 332 for the location of the line (A-A').

a Martin middle-school class successfully lobbied the Tennessee Legislature to change the Tennessee state rock from agate (which is a mineral and not a rock) to limestone. In 2009, agate became the Tennessee state mineral.

TN 78
DYERSBURG—KENTUCKY STATE LINE
36 miles

Large earthquakes in the New Madrid Seismic Zone occur infrequently, but their effects on the landscape often endure for centuries. For example, the 1811–1812 New Madrid earthquakes triggered more than two hundred landslides and slumps along the Chickasaw Bluffs between Memphis and Cairo, Illinois. These mass wasting events, each more than 200 feet across, are most heavily concentrated between Dyersburg and the Kentucky state line. Heavy vegetation and erosion have obscured most of the slides, but scallop-shaped landslide headwalls and scarps remain visible along the bluffs between Fort Pillow State Historic Park and Reelfoot Lake.

Five miles north of Dyersburg, the highway descends about 100 feet in elevation from the Chickasaw Bluffs to the Mississippi River Valley. The Chickasaw Bluffs remain visible 2 to 5 miles east of TN 78 between Ridgely and the Kentucky state line.

Look for circular, domed areas of lighter soil in the surrounding fields between Bogota and Tiptonville. These features, especially evident in fallow fields or where crops have been recently cut or harvested, are sand blows that may be tens of feet wide, hundreds of feet long, and up to 6 feet thick. During an earthquake sand blows and other liquefaction features most commonly form where the water table is shallow and sediments are unconsolidated, such as on the Mississippi River's floodplain. Under normal conditions, water occupies pore space between sand grains. With earthquake-induced severe ground shaking, water pressure increases and breaks the frictional bonds between the grains, and they become surrounded by water. The pressurized sand slurry

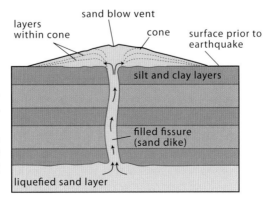

Sand blows form as earthquake shaking increases water pressure, which causes the sand to liquefy and forces it upward and onto the surface.

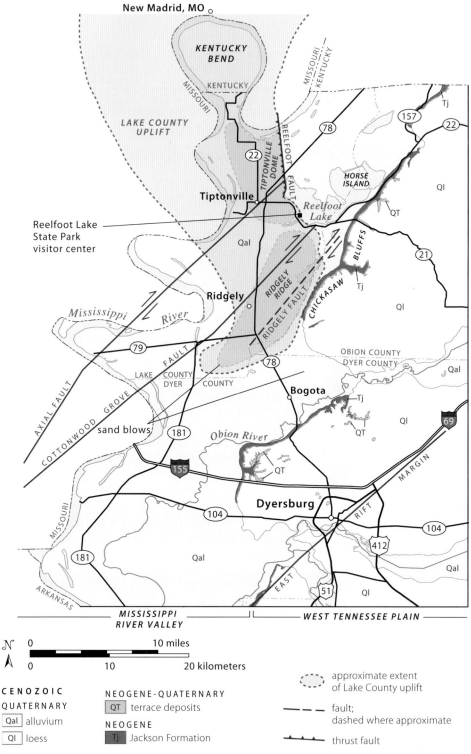

The geology of northwest Tennessee is dominated by structures of the Reelfoot rift and New Madrid Seismic Zone. Local uplift and subsidence along faults controls the location of land-forms. —Structural features after Hildenbrand, 1985; Purser and Van Arsdale, 1998; Stephenson et al, 1995

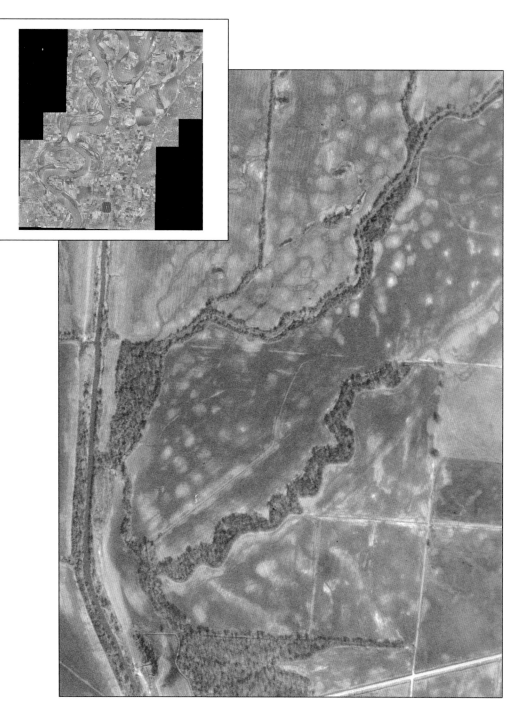

This black-and-white aerial photo highlights sand blows in farmland on the Mississippi River floodplain in Lake County west of Miston and Bogota. Most local sand blows formed during the New Madrid earthquakes of 1811–1812, but others formed during older earthquakes. —US Geological Survey image

squirts up through cracks in overlying sediments to form sand blows. When fresh, sand blows resemble small volcanoes with a central crater and sand gently sloping away from it.

The small town of Ridgely is built on the southern edge of a 15-by-30-mile-wide and up-to-30-foot-high ridge known as the Lake County uplift. Interaction between the Axial fault and New Madrid North fault has resulted in compression on the Reelfoot thrust fault, pushing the area around Ridgely upward periodically since Cretaceous time. The Lake County uplift includes two actively rising areas: Ridgely Ridge and the Tiptonville Dome. The 16-foot-high Ridgely Ridge, squeezed up between the Cottonwood Grove and Ridgely faults, extends northward from Ridgely to the southern shore of Reelfoot Lake. The Cottonwood Grove fault merges with the Axial fault northwest of Dyersburg.

Tiptonville lies on the southern edge of the Tiptonville Dome, an irregularly shaped high spot that is 9 miles wide, is 7 miles long, and rises up to 30 feet above the surrounding floodplain. The Reelfoot thrust fault separates the dome's eastern edge from the Reelfoot Lake basin. Most of the Tiptonville Dome's uplift has occurred during the last 2,000 years.

A memorial to the Battle of Island Number Ten sits at the junction of TN 22 and Cates Landing Road North, 5 miles north of Tiptonville. The Mississippi River and the Tiptonville Dome played an important role in the movement of troops during the battle in the spring 1862. Confederate troops controlled Tiptonville and held five gun batteries on Kentucky Bend and five on Island Number Ten (just offshore), which was considered a critical position in terms of control of the Mississippi River. The island was not really an island but a large sandbar only about 10 feet higher in elevation than the river's low-water point. The Confederate army considered the island impenetrable from land, at least from the Tennessee side, due to the swampy areas surrounding Reelfoot Lake—rainfall and flooding were high that year. However, their withdrawal or reinforcement would also have to be through Tennessee via the Tiptonville Road.

A flotilla of Union Navy ironclad ships sailed past the Confederate batteries during the night. They anchored near New Madrid, Missouri, and from there launched an attack on the Island Number Ten batteries. Confederate forces successfully withstood the bombardment for several weeks, but eventually they retreated to Tiptonville. During the siege, Union forces strengthened in the south, cutting off Confederate army supply routes at Fort Pillow, along the Tiptonville Road, and at the New Madrid river crossing. Union troops finally surrounded Confederate troops, who became isolated on the Tiptonville Dome during a spring flood. The defeat of the Confederate army during the Battle of Island Number Ten gave Union forces control of the Mississippi River to Fort Pillow. Island Number Ten, along with the gun batteries, and the original town of New Madrid, Missouri, are now submerged beneath the Mississippi River.

One mile north of the battle memorial, TN 22 turns sharply westward and crosses the Mississippi River's meander neck of the Kentucky Bend, here less than 1 mile wide. The Mississippi River, favoring a shorter path, will eventually cut off the Kentucky Bend at its narrowest point, and the bend will become a new oxbow lake. During the New Madrid earthquakes, movement along the Reelfoot fault created dams and waterfalls along the river. Eyewitnesses reported that the river flowed backward where the Reelfoot fault crosses the river east of the Kentucky Bend neck.

TN 78 crosses the trace of the Reelfoot fault about 3 miles north of Tiptonville. The fault does not reach the surface here, so the change in elevation of 10 to 30 feet is not a traditional fault scarp, but rather the result of a monocline, a fold that drapes over the buried thrust fault. The change in elevation can be seen in the fields on either side of the highway. This is the only known location in the New Madrid Seismic Zone where there is a surface expression of faulting. Many faults likely remain unknown and buried beneath sediments. A number of geologists dug trenches across the fault trace near here in order to catalog paleoseismic and structural features, as well as to constrain the timing of faulting by dating organic material. Their studies showed that there were three episodes of faulting during the last 2,400 years: between AD 780 and AD 1000, between 1260 and 1650, and in 1812. Based on these dates, the estimated recurrence interval for large earthquakes in the New Madrid Seismic Zone is every 400 to 500 years.

North of the Reelfoot fault monocline, TN 78 skirts Reelfoot Lake's western shore on top of the Mississippi River's eastern floodplain. In this 2-mile-wide strip, much of the fertile alluvial soil is devoted to cotton farming. Close to the river, many fields follow the shape of abandoned river meanders and scroll bars, asymmetrical, meander-parallel ridges that are separated by low areas called swales.

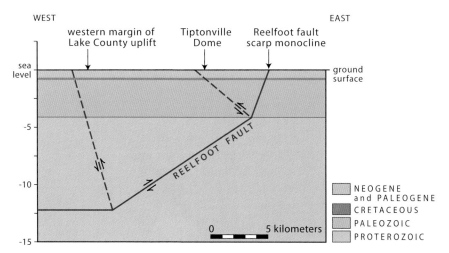

The Reelfoot fault dips westward about 75 degrees to the top of Proterozoic-age rocks. Seismicity shows that the fault dip shallows to near 30 degrees at about 7 miles of depth. At this depth, heat and pressure in the Earth's crust become so great that rocks behave plastically rather than brittlely. Smaller faults, called back thrusts, are formed from movement along the Reelfoot fault. —Modified from Purser and Van Arsdale, 1998

REELFOOT LAKE STATE PARK

Reelfoot Lake State Park is located on the eastern edge of the Mississippi River floodplain in northwestern Tennessee about 1 mile east of Tiptonville. Reelfoot Lake, Tennessee's largest natural lake (40 acres), supports a diverse abundance of animals and aquatic plants and is also loaded with crappie, bass, and catfish. Nearly three hundred species of birds, including bald eagles, fly along the Mississippi Migratory Flyway between northern Canada and the tropics and spend time at Reelfoot Lake. The lake's depth averages only about 6 feet; it is 18 feet at its deepest in the southern end. Bald cypress trees give the low-lying park an eerie, otherworldly feel.

Expansive views and public access options can be found along the lake's south shore on TN 22. The park's visitor center is located northwest of the spillway and has interesting displays on local human and natural history. Shoreline boardwalks take visitors up close to the lake and bald cypress trees.

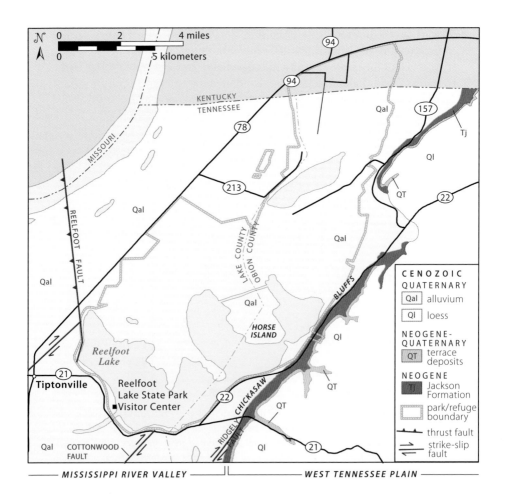

Stands of bald cypress trees grow in Reelfoot Lake. —Chuck Sutherland photo

Reelfoot Lake is also called Earthquake Lake because its formation is attributed to the February 1812 earthquake on the Reelfoot fault. Prior to the earthquake, the low, swampy area was where the ancient Reel Foot River flowed west to meet the Mississippi south of Tiptonville. During the earthquake, land on the southwest side of the Reelfoot fault was uplifted approximately 5 feet, and land on the north side subsided up to 3 feet. The net effect was the damming of the Reel Foot River and the formation of Reelfoot Lake. Most trees were drowned as the basin filled, and stumps from the old forest are preserved just below the lake surface.

Some bald cypress trees survived the earthquake-induced subsidence and flooding and yielded a wealth of information about Reelfoot Lake Formation. Each year all trees add a new layer of cells just below the bark. In spring and early summer, with frequent rainfall, cells grow large. As the weather dries and cools during fall months, the new cells that develop are smaller and more densely spaced. The visual contrast between the more compact cells (dark) and the larger cells (light) resembles a ring. By examining tree rings, geoscientists can determine a tree's age and also identify specific years when the tree grew a lot and years when the tree didn't grow at all.

Following the February 1812 earthquake, bald cypress trees were suddenly immersed in water. Thus, post-1812 tree rings are all large and light in color, reflecting the fact that there was no longer a late-summer drought to produce dark rings. The wood of Reelfoot Lake trees pre-dating the 1812 growth also contains

Tree rings in this approximately 0.2-inch-wide core taken from a Reelfoot Lake bald cypress show a change from river to lake conditions following the February 1812 New Madrid earthquake. Year 1810 is marked with a single pinprick at the left. The 1812 growth ring, marked with twin pinpricks, is very thin due to earthquake damage. The 1814 growth ring is very large due to earthquake-induced subsidence and the creation of Reelfoot Lake, which supplied the tree with lots of water. The enhanced growth only lasted for about ten years. —Malcolm Cleveland, University of Arkansas–Fayetteville, Geosciences Dept. Tree-Ring Laboratory photo

lots of cracks before, but the wood that grew after does not. The cracks likely formed from the intense shaking. Cores taken from trees outside of Reelfoot Lake do not show either the growth spurt or the cracks, further proof that the area comprising Reelfoot Lake was shaken and then submerged as a result of the fourth New Madrid earthquake.

In the early 1900s, more than twenty exploratory wells were drilled in the deep sediments that accumulated in the buried rift in hopes of finding oil and gas reserves. To date, there are no producing wells within the region. The visitor center has a small display about an oil well that was drilled at Samburg.

MUSEUMS AND NATURE CENTERS

EAST TENNESSEE

American Museum of Science and Energy
115 Main St. E
Oak Ridge, TN 37830
865-294-4531
amse.org

Bays Mountain Park and Planetarium
853 Bays Mountain Park Rd.
Kingsport, TN 37660
423-229-9447
baysmountain.com

Candoro Marble Arts and Heritage Center
4450 Candora Ave.
Knoxville, TN 37920
candoromarble.org
865-214-7383

Coker Creek Welcome Center
12197 New Highway 68
Tellico Plains, TN 37385
423-261-2286
cokercreek.org

Creative Discovery Museum
321 Chestnut St.
Chattanooga, TN 37402
423-756-2738
cdmfun.org

Discovery Park of America
830 Everett Blvd.
Union City, TN 38261
731-885-5455
discoveryparkofamerica.com

Ducktown Basin Museum
212 Burra Burra St.
Ducktown, TN 37326
423-496-5778
ducktownbasinmuseum.com

Gray Fossil Site and Museum
1212 Suncrest Dr.
Gray, TN 37615
423-439-3662
http://gfs.visithandson.org

Hands On! Regional Museum
315 East Main St.
Johnson City, TN 37601
423-434-4263

The Muse
516 N Beaman St.
Knoxville, TN 37914
865-594-1494
themuseknoxville.org

Ijams Nature Center
2915 Island Home Ave.
Knoxville, TN 37920
865-577-4717
ijams.org

Tennessee Aquarium
1 Broad St.
Chattanooga, TN 37402
800-262-0695
https://www.tnaqua.org

The University of Tennessee McClung
  Museum of Natural History and Culture
1327 Circle Park Dr.
Knoxville, TN 37916
865-974-2144
mcclungmuseum.utk.edu

WonderWorks—Pigeon Forge
100 Music Rd.
Pigeon Forge, TN 37863
865-868-1800
wonderworksonline.com/pigeon-forge

MIDDLE TENNESSEE

Adventure Science Center
800 Fort Negley Blvd.
Nashville, TN 37203
615-862-5160
adventuresci.org

Beaman Park Nature Center
5911 Old Hickory Blvd.
Nashville, TN 37015
615-862-8580
nashville.gov/Parks-and-Recreation/
Nature-Centers-and-Natural-Areas/
Beaman-Park-Nature-Center.aspx

Discovery Center
502 SE Broad St.
Murfreesboro, TN 37130
615-890-2300
explorethedc.org

Earth Experience—Middle Tennessee
  Museum of Natural History
816 Old Salem Rd.
Murfreesboro, TN 37129
615-900-8358
theearthexperience.org

Mount Pleasant—
  Maury Phosphate Museum
108 Public Square
Mt. Pleasant, TN 38474
931-379-9511

Savage Gardens
318 Savage Garden Rd.
Rocky Top, TN 37769
865-426-6495
*Open March-May

Shelby Bottoms Nature Center
1900 Davidson St.
Nashville, TN 37206
615-862-8539
nashville.gov/Parks-and-Recreation/
Nature-Centers-and-Natural-Areas/
Shelby-Bottoms-Nature-Center.aspx

Hands-On Science Center
101 Mitchell Blvd.
Tullahoma, TN 37388
931-455-8387
hosc.org

Warner Park Nature Center
7311 Highway 100
Nashville, TN 37221
615-862-8555
nashville.gov/Parks-and-Recreation/
Nature-Centers-and-Natural-Areas/
Warner-Park-Nature-Center.aspx

WEST TENNESSEE

Coon Creek Science Center
2983 Hardin Graveyard Rd.
Adamsville, TN 38310
901-636-2362
memphismuseums.org/
coon-creek-science-center/
*Visitors to the center are limited to
organized groups (call ahead)

Lichterman Nature Center
5992 Quince Rd.
Memphis, TN 38119
901-636-2211
memphismuseums.org/
lichterman-nature-center/

Mississippi River Museum and Mud
  Island River Park
125 N. Front St.
Memphis, TN 38103
901-576-7241
mudisland.com

Tennessee River Museum
495 Main St.
Savannah, TN 38372
731-925-8181
tennesseerivermuseum.org

The University of Memphis C. H. Nash
  Museum Chucalissa
1987 Indian Village Dr.
Memphis, TN 38109
901-785-3160
memphis.edu/chucalissa

GLOSSARY

Acadian orogeny. A Late Devonian deformation event involving exotic terranes colliding with the eastern North American margin that mainly affected the northern Appalachian Mountains.

active margin. A continental margin that is also a plate boundary where earthquakes and deformation occur.

Alleghanian orogeny. A late Paleozoic mountain building event that resulted from the collision of Africa with the east coast of North America. The event produced the fold-and-thrust belt deformation of the Valley and Ridge physiographic province, as well as the deformation, metamorphism, and intrusions of plutons in the Appalachian Mountains.

alluvial fan. A cone-shaped mass of sediment deposited by a stream as it exits the mountains and enters a broad valley. The apex of the cone points upstream.

alluvium. A general term for clay, silt, sand, gravel, and other unconsolidated sedimentary material deposited in relatively recent geologic time by running water.

anticline. A fold in which layered rocks have been bowed upward, producing an archlike profile.

anticlinorium. A regional-scale anticlinal structure composed of smaller-scale folds.

Appalachian Basin. A regional foreland basin containing rocks of Cambrian to Pennsylvanian age. These rocks are found in the Valley and Ridge and Cumberland Plateau of East Tennessee.

aquifer. A porous underground body of rock from which water can be obtained.

aragonite. A mineral made of calcium carbonate of which modern mollusk shells are composed.

ash. Tiny fragments of volcanic rock blown into the air and distributed across the countryside near an erupting volcano.

asthenosphere. The layer of Earth below the lithosphere that is part of the upper mantle.

barrier island. An island of sand forming part of the outer coastline that remains out of water at high tide. The narrow, linear sand deposit, parallel to the coastline, lies adjacent to a wider, landward deposit predominantly composed of clay deposited in a marsh or lagoon.

basalt. A fine-grained, dark-colored volcanic igneous rock made up mostly of the calcium-rich minerals plagioclase feldspar and pyroxene. It is the very abundant extrusive equivalent of gabbro.

basement. The igneous and metamorphic rocks upon which a sequence of sedimentary rocks were deposited.

basin. A low area in the landscape where water may accumulate as a lake. Also, a large-scale downwarping of the Earth's crust in which relatively thick sequences of sediments are deposited.

bed. A single layer of sedimentary rock. The layering of beds is called bedding. The boundary between beds is a **bedding plane**.

bedrock. The hard rock at or near the surface that has not been moved by erosion or human activity. It is commonly concealed by younger uncemented river, lake, glacial, or wind deposits and soil.

bentonite. A soft, potassium-rich clay formed by the alteration of volcanic ash in water. Bentonite swells with the addition of water and contracts when dry.

bituminous coal. A sedimentary rock formed from peat that is compressed and heated at a low temperature. It is the most common form of coal.

bioherm. A dome-shaped reef made of siliciclastic mud, broken shells, and other biological material.

biotite. A dark, platy mineral in the mica group.

Blue Ridge. A mountainous physiographic province extending the length of East Tennessee.

bluff. High cliffs overlooking a plain or body of water.

brachiopod. An invertebrate animal with two unequal shells (unlike clam shells), each of which is bilaterally symmetrical. Brachiopods were abundant and diverse until Cenozoic time with only a few living today.

braided river. A river with a floodplain composed of many interconnected, shifting channels separated by coarse sand or gravel bars.

breccia. A sedimentary or volcanic rock containing angular, pebble-sized to larger rock fragments. Collapse breccia forms in a sinkhole due to the collapse of a cavern.

bryozoan. A group of invertebrate marine colonial animals that secrete calcareous skeletons with varied forms. Some colonies are branching; they resemble plants but are animals.

burrow. A trace left by an organism, such as a worm, as it ate its way through sediment or dug a home.

calcareous. Said of a rock containing calcium carbonate along with other constituents.

calcite. A light-colored mineral composed of calcium carbonate that is the main constituent of limestone, most marble, and many marine fossils.

calcium carbonate. A chemical compound of calcium, carbon, and oxygen that can crystallize as either calcite or aragonite.

carbonate. Rocks such as limestone or dolostone/dolomite that are formed with calcium and/or magnesium carbonate.

cement. The substance, usually composed of silica (quartz), calcium carbonate minerals, or iron oxide, that binds the grains of a sedimentary rock.

cephalopod. A group of marine invertebrate animals with well-developed eyes and head surrounded by tentacles. Modern examples, such as octopuses and squids, don't have shells, but fossil examples had either straight or coiled shells.

channel fill. An alluvial deposit found in modern and ancient streambeds.

chert. A sedimentary rock composed of quartz crystals too small to see with the naked eye. It forms as a chemical deposit, found primarily as nodules precipitated from water percolating through limy sediments after deposition, but it can also be precipitated directly from water on the seafloor.

clastic. A rock made mainly of broken fragments of other rocks or minerals that have been transported some distance from their place of origin.

clay. A group of very fine-grained minerals composed chiefly of aluminum and silica. The term **clay** is also used to describe very fine particles of other minerals. Clay is so fine that it does not feel gritty when rubbed between the fingers.

coarse-grained. Said of sedimentary rocks that have clasts, or particles, that are relatively large, usually averaging 2 millimeters in diameter or larger. Also said of igneous rocks with relatively large crystals.

cobble. A course fragment of rock between 2.5 and 10 inches in diameter. Cobbles commonly, but not necessarily, have been somewhat rounded by abrasion.

coke. A hard, gray, and porous combustible material made from coal that has been heated to drive off volatile components.

concretion. A mass of a hard mineral precipitated from a solution within a softer sedimentary or volcanic rock.

conglomerate. A course sedimentary rock made up of pebbles, cobbles, and/or boulders eroded from older rocks. The large size implies a vigorous process of deposition, such as that of a mountain stream.

conodont. A microscopic marine fossil thought to be mouth parts of an extinct, swimming wormlike animal. Conodonts are useful for correlating ancient strata.

continental shelf. The submerged margin of a continent. Modern continental shelves extend from the coastline to water depths of about 600 feet.

corals. Marine, bottom-dwelling, mostly colonial animals that secrete an external skeleton composed of calcium carbonate. Their skeletons form major components of modern and ancient reefs.

cove. A steep-walled hollow at the head of a small canyon.

craton. A part of the Earth's crust, usually in the interior of a continent, that has not been pervasively deformed for at least 1 billion years.

crinoid. A group of invertebrate animals, also called "sea lilies," related to sea stars and sea urchins. They resembled a plant, with a stem attached to the sea bottom and arms radiating from the top, and were abundant in the Paleozoic Era.

crossbedding. Laminations, or crossbeds, in sand or sandstone that are inclined about 30 degrees to the main bedding. These inclined beds represent the lee, or downwind, faces of dunes or ripples, and their downslope direction indicates the direction of the wind or water current that deposited them.

crust. The outermost layer of Earth. **Oceanic crust**, made of basalt and rocks of similar composition, ranges from 3 to 6 miles thick. **Continental crust**, made mainly of lighter-colored, less dense rock, such as granite or gneiss, often with a veneer of sedimentary rock, normally ranges from 20 to 40 miles thick.

Cumberland Plateau. A flat-topped highland with flat-lying sedimentary rocks that contain most of Tennessee's minable coal.

debris flow. A mass of soil, mud, and rock that may move slowly or up to 80 miles per hour.

delta. A body of sediment deposited where a river enters a standing body of water.

deposition. The process of sediment settling out of water or air.

detachment thrust fault. A low-angle thrust fault, subparallel to bedding, that originates in sedimentary layers that more easily assist fracture and movement, such as shale or coal layers that are mechanically weak.

diamictite. A rock containing poorly sorted particle sizes, usually of glacial origin.

dike. A tabular body of igneous rock that cuts across the structure of older adjacent rock into which it was intruded as fluid magma.

dimension stone. Building stone that is quarried and prepared as regularly shaped blocks.

dip. The downslope direction (the direction water would run) on an inclined (or dipping) bedding surface.

dissected. Said of an elevated landscape that has had many valleys cut into it by streams.

dolomite. A sedimentary rock akin to limestone that contains magnesium as well as calcium carbonate. Dolomite typically forms when fluids moving through buried limestone precipitate magnesium. The term also refers to a mineral that makes up the rock dolomite.

dolostone. A rock composed mainly of the carbonate mineral dolomite.

dome. A broad, roughly circular upwarp in which strata dip in all directions from the top. The term is generally applied to large features, such as the Nashville Dome.

drainage basin. The area, or watershed, in which all water drains into a river.

drainage divide. The boundary between two watersheds, such that water on either side of it flows in different directions.

echinoderm. A biological family that includes crinoids, starfish, and sand dollars.

erosion. A general term for several processes that loosen, dissolve, or weather and then transport earthen materials and thus wear away landscapes.

erosional surface. A land surface that develops as earthen materials are removed by natural agents, such as wind, running water, or ice. When an erosional surface on older rock is covered with younger rock, the boundary is called an unconformity.

escarpment. The steep face of a ridge or plateau along which the land drops abruptly to a lower level.

estuary. The part of a river near its mouth that is influenced by tides.

fault. A fracture along which the rocks on either side have been displaced from inches to miles.

fault zone. A relatively narrow region in which multiple faults, more or less parallel but often interconnected, have developed.

feldspar. The most abundant mineral group in Earth's crust. Feldspars are divided between potassium-bearing feldspars and calcium-and sodium-bearing plagioclase feldspars. They are especially characteristic of igneous rocks. Feldspar is not as common as quartz in soil or sedimentary rocks because weathering alters feldspar to clay.

fine-grained. Said of sedimentary rocks that have clasts, or particles, that are relatively small, usually averaging less than 2 millimeters in diameter. Also said of igneous rocks with relatively small, hard-to-see crystals.

fissile. Rock that can be split along closely spaced planes.

floodplain. An area adjacent to a riverbed that may lie underwater when the river overflows its banks.

floodplain deposit. Silt and clay deposited by floodwaters on a floodplain.

fold. Rock layers that have been bent, usually as a result of compressive tectonic forces. A slight fold is called open or gentle. A V-shaped fold is called tight.

foliation. Parallel surfaces or layers in metamorphic rock caused by the growth, flattening, and/or dissolving of mineral grains under stress during metamorphism.

foreland basin. A linear basin that forms adjacent and parallel to actively forming mountains that receives sediments eroded from the mountains.

formation. The basic subdivision of sedimentary rocks that can be mapped from place to place.

fossil. Any remains or traces of animals or plants preserved in sediment or sedimentary rocks. Impressions, tracks, burrows, and other traces that are not actual remains are called **trace fossils**.

fossiliferous. Said of rocks bearing fossils.

gabbro. A dark-colored, coarse-grained intrusive igneous rock composed mostly of calcium plagioclase feldspar and pyroxene. When the same magma erupts at the surface, it forms basalt.

gap. A sharp break, pass, or opening in a mountain range formed by the action of wind or water.

garnet. A group of red or brown semiprecious minerals that are common in metamorphic rocks.

gastropod. Any mollusk belonging to the class Gastropoda, such as snails.

geode. A cavity in rock lined with crystals. If the surrounding rock weathers away, the geode may remain as a round rock that reveals its crystals when broken.

geologic time scale. A chronologic arrangement or sequence of geologic events usually presented in the form of a chart showing the geologic time units.

glade. A clearing between slopes. In Middle Tennessee, glades usually form on flat areas of carbonates.

gneiss. A coarse-grained metamorphic rock that has a striped appearance caused by alternating bands of light-colored minerals (quartz and feldspar) and bands of dark-colored, platy or flaky minerals (biotite and hornblende).

graded bedding. Bedding in which the grain size gradually gets finer upward through the bed.

granite. A light-colored, coarse-grained intrusive igneous rock made mostly of plagioclase, potassium feldspar and quartz, but which may also contain mica and/or hornblende.

granitic gneiss. Gneiss that is dominated by quartz and feldspar, with relatively thin bands of dark minerals. It most likely formed from the metamorphism of granite.

gravel. An accumulation of loose fragments that are larger than 2 millimeters in diameter and have been at least somewhat abraded, or rounded. Gravel includes pebbles, cobbles, and boulders.

graywacke. A sedimentary rock similar to sandstone but containing both sand and significant amounts of clay. Metamorphosed graywacke is called **metagraywacke**.

Grenville orogeny. A major deformational event that occurred between 1,100 and 880 million years ago, during the Precambrian Era, and can be traced through the Appalachians and into Texas. It is thought that the orogeny was the result of the collision of continents that took place during the assembly of the supercontinent Rodinia.

group. A formal rock unit containing two or more formations.

gypsum. A mineral or rock composed of calcium sulfate that formed from the evaporation of water (making it an evaporite rock).

hanging wall. The rock overlying a fault.

headward erosion. The lengthening of a stream as rock and soil is eroded around its headwaters.

heavy minerals. Minor constituents in rocks that, when eroded from a rock, tend to concentrate as dark layers of sand on beaches because of their high density.

hornblende. A black mineral that usually has an elongate shape. The most common mineral of the amphibole group.

hot spot. A volcanic center, persistent for at least a few tens of millions of years, that is thought to be the surface expression of a rising plume of hot mantle material.

Iapetus Ocean. A sea that existed east of North America before Europe and Africa collided with North America late in the Paleozoic Era.

ice age. A time of extensive continental-scale glacial activity.

ice sheet. A large, thick glacier that spreads outward from a central area.

igneous. Rock that cooled from magma either within the Earth (intrusive or plutonic) or at the surface (extrusive or volcanic).

index fossil. A fossil, also called a **guide fossil**, that identifies and dates the rock unit in which it's found. Index fossils are easily found, easily distinguished from other fossils, geographically widespread, and preserved in a variety of sedimentary rocks that formed in a restricted period of time.

intrusive. Rocks that cooled from magma that penetrated other rocks.

island arc. An offshore curving line of volcanoes above a subduction zone.

joint. A crack in rock along which no movement has occurred, so it is not a fault. Joints often occur parallel to each other in groups, or sets.

kaolinite. A common, earthy white, grayish, or yellowish clay mineral.

karst. A distinctive type of topography that formed from the dissolution of carbonate rocks and is characterized by sinkholes, caves, and underground streams.

lagoon. A small water body separated from or partially connected to a larger body. For example, open water lying between barrier islands and the mainland.

Laurentide ice sheet. The most recent ice sheet to cover northeastern and north-central North America. It is named for the Laurentian Highlands of northeastern Canada.

lava. Melted rock, or magma, that erupts at Earth's surface.

lens. A mass of rock that is thicker in the middle than around the edges.

levee. An earthen embankment built parallel to a river and on top of natural levees in order to protect the area behind it from floodwaters.

lignite. A brownish-black, low-grade coal.

limestone. A sedimentary rock composed of calcium carbonate. It commonly is largely made up of the calcareous skeletons of invertebrate fossils.

limonite. A brown iron oxide mineral of variable composition.

liquefaction. A process by which loosely packed sediment changes to a liquid state. For example, when an earthquake shakes water-saturated sand, silt, and clay, they lose strength and the ability to support weight.

lithosphere. The outer, relatively rigid layer of the Earth that consists of the entire crust plus the uppermost mantle. **Lithosphere plates**, the large, rigid units of the outer zone of Earth (60 to 150 miles thick), are capped by continental and/or oceanic crust. Earth's major earthquake zones define the margins of these plates, which move slowly over the pliable mantle beneath.

loess. Silt picked up from glacial streambeds and redeposited by the wind. It typically forms a cover over the landscape that thins with distance downwind from braided glacial rivers.

magma. Molten rock. Termed **lava** where it erupts at the surface of the Earth.

mammoth. A large, extinct, elephant-like, tusked mammal with a high, foreshortened skull. It was widely distributed during the Pleistocene ice ages. Its flat-crowned teeth were adapted for grazing, so its preferred habitat was tundra grasslands.

mantle. The largest division of the Earth's interior (80 percent), which lies between the lithosphere and the very dense core. It is rich in iron, magnesium, and calcium.

marble. A metamorphic rock mainly composed of carbonate minerals and derived from limestone or dolomite.

marsh. A wetland dominated by grasses as opposed to trees.

massive. Said of a rock layer (such as a thick sandstone bed) or rock type (such as granite) without evident layering.

mastodon. A large, extinct, elephant-like, tusked mammal that was widely distributed during the Pleistocene ice ages. Mastodon means "nipple tooth," describing the pattern of its tooth cusps, which were adapted for browsing in the animal's preferred habitat of open spruce woodlands.

meander. A looplike bend in a river that tends to form in flatlands where there is loose, relatively fine sediment.

member. A formal lithostratigraphic unit representing some specially developed part of a formation. It is ranked lower than a formation and higher than a bed.

meta. A prefix used to denote the previous identity of a metamorphic rock; for example, a metasedimentary rock was originally a sedimentary rock. In

Tennessee the prefix is mainly used to describe rocks of the Ocoee Super-group, in which pressure and heat resulting from burial, compaction, and Paleozoic mountain building caused sediment grains to partly recrystallize, but original bedding and sedimentary structures remain largely intact.

metamorphic. Said of minerals and rocks with compositions and textures that were changed by heat and/or pressure. For example, shale that was meta-morphosed to slate and sandstone to quartzite.

metamorphism. The process through which the texture and often the miner-alogy of rock (by the formation of new crystals, or recrystallization) changes due to heat and pressure but without the rock melting.

mica. A group of minerals that break into flat sheets and have a glittery appear-ance. The two most common types are **muscovite**, which is clear or silvery, and **biotite**, which is black.

mineral. A naturally occurring chemical element or compound with a charac-teristic crystal form.

Mississippi Embayment. A 200-mile-wide-by-300-mile-long trough filled with sediment. It tilts gently southward toward the Gulf of Mexico and crosses parts of Illinois, Kentucky, Missouri, Tennessee, Arkansas, Alabama, and Louisiana.

mold. A cavity in sedimentary rock that retains the shape of a fossil that dissolved, such as a shell.

mollusk. A phylum of animals that usually have a shell or pair of shells, including clams, snails, and squids.

monocline. A local steepening in otherwise flat-lying or gentle dipping rock layers.

mosasaur. A family of large marine reptile predators of the Cretaceous Period.

mudstone. A sedimentary rock made mainly of clay. Unlike shale it doesn't tend to split into thin pieces.

muscovite. A clear to silvery mineral of the mica group.

nodule. A rounded fist-sized or smaller concretion usually found in limestone or dolomite.

normal fault. A fault along which one fault block slides down a sloping fault surface relative to the fault block on the other side of the fault. A normal fault forms as the result of forces that are pulling an area apart.

olivine. A glassy green or brown mineral that is common in gabbro and basalt.

ooid. Approximately 1-millimeter-wide spheres composed of microscopic, onion-like layers of calcium carbonate. Grains that were agitated in very shallow water acted as nuclei upon which the calcium carbonate precipitated.

oolite. A sedimentary rock composed of ooids.

ore. A mineral or aggregate of minerals from which one or more valuable substances, especially metals, can be profitably extracted.

orogeny. The process of mountain formation.

ossicle. Any of the numerous individual calcified elements or pieces of the skeleton of many echinoderms.

ostracods. Microscopic arthropods with protective shells of varying shapes and ornamentation.

outcrop. An exposure of bedrock.

oxbow. A looping stream meander with an extreme U-shaped curvature in which only a neck of land is left between two parts of the stream.

oxide. A compound in which oxygen combines with a positively charged ion. Geologically, oxide minerals include both metallic ores and gems.

Pangea. A supercontinent that existed from about 300 to 200 million years ago and included most of the continental crust of the Earth.

passive margin. A plate boundary formed by rifting and lacking tectonism.

pebble. A rock particle between the size of sand and a cobble—that is, between about 2 millimeters and 2.5 inches in diameter.

pelecypod. An aquatic bivalve mollusk.

period. A formal unit of geologic time with boundaries based on transitions in the global fossil record.

phyllite. A fine-grained metamorphic rock that is similar to slate but contains foliation surfaces that are shiny and silvery due to mica grains that are barely large enough to catch the light. Phyllite has been "cooked" more than slate, but not as much as schist.

physiographic province. A geographic region defined by differences in the landscape. Tennessee has three physiographic provinces, each of which is divided into subprovinces.

placer deposits. A sedimentary mineral deposit in which water currents and settling have separated valuable, heavier minerals, such as gold, from other sediment.

plagioclase. A mineral in the feldspar group containing sodium and/or calcium.

plateau. An elevated, relatively flat area with at least one distinct edge called an escarpment.

plate tectonics. The observation that Earth's lithosphere (its crust plus the rigid uppermost mantle) consists of a mosaic of tectonic plates. Most large-scale structures of the outer Earth are formed by the relative movements of these plates. For example, mountains form where two plates collide.

pluton. A solidified body of intrusive igneous rock, such as granite.

pyrite. A mineral made of iron sulfide. Also called fool's gold.

pyroxene. A group of mostly dark, stubby minerals that are rich in iron, calcium, magnesium, and silica and occur in igneous and metamorphic rocks.

quarry. A place where rock is removed for use as is.

quartz. One of the most common minerals in the Earth's crust. The most common variety is colorless and clear like glass. Quartz is composed of silicon and oxygen, is the main constituent of most sand, and is common in sedimentary rocks and light-colored igneous rocks.

quartzite. A sandstone metamorphosed by heat and/or pressure so that the rock breaks across individual sand grains rather than around them.

reef. Densely populated areas of the seafloor in which the calcareous skeletons of animals form mounds. Today, reefs develop in warm, shallow, well-lit tropical waters that are unusually rich in nutrients and oxygen.

regression. The retreat of the sea from land areas and the consequent geologic evidence of such withdrawal, such as nearshore shallow-water deposits overlying offshore, deep-water deposits.

residuum. The soil left behind after carbonate minerals have dissolved from limestone or dolomite due to chemical weathering in a humid climate.

rhyolite. A light-colored, fine-grained volcanic rock (an extrusive igneous rock) containing the same proportions of quartz and potassium feldspar as granite.

rift. A long, narrow, down-dropped zone where Earth's crust is separating. The process of a tectonic plate being pulled apart or splitting is called rifting.

ripple mark. An undulatory surface on loose, granular sand or fine gravel sculpted by either wind, water currents, or waves. The marks can be preserved in sedimentary rocks.

sand. Loose particles, most typically quartz, that are larger than silt and finer than gravel (from a fraction of a millimeter to about 2 millimeters in diameter).

scarp. A linear cliff produced by faulting or erosion. The term is an abbreviation for escarpment.

schist. A medium- to coarse-grained metamorphic rock that is rich in platy minerals, such as mica, that are oriented so as to produce a conspicuous layering in the rock.

sediment. Earth material that has settled out of water or air. It can consist of pieces of preexisting rock, body parts of organisms, or mineral crystals that precipitated out of water.

sedimentary rock. Sediment that has been naturally compacted and/or cemented to form solid rock.

seismicity. The phenomenon of movements, or earthquakes, in the Earth's crust.

shale. A fine-grained sedimentary rock made mainly of clay that tends to split into thin pieces parallel to its bedding.

shatter cones. Clusters of nested, conically shaped broken zones in rocks that formed from very high-velocity impacts, such as large meteorites striking the Earth's surface.

shear. A type of deformation, usually in response to compression, that occurs when two rocks slide past each other, resulting in crushed and brecciated rock with parallel fractures.

silica. Silicon dioxide, the compound that makes up quartz in all its varieties, including chert.

silicastone. A chert-rich carbonate or siltstone. The dissolution of carbonate may transform a chert-rich carbonate to silicastone.

silt. Small particles of rock larger than clay but finer than sand. When rubbed between fingers or teeth, silt feels gritty.

sinkhole. A surface depression that resulted from the collapse of an underlying cavity.

slate. A fine-grained metamorphic rock formed from the weak metamorphism of shale. It is tougher than shale because it contains microscopic mica in place of clay minerals, and it splits along the foliation, called **slaty cleavage,** produced by the lining up of mica.

stratigraphy. The science of rock strata, including the arrangement of rock layers and their relationships.

stratum. A single bed of like material. The plural is **strata**.

stream capture. The event in which a stream, usually through headward erosion, cuts into the valley of another stream, causing the upper part of the other stream to become its tributary.

stream terrace. A former floodplain that lies at a higher elevation than the stream's current floodplain. The flat area is usually bounded by an upslope escarpment on one side and a downslope escarpment on the other.

strike. The direction or trend taken by a planar geologic structure. For example, a bedding or fault plane as it intersects the horizontal.

strike-slip fault. A fault showing sideways movement, or offset, along a near-vertical fault.

stromatolite. A convex-up mound or columnar-shaped structure, primarily in limestone, formed by complex photosynthetic microbial communities whose mucous covering trapped very fine sediment particles to produce a distinctive, very fine lamination.

structure. A fold, fault, or other geologic feature that result from deformational forces in the Earth's crust.

subduction. The process by which the edge of a tectonic plate capped by oceanic crust descends below an adjacent plate into the asthenosphere, where it melts. The molten rock can make its way back to the surface through volcanoes or as intrusions in the Earth's crust.

sulfide. A compound containing sulfur. Sulfide minerals often contain valuable metals, such as copper and zinc.

supercontinent. An ancient continent that contained all or most of the world's continental landmass.

supergroup. A stratigraphic unit composed of several associated groups.

suture. A zone of collision between two lithospheric plates.

syenite. A coarse-grained igneous rock resembling granite but lacking quartz because the magma it formed from was deficient in silica.

syncline. A fold in which layered rocks have been bowed downward, producing a smile-like profile.

synclinorium. A regional-scale synclinal structure composed of smaller-scale folds.

talus. Angular rock fragments that accumulate at the base of a steep cliff.

tectonic. The forces responsible for large-scale deformation of the Earth's crust.

tectonic plate. A rigid section of the Earth's lithosphere that moves independently of adjacent plates and interacts with them at its boundaries.

thrust fault. A fault dipping less than 45 degrees that formed by tectonic forces of horizontal compression. Generally the rock above the fault, called a **thrust sheet**, moved upward and over the rock below it. When multiple thrust sheets overlap, they are said to be imbricate.

tidal flat. A broad, flat area along a coastline across which seawater ebbs and flows with the rising and falling tide. Depending on the intensity of tidal currents, some are sandy and some are muddy.

topographic inversion. A phenomenon in which former topographic lows coincide with current structural highs, and vice versa. For example, valleys eroded on the crests of anticlines form topographic lows, and synclines often form ridges, or topographic highs.

trace fossil. A fossil, such as a burrow or a fecal pellet, that preserves evidence of past life but is not the actual skeletal remains.

transgression. The expansion of the sea over land areas and the consequent geologic evidence, such as deep-water deposits overlying shallow-water deposits.

trend. The compass direction of a linear feature as projected onto a horizontal plane.

trilobite. An extinct arthropod with an external calcareous skeleton and appendages for swimming and walking.

tuff. Consolidated or cemented volcanic ash.

unconformity. A break or gap in any sequence of strata that implies an interval of time during which no strata were deposited or strata were eroded before deposition began again.

Valley and Ridge. A physiographic province in East Tennessee that consists of long, parallel ridges separated by valleys.

vein. A mineral deposit that formed along a crack in rock by the precipitation of minerals from water. Quartz and calcite are the most common vein materials.

volcanic ash. Fine rock fragments from an explosive volcanic eruption.

watershed. The area that drains into a stream.

weathering. The process by which rocks break down near Earth's surface due to exposure to air, water, and the action of organisms. An unweathered rock surface is called "fresh."

CITED REFERENCES

2006. Digital Geologic Units of Great Smoky Mountains National Park and Vicinity, Tennessee and North Carolina (NPS, GRD, GRE, GRSM, GRSMGLG)

Archer, A. W., and S. F. Greb. 1995. An Amazon-scale drainage system in the Early Pennsylvanian of central North America. *Journal of Geology* 103: 611–28.

Brahana, J. V., and R. E. Broshears. 2001. *Hydrogeology and Groundwater Flow in the Memphis and Fort Pillow Aquifers in the Memphis Area, Tennessee.* Water-Resources Investigations Report 89-4131, Tennessee Department of Environment and Conservation, Division of Water Supply.

Braile, L. W., W. J. Hinze, G. R. Keller, E. G. Lidiak, and J. L. Sexton. 1986. Tectonic development of the New Madrid rift complex, Mississippi Embayment, North America. *Tectonophysics* 131: 1–21.

Byerly, D. W. 2013. *The Last Billion Years: A Geologic History of Tennessee.* Nashville: University of Tennessee Press.

Byerly, D. W., K. R. Walker, W. W. Diehl, M. Ghazizadeh, R. E. Johnson, C. T. Lutz, A. K. Schoner, W. A. Simmons, J. C. B. Simonson, L. J. Weber, and J. E. Wedekind. 1986. Thorn Hill: A classic Paleozoic stratigraphic section in Tennessee. In *Centennial Field Guide, Southeastern Section*, vol. 6. Geological Society of America, ed. T. L. Neatherly, p. 131–36.

Clark, S. H. B., G. T. Spanski, D. G. Hadley, and A. H. Hofstra. 2005. *Geology and mineral resource potential of the Chattanooga 1°X2° Quadrangle, Tennessee and North Carolina: A Preliminary Assessment.* US Geological Survey Bulletin 2005.

Cleland, H. F. 1911. The formation of North American natural bridges. *Popular Science Monthly* 78: 418–27.

Crawford, J., and A. D. Hoagland. 1968. The Mascot–Jefferson City zinc district, Tennessee. In *Ore Deposits of the United States 1933–1967 (Graton-Sales Volume).* American Institute of Mining, Metallurgical Petroleum Engineers, ed. J. D. Ridge, p. 242–56.

Csontos, R., and R. Van Arsdale. 2008. New Madrid seismic zone fault geometry. *Geosphere* 4 (5): 802–13.

Dean, C. S. 1989. Geology of the Cumberland Gap area as interpreted from the pilot bore of the Federal Highway Administration highway tunnel project. In *Cumberland Mountain: The Inside Story*. Kentucky Geological Survey Series 11, eds. C. S. Dean and S. O. Moshier, p. 4–9.

Diegel, F. A. 1986. Topological constraints on imbricate thrust networks, examples from the Mountain City window, Tennessee, USA. *Journal of Structural Geology* 8 (3/4): 269–79.

Dow, L. 1848. *History of Cosmopolite; or, the Four Volumes of Lorenzo Dow's Journal*. Wheeling, VA: Joshua Martin, p. 344–46.

Fisk, H. N. 1944. *Geological investigation of the alluvial valley of the Lower Mississippi River*. US Department of the Army, Mississippi River Commission.

French, B. M. 1998. *Traces of Catastrophe: A Handbook of Shock-Metamorphic Effects in Terrestrial Meteorite Impact Structures*. LPI Contribution No. 954. Houston: Lunar and Planetary Institute.

Greb, S. F., P. E. Potter, D. L. Meyer, and W. I. Ausich. 2008. *Mud Mounds, Paleoslumps, Crinoids, and More: The Geology of the Fort Payne Formation at Lake Cumberland, South-Central Kentucky*. Field Trip for the Kentucky Chapter of the American Institute of Professional Geologists.

Hadley, J. B., L. S. Wiener, C. E. Merschat, S. W. Maher, D. L. Royster, J. H. Aycock, and J. P. McElrath. 1974. *Geology along Interstate 40 through Pigeon River Gorge, Tennessee–North Carolina*. Tennessee Academy of Science Geology, Geography Section and Safford Centennial Society Spring Field Trip.

Hao, Y., M. B. Magnani, K. McIntosh, B. Waldron, and L. Guo. 2013. Quaternary deformation along the Meeman-Shelby fault near Memphis, Tennessee, imaged by high-resolution marine and land seismic reflection profiles. *Tectonics* 32 (3): 501–15.

Hardeman, W. D., R. A. Miller, and G. D. Swingle. 1966. *Geologic Map of Tennessee*. Tennessee Division of Geology, State Geologic Map, 4 sheets, scale 1:250,000.

Harris, L. D., and R. C. Milici. 1977. *Characteristics of Thin-Skinned Style of Deformation in the Southern Appalachians, and Potential Hydrocarbon Traps*. US Geological Survey Professional Paper 1018.

Hatcher, R. D., Jr., P. J. Lemiszki, and J. B. Whisner. 2007. Character of rigid boundaries and internal deformation of the southern Appalachian foreland fold-thrust belt. In *Whence the Mountains? Inquiries into the Evolution of Orogenic Systems: A Volume in Honor of Raymond A. Price*. Geological Society of America Special Paper 433, eds. J. W. Sears, T. A. Harms, and C. A. Evenchick, p. 243–76.

Hatcher, R. D., Jr., J. B. Whisner, J. R. Thigpen, N. E. Whitmer, and S. C. Whisner. 2004. *Southern Appalachian Foreland Fold-Thrust Belt: Field Trip Guide, 4-D Framework of Continental Crust*. 17th International Basement Tectonics Conference, eds. R. D. Hatcher, C. E. Merschat, and J. B. Whisner.

Hildenbrand, T. G. 1985. Rift structures of the northern Mississippi Embayment from the analysis of gravity and magnetic data. *Journal of Geophysical Research* 90 (B14): 12,607–22.

Horne, J. C., J. C. Ferm, F. T. Caruccio, and B. P. Baganz. 1978. Depositional models in coal exploration and mine planning in Appalachian Region. *The American Association of Petroleum Geologists Bulletin* 62 (12): 2379–2411.

Khetani, A. B., and J. F. Read. 2002. Sequence development of a mixed carbonate-siliciclastic high-relief ramp, Mississippian, Kentucky, USA. *Journal of Sedimentary Research* 72 (5): 657–72.

Kneberg, M. D. 1952. The Tennessee area. In *Archaeology of Eastern United States*. University of Chicago Press, ed. J. B. Griffin, p. 190–98.

Knoll, M. A., D. B. Potter Jr., and C. Van de Ven. 2015. Geology, hydrology, and water use history atop the Cumberland Plateau in the Sewanee and Tracy City, Tennessee, area. In *Diverse Excursions in the Southeast: Paleozoic to Present*. Geological Society of America Field Guide 39, ed. A. E. Holmes, p. 197–218.

Lemiszki, P. J., and M. S. Kohl. 2006. Geologic excursion across part of the southern Appalachian foreland fold-thrust belt in northeastern Tennessee. In *Field Trip Guidebook, Southeastern Section*. Geological Society of America, eds. T. C. Labotka and R. D. Hatcher, p. 37–64.

Lloyd, O. B., Jr., and W. L. Lyke. 1995. *Ground Water Atlas of the United States: Segment 10, Illinois, Indiana, Kentucky, Ohio, Tennessee, Hydrologic Atlas 730-K*. US Geological Survey.

Luther, E. T. 1977. *Our Restless Earth: The Geologic Regions of Tennessee*. Knoxville: The University of Tennessee Press.

Marshak, S. 2015. *Earth: Portrait of a Planet*. 5th ed. New York: W. W. Norton.

Martin, P., P. Arroucau, and G. Vlahovic. 2014. Shear-wave splitting study of crustal anisotropy in the New Madrid Seismic Zone. *Bulletin of the Seismological Society of America* 104: 1100–10.

Martin, R. V., and R. B. Van Arsdale. 2017. Stratigraphy and structure of the Eocene Memphis Sand above the eastern margin of the Reelfoot rift in Tennessee, Mississippi, and Arkansas, USA. *Geological Society of America Bulletin* 178 (7-8): 970–96.

Milam, K. A., J. C. Evenick, and B. Deane, eds. 2005. *Field Guide to the Middlesboro and Flynn Creek Impact Structures, Impact Field Studies Group*. 69th Annual Meteoritical Society Meeting, September 16–18, Gatlinburg, TN.

Milici, R. C. 1967. The Physiography of Sequatchie Valley and adjacent portions of the Cumberland Plateau, Tennessee. Tennessee Division of Geology Report of Investigations 22.

Miller, J. A. 1990. *Groundwater Atlas of the United States: Alabama, Florida, Georgia, and South Carolina*. USGS HA730-G.

Miller, R. A. 1974. *The Geologic History of Tennessee*. Tennessee Division of Geology Bulletin 74.

Miller, R. A. 2014. *The Geologic History of Nashville and the Surrounding Middle Tennessee Region*. Nashville: South Harpeth Publishing.

Mitra, S. 1988. Three-dimensional geometry and kinematic evolution of the Pine Mountain thrust system, southern Appalachians. *Geological Society of America Bulletin* 100: 72–95.

Moore, H. L. 1988. *A Roadside Guide to the Geology of the Great Smoky Mountains National Park*. Knoxville: The University of Tennessee Press.

Moore, H. L. 1994. *A Geologic Trip Across Tennessee by Interstate 40*. Knoxville: The University of Tennessee Press.

Muhs, D. R. 2017. The geochemistry of loess: Asian and North American deposits compared. *Journal of Asian Earth Sciences* 155. https//doi.org/10.1016/j.jseas2017.10.032.

Muir, J. 1916. *A Thousand-Mile Walk to the Gulf*. Boston: Houghton Mifflin.

Penick, J. L., Jr. 1981. *The New Madrid Earthquakes*. Rev. ed. Columbia: University of Missouri Press.

Pride, T. E., A. E. Ogden, M. J. Harvey, and D. B. George. 1988. The effect of urban development on spring water quality in Cookeville, Tennessee. In *Proceedings of the Second Conference on Environmental Problems in Karst Terranes and their Solutions*. National Water Well Association, p. 97–120.

Purser, J. L., and R. B. Van Arsdale. 1998. Structure of the Lake County uplift: New Madrid seismic zone. *Bulletin of the Seismological Society of America* 88 (5): 1204–11.

Safford, J. M. 1869. *Geology of Tennessee*. Nashville: Tennessee General Assembly.

Saucier, R. T. 1987. *The New Madrid, Missouri, Earthquake Region—Geological, Seismological, and Geotechnical Studies*. US Geological Survey Professional Paper 1336—A, eds. D. P. Russ and A. J. Crone.

Southworth, S., P. G. Chirico, and T. Putbrese. 1999. *Geologic map of [parts of the] Cades Cove and Calderwood quadrangles, Tennessee and North Carolina, Great Smoky Mountains National Park*. USGS Open-File Report OF-99-175, scale 1:24,000.

Stephenson, W. J., Shedlock, K. M., and Odum, J. K. 1995. *Characterization of the Cottonwood Grove and Ridgely Faults near Reelfoot Lake, Tennessee*. USGS Professional Paper 1538-I.

Troost, G. 1841. *Sixth Geol. Rept. of the State Geologist of the State of Tennessee*. Nashville.

Van Arsdale, R. B., and R. T. Cox. 2007. The Mississippi's Curious Origins. *Scientific American* 296 (1): 76–82.

Van der Plujim, B. A., and S. Marshak. 2004. *Earth Structure*. 2nd ed. New York: W. W. Norton.

Walker, K. R., ed. 1985. *The Geological History of the Thorn Hill Paleozoic Section (Cambrian-Mississippian), Eastern Tennessee*. Studies in Geology 10. Knoxville: The University of Tennessee Department of Geological Sciences.

Walker, K. R., G. Shanmugam, and S. C. Ruppel. 1983. A model for carbonate to terrigenous clastic sequences. *Geological Society of America Bulletin* 94 (6): 700–12.

Wells, F. G., and M. D. Foster. 1933. *Ground-Water Resources of Western Tennessee*. US Geological Survey Professional Paper 656.

Wilson, C. W. 1948. Channels and channel-filling sediments of Richmond age in south-central Tennessee. *Geological Society of America Bulletin* 59 (8): 733–66.

Willsey, S. 2017. *Geology Underfoot in Southern Idaho*. Missoula, MT: Mountain Press.

Wilson, C. W., Jr., and R. G. Stearns. 1958. Structures of the Cumberland Plateau, Tennessee. *Geological Society of America Bulletin* 69 (10): 1283–96.

Wolfe, W. J., C. J. Haugh, A. Webbers, and T. H. Diehl. 1997. *Preliminary Conceptual Models of the Occurrence, Fate, and Transport of Chlorinated Solvents in Karst Aquifers of Tennessee*. US Geological Survey Water-Resources Investigations Report 97-4097.

INDEX

MARCY DAVIS earned an MS in geology at the University of Texas in Austin in 2001. She currently works as a research scientist associate at the University of Texas Institute for Geophysics, supporting field science teams working in such far-flung regions of the world as Antarctica, Greenland, New Zealand, the Arctic and Caribbean Oceans, and the United States. Marcy is also a prolific science writer with contributions to Polar Field Resources Field Notes as well as to the Earth and Sky radio series. While researching her family history, Marcy spent time in Tennessee and learned about the geology of the area. Marcy lives and works in Austin along with her husband, Dan, and their cat, Lucille.